MW00838129

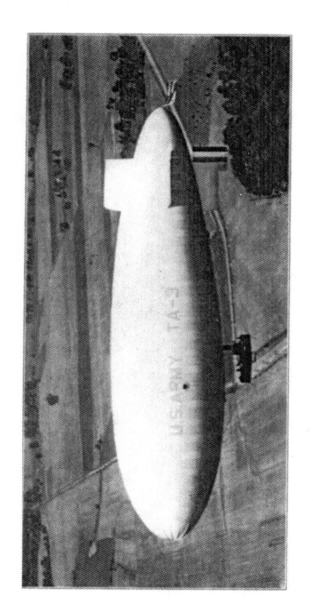

Plate I.   United States Army Airship *TA*-3

(Official Photograph, Air Corps, U. S. Army)

PRESSURE AIRSHIPS

PART I—NONRIGID AIRSHIPS

By THOS. L. BLAKEMORE, S.B., M.S.A.E.

Chief, Balloon and Airship Branch
Engineering Division, U. S. Army Air Corps

PART II—SEMIRIGID AIRSHIPS

By W. WATTERS PAGON, A.B., S.B., M.C.E.

Mem. Am. Soc. C.E.; Member Special Committee on Design of Navy
Airship ZR-1 and Army Airship RS-1

University Press of the Pacific
Honolulu, Hawaii

Pressure Airships

by
Thomas L. Blakemore
W. Watters Pagon

Afterword by Adam Starchild

ISBN: 1-4102-0439-1

University Press of the Pacific
Honolulu, Hawaii
http://www.universitypressofthepacific.com

AUTHORS' PREFACE

Pressure Airships has been adopted as the most comprehensive title for this volume to include both the nonrigid and semirigid classes of airships in which the shape of the envelope is due to maintenance of positive pressure of gas therein. Part I treats of the nonrigids, while Part II relates to semirigids. However, the scope of this work does not embrace the new type of metal-clad airship that requires internal pressure.

The smaller sizes of pressure airships as developed in the United States have been primarily for military and naval purposes, such as scouting, transportation, ship convoys, harbor defense, anti-submarine offensive operations, and as a preliminary stage of training for the crews of rigid type airships. The larger sizes, such as the Italian types of semirigids, have proved their commercial capabilities by numerous long voyages, the best known being the highly successful journey of the *Norge* from Rome to Teller, Alaska, via the North Pole.

This volume results from the experience gained by the authors in design and consulting capacities with the United States Navy and Army, during and since the World War. However, the scope is not limited to American practice, as European sources of information have been drawn upon freely, particularly regarding semirigids.

In selecting and arranging the data to be included herein, the authors had in view making the book useful for students, aeronautical engineers, designers, constructors and inspectors. The development progress in the United States has been gradual with constantly increasing efficiency of performance resulting from extensive research and the compilation of flight data; this is being continued in a way that insures even greater reliability, safety and operation performance for the future. The reader should bear in mind that information relating to principles of airship design, aerostatics, gases, fabrics, and power plants, that ordinarily would be included in a book on airships, is omitted from this volume because of being described fully in other volumes of the Ronald Aeronautic Library; footnote references at appropriate points state where such allied information is available.

The author of Part I gratefully acknowledges his indebtedness to Majors H. A. Strauss and F. M. Kennedy of the Army Air Service for advice and encouragement; also to Mr. H. T. Kraft, Chief Aeronautical Engineer of the Goodyear Tire and Rubber Company, to Mr. J. R. Gammeter, Process Engineer, and to Mr. A. G. Maranville, Aeronautical Sales Engineer of the B. F. Goodrich Rubber Company, for furnishing technical information regarding products of these companies. The author has profited much from the excellent advice of Lieut. Colonel J. A. Paegelow, Commanding Officer, and Captain H. C. Gray, Engineering Officer of Scott Field, and Lieut. R. E. Robillard at McCook Field, relating to subjects of construction and erection of airships.

The author of Part II is particularly indebted to his assistant Mr. W. W. Troxell, for valuable aid in deriving the new theory pertaining to semirigids; to Mr. Starr Truscott and Mr. C. P. Burgess, Aeronautical Engineers of the Bureau of Aeronautics, U. S. Navy; to several officers and engineers of the Army Air Corps at McCook and Scott Fields for data relating to Airship RS-1; and to executives of the National Advisory Committee for Aeronautics for advice and information supplied by them.

THOS. L. BLAKEMORE

W. WATTERS PAGON

January 5, 1927.

CONTENTS

Part I—Nonrigid Airships

CHAPTER XIII

CHAPTER XIV

CHAPTER XV

CHAPTER XVI

APPENDIX I

APPENDIX II

APPENDIX III

LIST OF ILLUSTRATIONS

PRESSURE AIRSHIPS

PART I

NONRIGID AIRSHIPS

By

THOS. L. BLAKEMORE, S.B., M.S.A.E.

Chief, Balloon and Airship Branch, Engineering Division,
U. S. Army Air Corps

CHAPTER I

GENERAL CONSIDERATIONS

The principles of airship design that determine the dimensions, shape and horsepower of any airship to accomplish a required performance, are set forth in another volume of the Ronald Aeronautic Library; therefore Part I of this volume is limited to the more specific design considerations of the component parts of pressure airships, together with descriptions of various types of construction of nonrigids.

Nonrigid airships maintain the shape of the gas-filled hull or envelope solely by means of the internal pressure of the gas therein. The compensation for contraction and expansion of the gas is produced by an air-filled ballonet (one or more) located at the bottom and inside of the elongated fabric hull. The top of the fabric ballonet is free to move up and down: it separates the lower part of the gas compartment from the air-filled ballonet.

The principle of operation is that the predetermined internal gas pressure is maintained by blowing air into the ballonet through a scoop placed in rear of the propeller, or a separate blower may be provided for that purpose. The air pressure acting on the movable ballonet diaphragm, thus produces a constant pressure within the gas containers regardless of pressure variations caused by changes of temperature or altitude. Automatic pressure release valves in both the air ballonet and gas compartments aid in regulating the pressures within proper limits.

Following are the principal advantages and disadvantages of the nonrigid class of airships:

3

Advantages. Transportability, and the elimination of the heavy rigid members as required in the semirigid and rigid airships.

Disadvantages. Heavy fabrics; short life of fabrics owing to high gas pressure; inaccessibility to repair during flight; unreliability of the pressure.

The representative types of the nonrigid class are the Astra-Torres developed by the French, and the Parseval of German origin.

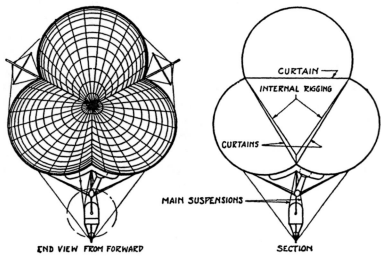

END VIEW FROM FORWARD   SECTION

Figure 1. Astra-Torres Envelope for Airships

Types of Nonrigids

Astra-Torres (Figure 1). This type was invented in Spain by Señor Torres and developed in Paris by the Astra Company. The envelope has a cross-section of the ace-of-clubs shape, the major part of the car suspension being inside the envelope. The interior of the envelope is divided into four compartments by three longitudinal diaphragms which form a triangle and retain the shape to the envelope cross-section. Passage holes in these diaphragms permit the pressure of the gas to equalize. The suspension bridles which hang from the two top ridges are independent of these diaphragms, and pass through the bottom ridge by means of gas tight expansion sleeves. There are four ballonets, two forward and two aft, outside the diaphragms, which are cross-connected by an equalizing air duct on the underside of the envelope. Air from the blower is transmitted to the ballonets through an air duct on the underside of the envelope.

With respect to the car suspension the Astra-Torres appears to have the following points in its favor.

The car suspension is attached above instead of below the center line of the envelope, with the result that the height of the ship can be reduced.

The head resistance due to rigging is reduced considerably as the greater part of the rigging is enclosed.

The Astra system, however, has not been an unqualified success owing to its complication, uncertainty of adjustment, difficulty of inspection and repair, poor form of envelope, and difficult ballonet leads. Furthermore, the advantage previously mentioned is counteracted by the tendency for the envelope to buckle earlier than would be the case were the riggings attached lower down. This will become apparent by comparing the exterior rigging of the familiar fish-form of airship envelope with the Astra system.

Parseval. The Parseval design of envelope and suspension has been an unqualified success. The torpedo-shaped envelope is the result of tests at Göttingen to obtain a shape giving the least head resistance for a given volume. The arrangement of control surfaces was also studied by models in the wind tunnel. The strength of the envelope fabric required is determined from the pressure distribution data obtained from the wind tunnel, and while there is no theory for the layout of the trajectory bands, they are

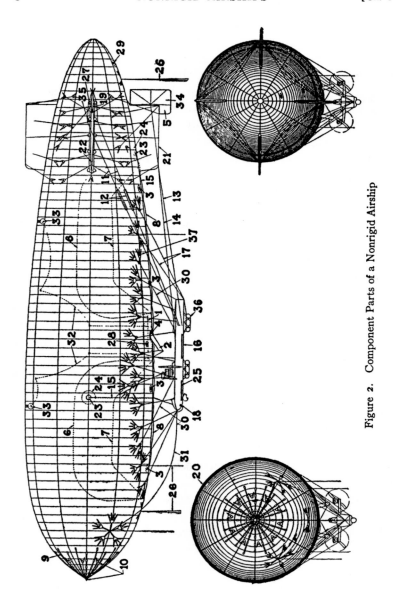

Figure 2.   Component Parts of a Nonrigid Airship

checked on a water-model. These bands are not adjustable, but are pulled taut and seem to stay so.

These bands do not embrace plane sections of the balloon, but follow a curved path, so that they become nearly vertical as they approach the upper surface, thus bringing the vertical load on top of the envelope, but placing a slightly greater proportion of the compressive force on the lower half.

The essential parts of the nonrigid airship are shown in Figure 2. Referring to the numbers on this figure, the parts are:

Part No.	Name of Part	Part No.	Name of Part
1	Air duct to ballonet	19	Elevator, balanced
2	Air scoop	20	Envelope
3	Air valve	21	Fin
4	Air damper valve	22	Stabilizer
5	Balanced portion of rudder	23	Gas valve
6	Ballonet diaphragm	24	Gas valve petticoat
7	Ballonet shoe	25	Hand rail
8	Cables, air valve operating	26	Handling lines
9	Bow (nose) stiffening	27	Horn (rudder, elevator)
10	Bow mooring unit	28	Inflation sleeve
11	Cables, elevator control	29	Deflation sleeve
12	Elevator control guide attachment	30	Martingales
13	Cables, rudder control	31	Mooring line; drag-rope bridle
14	Cables, emergency control for rudder, also named the "jury rig"	32	Rip-cords
		33	Rip-panels
15	Cables, gas valve operating	34	Rudder (balanced)
16	Car	35	Fairlead, elevator control cable
17	Car suspension	36	Bumper bags; pontoons
18	Drag-rope stowage	37	Rope finger patches

CHAPTER II

DESCRIPTION OF TYPES

References. For an account of early history including British Navy and Army airships, the reader is referred to the Royal Naval Air Service Training Manual, Chapter XII on "History of Airships." This account, though brief, is very complete. Further references are as follows:

"Present Status of Airships in Europe," by J. C. Hunsaker, U. S. N., *Journal Franklin Institute*, June, 1914.
"Applied Aerodynamics," by L. Bairstow, 1920.
"Aerial Navigation," by Dr. A. F. Zahm.
"British Airships," by George Whale.
"My Airships," by Santos Dumont.

United States

Figures 3 and 4 show silhouettes of the various airships described in this chapter. For the general characteristics of nonrigid airships, reference is made to Table 1, pages 12–15.

Navy Class A. This airship, the first constructed for the Navy, was begun in the autumn of 1915 and not completed until early in 1917. It was constructed by the Connecticut Aircraft Company and was modeled on the Parseval type. The envelope was assembled from continuous longitudinal gores of long lengths of fabric instead of rings and gores as is customary at present. The car was suspended by a rope rigging from a suspension band attached to the envelope, and was an open scow-shaped structure with two girders of tubular members projecting from it at the end. The two 4-bladed propellers were driven through two over-

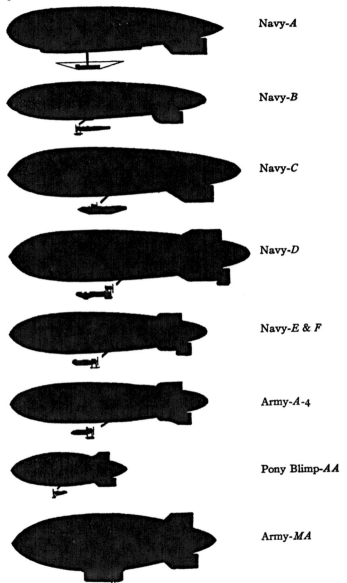

Navy-*A*

Navy-*B*

Navy-*C*

Navy-*D*

Navy-*E* & *F*

Army-*A*-4

Pony Blimp-*AA*

Army-*MA*

Figure 3.   Silhouettes of American Airship Types

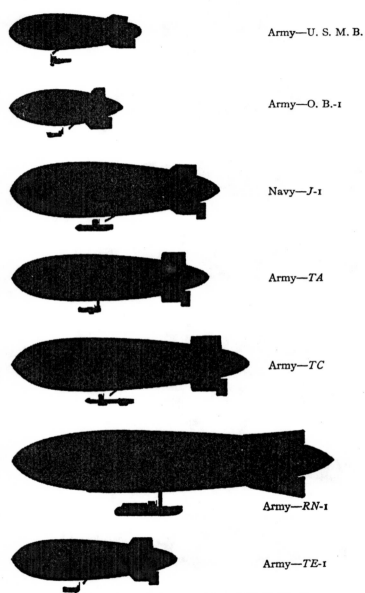

Army—U. S. M. B.

Army—O. B.-1

Navy—*J*-1

Army—*TA*

Army—*TC*

Army—*RN*-1

Army—*TE*-1

Figure 4.   Silhouettes of American Airship Types

head cross-shafts and gear case, the Sturtevant engine being carried in the car. An air blower was driven by a 1½ hp. air-cooled, single-cylinder Indian motor. The performance was considered very creditable in view of the limited amount of information on airship construction available at the time.[1]

Navy Class B.[2] This type airship was very similar to the S.S. or submarine scout type airship developed by the British Admiralty. In order to secure a type of airship that could be quickly constructed, the expedient was adopted of swinging a fuselage of an ordinary B.E.2C airplane, minus the wings, rudder and elevators, beneath the envelope. This improvised design received the slang designation of "blimp." In the United States Navy design, the engine was mounted at the forward end of the car driving a tractor propeller. Three seats in tandem were arranged behind the engine, with fuel and ballast tanks to the rear of these. One of the ships accomplished a flight duration record of 40 hrs. Nine airships of this class were built by the Goodyear Tire & Rubber Co., five by the B. F. Goodrich Co., and two by the Connecticut Aircraft Co.

Navy C.[2] This airship was designed to be used offensively against submarines, and accordingly was made to carry four 270 lb. bombs. Furthermore, to overcome the unreliability of the preceding single-engine Class *B* airship, this one was designed to carry a twin-engine power plant. The engines were mounted on outriggers on the car driving two-bladed pusher propellers. The envelope was a modification of the British Navy S.S. Zero airship envelope. Subsequent investigation in the wind tunnel at the Washington Navy Yard has shown this form to be the best from a resistance and stability standpoint yet produced for non-

[1] For further details see article on Dirigible *DN-1*, by C. F. Smythe, *Aviation*, Dec. 1, 1916.
[2] For a more complete account of the development of the Navy Class *B* and *C* designs, the reader is referred to articles on "Airship Engineering Progress in the United States," by J. C. Hunsaker, Eng. D., *Aviation*, Aug. 15 and Sept. 1, 1919.

TABLE 1—GENERAL CHARACTERISTICS

Class and Type of Airship	Year	Volume (cu. ft.)	Length Overall	Extreme Height	Max. Dia. of Hull	Extreme Width Over Fins	Elongation Ratio	Ballonet % / Hull	Car Overall Length	Car Overall Width	Car Overall Height
U. S. A.											
Pony Blimp A	17–18	35,350	95.5	40	28	29	3.3	20	12	2.5	4
OA–1	20	35,350	95.5	38.5	28	29	3.3	20	12.1	2.8	4
U. S. MB	21	49,680	109	43	29.8	29.8	3.6	26	16	3	3.6
Navy A (DN–1)	15–17	110,000	175	50	35		5				
Navy B	17	84,000	163	46	31.5	40	5.1				
Navy C	18	181,000	196	54	42	53.6	4.6	29.3	40	4.5	4.75
Navy D	19	190,000	198	58	42	51.3	4.7	30.7	28	4.75	4
Navy E	18	95,000	162	49.5	33.5	40	4.8	28	20	3	4
Navy F	18	95,000	162	48.5	33.5	39	4.8	28	18	3	4
OB–1	22	43,030	94.8	41.5	30.8	32.7	3	20	13.9	3	6.5
MA Military	21	180,000	169	56	48	50	3.4	33	29.9	5.5	7.5
Goodyear Navy Military J–1	22	173,000	170.5	58.5	45	45	3.8	30	30	4.5	4.2
A–4	19	95,000	162	47	33.5	39	4.8	25	18	2	4
TC–1-2-3 *	22	200,600	196		44.5		4.4	26	40	4.5	3
TA–1-2 *	23	130,160	162		39.3		4.1	30	18.5	4.5	4.1
TC–6 *	24	200,600	196		44.5		4.4	26	40	4.5	3
TE–1 *	26	80,200	136		34		4	25	13.16	4	3.8
TF–1 *	26	52,290	106	34.7	30.9		3.4	18	12	4.2	3.9
RN–1	21	326,500	264	75.9	49.5	62.7	5.3				
ENGLAND											
NS–7 (A. T.)		360,000	262	69.3		56.8	5.1				
S. S.	16	65,000	144		28		5.1				
Parseval	17	364,000	301		51		5.9				
S. S. Zero	17–18	70,000	143	46	32	39.5	4.4	33.3			
S. S. Twin	18	100,000	165	49		35.5					
C–12 (A. T.)		170,000	196	52		39.5					
C–Star–1 (A. T.)		210,000	218	57.5		49.3					
FRANCE											
Astra	15	495,000	295		54		5.4				
Astra	17	210,000									
Astra (Later)	17	234,000									
A. T.–O.		176,500	200	49.5	34.6		5.8				
A. T.–1-4		222,300	224	64.3	44.5	54.4	5				
A. T.–5-9		236,500	234	66	48.6	52.8	4.8				
A. T.–10-17		292,900	247	66	48.6	56.1	5.1				
A. T.–18		338,800	264	71.6	52.8	59.4	5				
A. T.–19 (Astra Type)	18	339,000	262.4	71.2	54.1	59	4.9	41.6	53.1	5.6	6.6
C. M. (Chalais Meud.)	18	176,500									
C. M.–1-4 (Chalais Meud.)	16	194,100	231	63.6	37.9	45.5	6.1				
C. M.–5	18	320,550	262.5	72.2	45.7	46.9	5.7	41.1	52.5	5.6	
C. M.–6-8 (Chalais Meud.)	18	321,200	287	70.9	46	48.6	6.2				
Capt. Caussin	17	321,900	273	75.9	46.2	47.8	5.9				
T (Chalais Meud.)	17	194,000	230			46					
Lorraine & Tunisie	16	370,600	306	78.3	46.2	50.8	6.6				
Zodiac		487,100	323	85.8	51.8	56.1	6.2				
Zodiac (D'Arl & Champ)	15–16	501,000	303	88.2	52.8	55.2	5.7				
Zodiac (Vedette)	16	77,600									
Zodiac (Vedette)	17	97,000									
Zodiac (Eclaireur)	17	219,000									
Zodiac (Croiseur)	17–18	430,000	331		50		6.6				
V. A.–1-3		70,600									
V. A.–4-5		70,600	142		29.7		4.8				
V. Z.–1-15 (Vedette Zodiac)	18	97,000	158	56.1	35.6	40.4	4.4				
V. Z.–16-23 (Vedette Zodiac)	18	109,400	158	56.1	36.3	40.4	4.4				
V. S.–1 (Zodiac)	17–18	328,000	262.5	72.2	50.2	59	5.2		54.7	4.9	
Z. D.–1-5 (Zodiac)	17	218,800	237	66	42.9	49.5	5.5				
Z. D.–6-8 (Zodiac)	17	330,000									
Zodiac U. S. N.		326,500	264	75.9	49.5	62.7	5.3				
GERMANY											
P. L.–16 (Parseval)	13	353,140	308.4		50.8		6.1				
P. L.–17	12	353,140	278.7		52.5		5.3				
P. L.–18	13	310,770	275.6		49.2		5.6				
P. L.–19	14	353,140	301.8	73.2	49.2		6.1				
P. L.–20-21	14	353,140	301.8		49.2		6.1				
P. L.–22	14	776,920	524.9		54.1		9.7				
P. L.–23	14	353,140	301.8		49.2		6.1				
P. L.–24	14	494,400	360.8		53.8		6.7				
P. L.–25 (Sea Patrol)	15	494,400	360.8	78.7	53.8		6.7				
P. L.–1	21	81,200	155.8	54.1	32.1	33.6	4.9				
P. L.–2	21	211,900	229.6	71.3	42.6	43.4	5.4				
P. L.–3	21	317,900	283.1	65.6	48.3	49.8	5.9				

* NOTE—These are helium inflated airships. Lift calculated at 55 pounds per 1,000 cu. ft.

LIFT (Lbs.)				WEIGHT (Lbs.)							
Total Lift @ .0644 lbs.	Useful Lift	Useful / Total %	Gross Weight Per H.P.	Fixed Weight	Crew	Armament	Radio	Ballast	Normal Fuel Gas and Oil	Car	Control Surfaces
2,390	930	38.9	59.8	1,460	352 (2)	...	...	130	240	261	160
2,390	893	37.4	47.8	1,497	352 (2)	...	...	278	263	497	...
3,354	1,195	35.6	27.9	2,159	600	...	...	182	413	927	158
7,438	1,604	21.6	53.1	5,834	1,232 (7)	...	...	...	...	...	...
5,680	2,080	36.6	56.8	3,600	528 (3)	300	100	200	700	...	...
12,239	4,639	37.9	40.8	7,600	704 (4)	1,200	250	200	1,500	...	...
12,239	4,339	35.5	49	7,900	704 (4)	1,200	250	440	1,550	1,344	615
6,424	1,883	29.3	42.8	4,541	528 (3)	...	...	530	640	...	...
6,424	2,134	33.2	51.4	4,290	528 (3)	...	...	...	1,170	...	...
2,908	1,146	39.4	58.2	1,763	360	...	...	206	186	292	237
12,172	4,521	37.1	46.8	7,651	1,056 (6)	...	...	1,000	2,250	1,005	...
11,698	4,698	40.2	45	7,000	880 (5)	1,080	...	400	1,260	...	...
6,424	2,224	34.7	71.4	4,200	540	...	...	390	1,294	800	622
11,584	4,116	35.5	38.6	7,468	1,000	1,100	106	425	2,691	3,110	520
7,542	1,871	25	53.8	5,671	800	...	...	300	771	2,583	386
11,584	4,073	35.2	38.6	7,511	1,000	...	106	425	2,648	3,335	557
4,630	1,334	28.8	46	3,296	800	...	...	200	334	1,025	318
2,870	933	32.5	57.4	1,937	600	...	...	150	183	637	237
21,027	...	...	42.1	...	1,760 (10)	1,760	...	1,628	...	...	...
23,184	7,384	31.8	44.6	15,800	1,760 (10)	...	...	...	...	...	...
4,186	1,236	29.5	52.3	2,950	...	...	...	...	...	...	...
23,442	5,742	24.5	65.1	17,700	...	...	...	...	...	...	...
4,508	319	7.1	60.1	4,189	528 (3)	...	...	...	...	...	...
6,440	1,690	26.2	42.9	4,750	880 (5)	...	...	...	...	...	...
10,948	3,467	31.7	36.5	7,481	880 (5)	...	...	...	...	...	...
13,524	3,086	22.8	36.6	10,438	880 (5)	...	...	...	...	...	...
31,878	14,630	45.9	72.5	17,248	1,056 (6)	...	...	...	...	...	...
13,524	...	...	39.8	...	...	...	...	...	...	...	...
15,070	5,438	36	37.7	9,632	...	...	...	...	...	...	...
11,367	...	...	37.9	...	704 (4)	440	...	880	...	...	...
14,316	...	...	44.7	...	880 (5)	528	...	880	...	...	...
15,231	...	...	21.2	...	880 (5)	550	...	1,474	...	...	...
18,863	...	...	47.2	...	1,056 (6)	1,276	...	1,826	...	...	...
21,819	9,967	45.7	43.6	11,852	1,232 (7)	1,760	176	2,552	2,750	...	...
21,832	8,980	41.1	43.6	12,852	1,232 (7)	1,760	176	2,534	2,750	528	...
11,367	3,751	33	35.5	7,616	880 (5)	...	...	1,100	...	...	...
12,500	...	...	41.7	...	880 (5)	550	176	...	3,132	...	...
20,643	4,903	23.8	44.9	15,740	...	...	...	...	3,132	...	...
20,685	4,945	23.9	41.4	15,740	880 (5)	1,320	...	1,980	...	...	...
20,730	11,098	53.5	43.2	9,632	1,056 (6)	1,760	...	1,980	...	...	...
12,494	4,206	33.7	39	8,288	880 (5)	...	...	...	...	...	...
23,867	9,979	41.8	54.2	13,888	1,232 (7)	1,760	...	2,200	...	...	...
31,369	...	...	71.3	...	1,232 (7)	2,200	...	3,080	...	...	...
32,264	13,896	43.1	73.3	18,368	1,232 (7)	2,200	...	3,080	...	...	...
4,997	...	...	35.7	...	...	...	...	...	...	...	...
6,247	...	...	52.1	...	...	...	...	...	...	...	...
14,104	...	...	32.1	...	...	...	...	...	...	...	...
27,692	...	...	61.5	...	...	...	...	...	...	...	...
4,547	...	...	56.8	...	352 (2)	176	...	110	...	...	...
4,547	...	...	53.5	...	528 (3)	176	...	220	...	...	...
6,247	...	...	39	...	528 (3)	220	...	605	...	...	...
7,045	...	...	23.5	...	528 (3)	220	...	704	...	...	...
21,123	...	...	48	...	...	...	...	...	...	...	...
14,091	...	...	20.1	...	880 (5)	550	...	1,364	...	...	...
21,252	...	...	42.5	...	...	...	...	...	...	...	...
21,027	...	...	42.1	...	1,760 (10)	1,760	...	1,628	...	...	...
22,742	6,097	26.8	63.2	16,645	...	...	...	...	...	...	...
22,742	4,753	20.9	67	17,989	...	...	...	...	...	...	...
20,013	...	...	55.6	...	...	...	...	...	...	...	...
22,742	5,873	25.8	63.2	16,869	...	...	...	3,447	...	...	...
22,742	...	...	63.2	...	...	...	...	...	...	...	...
50,032	...	...	83.4	...	...	...	...	...	...	...	...
22,742	5,873	25.8	56.9	16,869	...	...	...	...	...	...	...
31,839	9,275	29.1	75.8	22,564	...	...	...	...	6,720	5,623	...
31,839	11,314	35.5	75.8	20,525	...	...	...	...	772	441	...
5,230	1,803	34.5	32.7	3,427	880 (5)	...	...	...	2,300	1,764	...
13,646	5,410	39.6	45.5	8,236	1,760 (10)	...	...	...	3,880	3,439	...
20,473	8,897	43.5	39.4	11,576	2,816 (16)	...	...	...	...	...	...

TABLE I—GENERAL CHARACTERISTICS

CLASS AND TYPE OF AIRSHIP	ENGINE					PROP.			SPEED M.P.H.	
	Number	TYPE	H.P. of Each	Total H.P.	R.P.M.	Number	No. of Blades	Dia. In Feet	Full	Cruising
U. S. A.										
Pony Blimp A	1	Ace	40	40	2,000	1	2	7.0	40	
O4-1	1	Lawrance (3 Cyl.)	50	50	1,500	1	2	7.0	45	
U. S. MB	2	Lawrance	60	120	1,800	2	2	7.0	55	
Navy A (DN-1)	1	Sturtevant (8 Cyl.)	140	140		2	4		35	40
Navy B	1	Curtiss-OXX3	100	100	1,400	1	2		47	35
Navy C	2	Hispano-Suiza	150	300	1,400	2	2	8.5	60	40
Navy D	2	Union	125	250	1,400	2	2	8.5	58	40
Navy E	1	Thomas	150	150	2,000	1	2		56	35
Navy F	1	Union	125	125	1,400	1	2		52	35
OB-1	1	Lawrance	50	50	1,500	1	2	7	45	36
MA Military	2	Aeromarine	130	260		2	2	11.0	65	55
Goodyear Navy Military J-1	2	Aeromarine	130	260		2	2			
A-4	1	Curtiss OX	90	90	1,450	1	2	8.5	46	35
TC-1-2-3 •	2	Wright "I"	150	300	1,440	2	2	8.5	52	40
TA-1-2 •	2	Curtiss OX-5	80	160	1,250	2	4	8.0	45	36
TC-6 •	2	Lawrance	190	380	1,550	2	2	9.8	58	46
TE-1 •	2	Lawrance	40	80	1,325	2	2	7	45	35
TF-1 •	2	Lawrance	40	40	1,325	1	2	7	40	32
RN-1	2	Renault	250	500	1,300	2	2	11.5	49	
ENGLAND										
N. S.-7 (A. T.)	2	Flat	260	520		2	2		57.5	42.6
S. S.	1		80	80		1			45	38
Parseval	2	Wolseley-Maybach	180	360		2			42.5	28
S. S. Zero	1	Rolls-Royce (Hawk)	75	75		1	2		48.4	34.5
S. S. Twin	2	Rolls-Royce (Hawk)	75	150		2	2		57.5	42.5
C-12 (A. T.)	2	Sunbeam	150	300		2	4		52	
C-Star-1 (A. T.)	1	Berliet	110	110		2	2		57.5	40.3
	2	Flat	260	260						
FRANCE										
Astra	2	Chenu	220	440		2			40	
Astra	2	Renault	170	340		2				
Astra (Later)	2	Hispano-Suiza	200	400		2			50	
A. T.-O.	2	Sunbeam	150	300	2,000		4		46	
A. T.-1-4	2	Renault	160	320	1,300	2			45	
A. T.-5-9	2	Hispano-Suiza	200	400	2,000		4		49	
	2	Renault	160	320	1,300		2		45	
A. T.-10-17	2	Hispano-Suiza	200	400	2,000		4		49	
A. T.-18	2	Renault	250	500	1,300	2	4		49	
A. T.-19 (Astra Type)	2	Renault	250	500	1,300	2	4	10.2	50	
C. M. (Chalais Meud.)	2	Salmson Canton Unne	160	320		2	2		52	
C. M.-1-4 (Chalais Meud.)	2	Salmson	150	300	1,300		2		49	35
C. M.-5.	2	Salmson (Radial)	230	460	1,450	2	2	9.8	50	40
C. M.-6-8 (Chalais Meud.)	2	Salmson	250	500	1,300	2	2	9.67	49	40
Capt. Caussin.	2	Salmson Canton Unne	240	480	1,280	2	2		54	
T (Chalais Meud.)	2	Salmson Canton Unne	160	320		2	2		50	
Lorraine & Tunisie	2	Clement Bayard	220	440		2	2		43	
Zodiac	2	Zodiac	220	440		2	2			
Zodiac (D'Arl & Champ)	2	Zodiac	220	440		2	2		43	32
Zodiac (Vedette)	2	Anzani	70	140		2			50	
Zodiac (Vedette)	2	Renault	60	120		2			50	
Zodiac (Eclaireur)	2	Hispano-Suiza	220	440		2			50	
Zodiac (Croiseur)	2	Zodiac	225	450		2			47	
V. A.-1-3	2	Renault	80	80	1,700		4		37	
V. A.-4-5.	1	Rolls-Royce	85	85	1,350		4		43	
V. Z.-1-15 (Vedette Zodiac)	2	Renault	80	160	1,700	2	2		48	35
V. Z.-16-23 (Vedette Zodiac)	2	Hispano-Suiza	150	300	1,300		2		49	40
V. S.-1 (Zodiac)	2	Renault	220	440	1,300	2	2	11.4		
Z. D.-1-5 (Zodiac)	2	Hisp.-Suiza	200	400	2,000		4		49	35
	2	Renault	150	300	1,300		2		45	
Z. D.-6-8 (Zodiac)	2	Renault	220	400	1,300		2		50	
Zodiac U. S. N.	2	Renault	250	500	1,300		2		49	
GERMANY										
P. L.-16 (Parseval)	2	Maybach	180	360		2			42.2	
P. L.-17	2	Maybach	170	340		2			40.3	
P. L.-18	2	Maybach	180	360		2				
P. L.-19	2	Maybach	180	360		2		14.1	47.7	
P. L.-20-21	2	Maybach	180	360		2				
P. L.-22	3	Maybach	200	600					46.5	
P. L.-23	2	Maybach	200	400		2			43.4	
P. L.-24	2	Maybach	210	420		2			43.4	
P. L.-25 (Sea Patrol)	2	Maybach	210	420		4		14.1	43.5	
P. L.-1	1	Maybach	160	160					65	
P. L.-2	2	Maybach	160	320					65	
P. L.-3	2	Maybach	260	520					67	

Endurance Full Speed Hrs.	Full Speed Ml.	Cruising Speed Hrs.	Cruising Speed Ml.	Rate of Climb Ft. per Min.	Maximum (Ft.)	Rudder	Elevators	Lower Vert. Fin	Upper Vert. Fin	Horizontal Fins	Total Area	Rudder % Vert. Fin	Elevator % Horizontal	Type	Normal Load Gas (Lbs.)	Normal Load Oil (Lbs.)	Max. Load Gas (Lbs.)	Max. Load Oil (Lbs.)	Hourly Consump. Full Speed	Normal Speed
10	400	20			6,000	33	66	58	58	116	331	28.4	56.9	NB	240		240		24	
9	405		450		6,000	33	66	58	58	116	331	28.4	56.9		240	23	240	23		
7	385	14	560		6,000	37	74	716	628	143	388	27.5	51.7	NB	1,240	64	360	28	49.2	
2	70			700	6,000															
10.9	512	26.5	927		8,500	56	70	152		305	583	36.7	23.0	NB	670	30	670	30	61.5	26
14.8	890	31.2	1,250	1,000	8,600	82	110	372		420	962	24.0	28.1	NB	1,440	60	2,400	120	170	81
17	985	37	1,480	1,000	8,800	85	120	187	188	375	955	22.7	32.0	B	1,475	75	2,500	150	156	72
6.8	380	19.2	672		8,000	64	128	165		330	687	38.8	38.8	B	600	40	600	40	94	32
17.5	910	34.2	1,225	700	8,000	48	97	116	64	232	558	26.7	41.3	NB	1,130	40	1,200	60	76	36
7	315				6,000	99	198	174	174	348	894	29.4	29.4		172	14	336	60	27	
20	1,300	30	1,650		10,500	60	120	172	172	344	868	22.5	33.0				2,200	50		
					9,300	88	176	89	89	178	620	49.5	98.8	B	372	40			45	30
8.3	382	12.4	430	1,000	8,000	94	188	200	210	400	1,092	22.9	47	B	2,322	270	2,400	270	150	40
15	780	21	840	1,000	8,000	90	140	152	160	305	847	28.8	46	B	700	71	1,200	175	80	48
8.7	390	14.5	520	700		64	128	200	210	400	1,092	22.9	47	B	2,384	264	2,460	264	150	46
11	605	15	680	1,400		49	98	117	123	234	622	28.4	42	B	300	34	320	34	45	35
7	315	9	315	700		48	97	115	64	231	557	26.8	42	NB	165	18	200	18	40	32
8	320	10	320	700		248	253			595	1,228									
12	588																			
18	810	26	990		10,000									NB						
24	1,020	70	1,960		8,000									NB						
12	581	24	828											NB						
12	690	30	1,275																	
														B						
10	500																			
8	368																			
10	450																			
10	490																			
10	450																			
10	490																			
10	490																			
10	500					204	323			968	2,140	31.6	33.4	B			2,928			
7	343	15	525			237	194	355	226	473	1,485	40.8	41		2,952	180				
10	500	35	1,400																	
10	490	35	1,400																	
12	648																			
12	516																			
15	645																			
5	185																			
6	258																			
6	288	12	420																	
6	294	12	480																	
14		30																		
10	490	20	750																	
10	450																			
12	600																			
12	588																			
					6,560															
					6,560															
					6,560															
					8,200															
					7,872															
					8,200															
					8,200															
					8,200												1,043	113.4		
					7,540															
					8,200												5,072	551	212	13
5	325				8,200															
10	650				10,500															
10	670				13,120															

rigid airships. The Goodyear Tire & Rubber Co. constructed the envelope of 12 gores and placed the air duct inside, whereas the B. F. Goodrich Co. constructed their envelope of 20 gores and placed the air duct on the outside. In the previous design, the ballonets were placed in the nose and tail of the envelope, whereas this later design brought them close together for the purpose of reducing the tail droop. The control surfaces, however, were placed farther aft than was originally intended and this produced a slight drooping of the tail. The nose battens of this airship were of the box type construction instead of the flat type used in previous airships.

Navy Class D. This airship was designed to incorporate many improvements over the C class airship. The car was made shorter and lighter, the fuel tanks being installed on the envelope. The fins were designed with balance controls to facilitate maneuvering and a top fin was incorporated to reduce the lower vertical fin area and thereby increase the angle of clearance for the rudder, this angle being that subtended between a line drawn from the rudder to the rear of the car and the ground line. The engines were mounted higher and closer to the center line of the car, thus increasing propeller clearance. The cars for this type airship were constructed at the Naval Aircraft Factory, Philadelphia, Pa., and the envelopes at the Goodyear Tire & Rubber Co. of Akron, Ohio.

Navy Class E and F. The E airship was a special type built by the Goodyear Tire & Rubber Co. in which a Thomas geared engine was used, located in the rear of the car. The F airship was similar to the Class E; it was proposed to use this F-type for an engine testing airship; the car was constructed with that purpose in view. A Union engine, rated at 125 hp., was installed in the rear of the first car built. The fuel tanks for both E and F airships were installed in the envelope at the bottom between the ballonets. They were enclosed in gas-tight covers through which the suspension lines passed to patches cemented to the top of the envelope.

Army A-4. This type was modeled in general on the E and F types, the differences being: the fuel was contained in four cylindrical tanks suspended below the widest element on the outside of the envelope, thus allowing the ballonets to be brought closer together; the Curtiss OX-5 engine replaced the Thomas and Union engines.

Pony Blimp, AA. This airship was designed and constructed by the Goodyear Tire & Rubber Co., for sport purposes and commercial uses. The first airship of this class designated as the Type A Pony Blimp was equipped with a 40 hp. engine located in the rear of the car and driving a pusher propeller. The second airship designated as the AA Pony Blimp was equipped with a 3-cylinder air-cooled Lawrance radial type engine developing 50 hp. This engine was mounted in the forward end of the car as a tractor to facilitate starting by the pilot. The total fuel capacity of 40 gal. was carried in the car. One main tank of 35 gal. was mounted in the rear section and the balance of 5 gal. carried in a gravity tank. The gravity tank was fed from the rear tank by means of the standard Stewart vacuum system mounted directly into the gravity tank. This was the first instance where the vacuum system was used with success in an airship. A hand pump was also provided in case the Stewart system should fail. The gravity tank had a separate compartment for 5 gal. of reserve oil which fed through the engine pump by merely opening a valve. A discharge valve was installed in the main tank for the purpose of using the fuel as emergency ballast. The rudder was controlled by stirrups, and the elevators by a wheel mounted on the right side of the car.

The car was made easily detachable by removing the clevis pins at the cable suspension clips. Two seats were provided which, however, could accommodate three passengers, one being the pilot. An unusual feature of this design was the one ballonet in place of the usual two in nonrigid airships. Consequently, the method of adjusting trim by selective inflation of ballonets was sacrificed. This airship was considered very unstable owing to its bluntness of form, the elongation ratio being 3.3 which produces a relatively small moment arm for the aerodynamic load on the control surfaces. This no doubt could be overcome by increasing the area of the control surfaces, thereby sacrificing useful lift. Further description of this airship may be found in *Aviation*, April 16, 1920.

Army MA. The envelope of this airship was of the Pony Blimp form having an elongation ratio of 3.6. The Goodyear Tire & Rubber Co., the designer of the airship, adopted this form to decrease the head resistance and tail droop, which are important factors in airship envelope design. However, aerodynamic stability was sacrificed as in the Pony Blimp airship. No attempt was made to correct this later by increasing the control surface area owing to the policy adopted by the Army in 1923 to inflate all airships with helium gas instead of hydrogen, which necessitated the increase of volume of all existing airships in order to obtain the same useful lift as originally designed with hydrogen. The car of the *MA* airship was therefore slung under a *TC* envelope and no further investigation was made to determine the feasibility of increasing the controllability of the *MA* airship by altering the control surfaces.

The car is of the inclosed type. The two 135 hp. Aeromarine Model U6D engines are mounted longitudinally in the rear of the car with the propeller transmission between them including clutches, brakes, reverse gear and blower.

The tractor propellers 11 ft. in diameter, were mounted on outrigger tubes. The radiators are set on bosses located on the tubes. A detailed description of this airship is included in an article by H. T. Kraft, Chief Aeronautical Engineer of the Goodyear Tire & Rubber Co., published in *Aviation*, January 23, 1922.

Army, United States MB. A twin-engine, nonrigid airship was designed for experiment as an observation balloon. It was built on contract for the Engineering Division by the Airships, Inc., at Hammondsport, N. Y. The use of an engine-driven balloon for observation purposes greatly increases the range of activity and makes possible the removal of the base of operation from the immediate danger zone to a more suitable location with resultant economy of personnel and equipment. The advantages claimed for this type of airships are:

> It may be assembled at the operating base back of the front line.
>
> Concentration of personnel and supplies at operating base leaving only the winch crew at the observation point.
>
> Bedding down or housing all balloons at operating base and flying up to observation position.
>
> All gas generating and topping to be done at base.
>
> Increased radius of operation.
>
> To make equipment available for uses other than the direction of gun fire.
>
> Increases the utility of balloon companies by the handling of more than one observation point.

The principal feature of construction is the use of a single ballonet and a detachable engine outrigger. During trial flight, the following characteristics were observed: High speed for this type airship approximately 60 M.p.h.; the speed at which reverse control occurred was very low being about 7 M.p.h.; controllability satisfactory.

This equipment was later used in connection with the

project for exterminating the gipsy moth in the New England states.

A blower which was later developed for this airship is described under the subject of Blowers, page 99.

Army OB-1. The original designation of this airship was the *H*-1 type, having been constructed by the Goodyear Tire & Rubber Co. for the Navy to meet the following requirements as laid down by the Bureaus of Construction and Repair and Engineering:

> To be the smallest size possible to meet the required performance and load factor allowing inflation of the envelope in the well of an airship tender which measured 99 ft. in length by 35 ft. in width at the forward end with straight sides running aft to 27 ft. width at the aft end.
>
> Car to be easily and quickly detachable and attachable.
>
> The fins and rudders also to be arranged to permit easy and quick attachment and detachment.
>
> Car to be of the pusher type with portable cover.
>
> The water ballast container to be used for fuel when occasion demanded.
>
> The arrangement of the towing bridle and cable attachment to permit, (*a*) ease of attachment and detachment of towing cable, (*b*) the use of telephone cable, and (*c*) a break-away controlled from the car, releasing cable and telephone connections simultaneously.
>
> The bow of the envelope to be stiffened to provide for towing at 70 M.p.h.

The following observations were made during trial flights at Wilbur Wright Field, Fairfield, Ohio:

> The airship towed satisfactorily in moderate wind and handled much better than a Type *R* balloon would have done under similar conditions, due undoubtedly to the fact that sufficient pressure was maintained in the envelope throughout the test.
>
> The form of the envelope which was a Goodyear Pony

Blimp shape except that the elongation ratio was reduced to 3, is very inefficient.

For inland flying, the car could be equipped with bumpers; however, the car which was designed for landing on the water is also suitable for land use.

The pelican hooks provided for quickly detaching suspension lines was a special feature of the design which was considered very satisfactory.

A blower is essential to maintain sufficient pressure in the envelope. However, on a small ship it is a difficult matter to get a suitable blower installation for a reasonable sacrifice of useful lift.

It was observed that in order to maintain the required pressure in the envelope, the engine had to be run about 1,000 r.p.m.

Navy J-1. This airship, which was designed by the Bureau of Aeronautics, United States Navy, was constructed by the Goodyear Tire & Rubber Co. in 1922. The envelope was a modified Class C form with an elongation ratio of approximately 3.7. The principal features of design were as follows:

A single ballonet was provided.

The rip-panel extended transversely across the top of the envelope instead of longitudinally. This was done as there was not much to choose between the two positions owing to the ballonet being located over the car, making direct rip-cord leads impracticable, and owing to the blunt form of the airship.

The car was of a semi-monocoque type of construction similar to the type just previously furnished to the Army for two of the Class C ships turned over to it by the Navy, except that it was more sturdily built. The length of the car was reduced from that of the Class C by omitting the rear cockpit and placing the mechanic forward of the engine outrigger with his seat facing to the rear.

Pontoons were omitted; a central keel running along the bottom of the car.

The outrigger was of a cantilever type similar to the modified *C* car noted above and to the present *TC* airship car.

Army TA. In 1922, owing to the policy adopted by the Army Air Service, all ships were to be designed for helium inflation and no ships were under any circumstances to be flown with hydrogen. This policy made impracticable the further production of any airships of the *A*-4 or Class *C* types. Accordingly the Army *TA* airship was designed to replace the original *A*-4. The envelope form of the *A*-4 was retained, increasing its volume to 130,000 cu. ft.; the car was redesigned, the twin-engine power plant being located in the aft end of the car.

Army TC. To replace the Types *C* and *D* airships with a helium inflated airship, the Type *TC* was designed for advanced training. The special features of this design were as follows:

A double ballonet was provided, consisting of a single ballonet with partitions, as recommended by operating stations, in place of two single ballonets, the object being to reduce the tail droop by obtaining a more rigid envelope beam and increasing the lift in the region of the surfaces; reduction of the large pitching moments by providing the separate ballonets; an air compartment directly above the engine and propeller as a measure of safety against loss of helium due to possible tearing of the envelope by the propeller; elimination of the long air line joining the ballonet.

The car structure was designed to afford a factor of safety of 6 under static load. The original ships of this design were equipped with two single ballonets and 34 in. landing pontoons to provide sufficient ground clearance for the installation of bombs underneath the car.

The *TC*-4, 5, and 6, constructed in 1923 and 1924, were

Plate II.   Car for Airship *J*-1

Plate III.   United States Army Airship *TC*-5

Plate IV.   Outrigger for Port Engine, Airship *TC*-6

equipped with the double ballonet as indicated. The landing pontoons were reduced to 19 in. as the armament equipment had been omitted. The S.C.R.-134 radio set was installed in the second cockpit of the car. A space was also left in the aft end of the rear cockpit for the installation of a suitable blower. The car was strengthened to a load factor of 6 as noted above. The TC-7, 8 and 9 were equipped with two single ballonets owing to the difficulties encountered with the double ballonet having partitions as mentioned under subject of Ballonets.

The TC-6 airship was identical with the TC-4 and 5 except that the Wright 1-engine installation was replaced by two Lawrance J-1 engines driving tractor propellers, 9 ft. 10 in. in diameter which installation comprised the first air-cooled engine installation for nonrigid airships of this size and power. A saving of 400 lbs. was made in comparison with the previous TC airship by eliminating water cooling installation, although no saving was made in structural weight. With this modification, it is expected to increase the maximum speed of the airship from 54 M.p.h. to 60 M.p.h. With the combined reduction in weight and increased power an increase in range at full and half power of 10 per cent is expected.

Army RN-1. This airship was originally known as the ZDUS-1 at the time it was acquired from the French government by the United States Navy. It was later turned over to the United States Army and erected at Langley Field. As this ship was originally designed by the French government, a detailed description will be omitted here, the reader being referred to an article in the September 3, 1923, issue of *Aviation.* Modifications were made in the car at Scott Field in 1922 and 1923 to reduce its weight and to replace foreign equipment with standardized American equipment. The two Renault engines were replaced by two Packard type 1237 engines. Extensive alterations were made in the car, such as removing armament equipment and the heavy gun cockpit in the forward end. A new system of controls was installed and a winter top covered the forward half of the car.

Army TE-1. Designed by the Engineering Division, McCook Field, the *TE*-1 airship is intended to replace the present *TA* airship for the purpose of economizing in helium operation. This accounts for its reduction in volume and power. The envelope is of the Class *C* form with an elongation ratio of 4. The envelope and surfaces were constructed by the Airships, Inc., at Hammondsport, N. Y., and the car by the Aircraft Development Corporation of Detroit. The car is based on the monocoque form of construction, duralumin sheet being used throughout with the exception of the knee braces for the engine outriggers which are seamless steel tubing. A double ballonet is installed by which it is hoped to eliminate the difficulties encountered in this type of ballonet as described in Chapter III under Ballonets.

Germany

A new type of nonrigid airship has been proposed by H. Naatz, which is described in N.A.C.A. Technical Memorandum No. 277 on recent researches in airship construction. The essential features of this new type are summed up in the following advantages claimed for it as quoted in the Memorandum:

> The new type is as rigid as a rigid airship.
> It is just as strong as a nonrigid airship.
> It is not nearly so sensitive to injuries as a nonrigid airship due to the network under the envelope, and tears are not propagated so easily as in cloth envelopes.
> The gas cells are arranged the same as in rigid airships.

It is only slightly affected by the heat of the sun and by the weather, on account of the wide ventilating space.

It is lighter than a rigid airship.

It can be made of all dimensions, up to the largest, since the stresses are taken up by a metal network, which can be made as strong as desired.

This type of airship is in answer to the question "Will nonrigid airships be able to compete with rigid airships in size and performance?" Security against buckling in nonrigids is maintained by the mean internal pressure which remains the same for any geometrical enlargement of the airship and changes only in direct proportion to the dynamic pressure at the maximum velocity. However, the elimination of distortion which is difficult to accomplish in nonrigid airships becomes increasingly so with the increase in size of the ship. This difficulty is due to the considerable flexibility of nonrigid airships which are made of woven fabric which has the further disadvantage of stretching unequally. These fabric characteristics make the adaptation of stiffening frames, which are added to resist the distortion, increasingly difficult.

The foregoing facts led to the conception of making the envelope of material of less flexibility than the woven fabric. A steel band as compared with a strip of fabric of the same tensile strength was observed to have $1/150$ the elongation of the fabric. Briefly, the design is as follows: the envelope includes a network of steel tape of 1 meter mesh. This network completely surrounds the hull, being secured to the bottom girder of the longitudinal keel containing the walkway and is held down at the top by a network partition in the vertical plane of symmetry, this partition being attached to the top girder of the keel frame. The gas cells are inserted in the spaces between the partition and the network on both sides. The outer envelope is held at a distance of about 0.2 meters, forming an arc over the top at a somewhat greater distance. The space between the network and the envelope is connected with the space under the gas valve and subjected to a pressure of 2 to 6.1 lbs. per sq. ft. (See page 222 in Part II of this volume.)

The partition serves to give the airship a more circular cross-section, provides a convenient means for attaching the control surfaces, and permits the introduction of a walkway and the installation of valves on the top of the airship. The outer envelope serves as a weather proofing and is air tight. The network supports not only the pressure from the gas, but also the pressure in the outer envelope. The increased pressure in the airship is obtained from the relative wind during flight and from blowers when the airship is at rest. Through the adjustment of the inlet and outlet valves, ventilation of the air space is maintained to prevent the accumulation of inflammable gases and the overheating of the gas in the cells.

The transverse bulkheads upon which depends the static longitudinal stability, safety against increase of gas pressure at the ends and against the sinking of the airship from gas leakage, are made in the form of an undivided cylinder surface, by taking two cylinders which intersect each other in the middle partition and are tangential, or nearly so, to the network on the sides of the airship. The theory of this type of partition is that only the horizontal circumferential threads take up the stress when a pressure is exerted on the wall. The threads run into the envelope at angles varying from 0 to 30 degrees. Consequently, the tendency of the envelope to wrinkle is produced by constricting loads constituting only about ¼ of the tension of the bulkhead which is applied to edges directed obliquely to the axis of the airship. These wrinkles would hardly be noticeable as the loads are taken up chiefly by the peripheral tension in the envelope. The foregoing theory, the author states, has been substantiated by water model tests.

CHAPTER III

AIRSHIP HULL

Envelope

It is assumed that the designer has determined the size and form of the envelope that will provide the useful lift, speed and ceiling needed to fulfill a definite operating requirement.

Patterning. The envelope is divided into equal gores and patterned by the conic-frustum method. The curved sides of the patterns are joined along the panel seams. The width of the panels is the maximum that can be obtained from the fabric supplied.

The *conic-frustum* method of determining patterns is as follows:

Referring to Figure 5,

$$R = \frac{r_2 H}{r_2 - r_1}$$

$$\phi = \frac{\pi r_2}{NR} 57.296°$$

Where N = Number of gores, and
$$L_2 = 2 R \sin \phi$$
$$L_1 = 2(R - H) \sin \phi$$
$$d_2 = R \text{ versin } \phi$$
$$d_1 = (R - H) \text{ versin } \phi$$

Determine the maximum width of fabric to be used and choose H so that $H + d_1 +$ allowance for seam lap equals the maximum width approximately.

A simpler method adopted by manufacturers, which

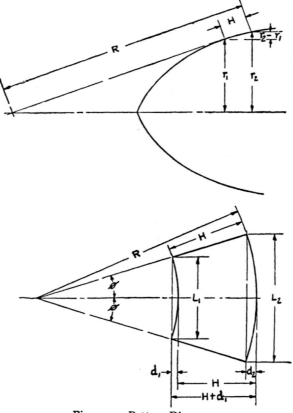

Figure 5.   Pattern Diagrams

introduces a negligible error, follows.   (Refer to Figures 5 and 6.)

$$\frac{R}{R - H} = \frac{L_2}{L_1}$$

$$R = \frac{L_2 H}{L_2 - L_1}$$

$$R = \frac{r_2 H}{r_2 - r_1}$$

$$L_2 = \frac{\pi\, r_2}{N} \qquad (1)$$

$$L_1 = \frac{\pi\, r_1}{N} \qquad (2)$$

Where N = Number of gores
Assume Arc L = Chord L in Figure 6,
Then

$$\frac{2R}{L} = \frac{L}{d}$$

Whence

$$d = \frac{L^2}{2R}$$

And similarly,

$$d_2 = \frac{L^2_2}{2R} \qquad (3)$$

$$d_1 = \frac{L_1^2}{2\,(R - H)} \qquad (4)$$

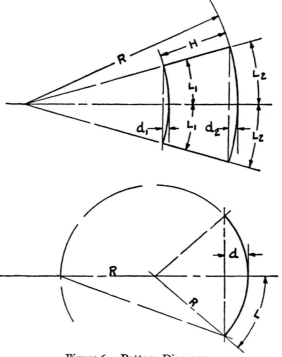

Figure 6.   Pattern Diagrams

In carrying out the foregoing methods, it is necessary for the designer to lay out the envelope curve to a scale as large as possible in order that the dimensions r_1 and r_2 obtained from the curve may be accurately determined. The minimum scale which has given satisfactory results is ½ in. equals 12 in.

It will be obvious that the pattern and layout calculations are minimized for an envelope curve that has fixed geometrical properties. For then the ordinates r_1 and r_2, or offsets of the curve, may be expressed as y functions of x; and y_1, and y_2, equivalents of r_1 and r_2 in the foregoing equations, are chosen so that $[(y_2 - y_1)^2 + (x_2 - x_1)^2]^{1/2} + d_1 +$ allowance for seam lap equals the maximum width of fabric approximately. It is further evident that

$$H = [(y_2 - y_1)^2 + (x_2 - x_1)^2]^{1/2} \qquad (5)$$

Seams. For cutting, cementing, sewing and taping of seams the reader is referred to these subjects as they appear under Inspection in Chapter VIII.

Seams are required to develop the full strength of the fabric that is joined, to be gas tight, and to be light in weight. During the development period necessary to determine the most satisfactory type of seam to meet the requirements, the results noted in the following paragraphs were obtained of interest to the engineer and designer.

For the following observations, reference is made to tests by the Bureau of Standards in cooperation with the joint Army and Navy Aircraft Board as reported in the N.A.C.A. Report No. 37 on "Fabric Fastenings," by E. Dean Walen and R. T. Fisher in 1919; report prepared by the Goodyear Tire & Rubber Co., for the Navy in 1919; and various Engineering Division Air Corps, United States Army tests conducted on balloon fabric seams subsequent to 1921.

Sewing. In all cases where a single thread was used

without cement, whether of silk, linen or cotton, the thread sheared indicating that single thread sewing was not sufficient in seams where the cement softens to any appreciable extent. For two rows of stitching, both cotton and linen threads sheared while the silk held, indicating that in cases of extreme cement softening silk thread is preferable. For three rows of thread the fabric tore at the needle holes. The type of construction used in these tests was a ¾ in. lap seam, the threads were ¼ in. apart and from 6 to 8 stitches per in. The cotton thread used was the ONT cord soft-finish left twist, number 30 averaging 3.5 lbs. strength for the upper bobbin. The fabric employed in these tests was airship envelope type having a strength of about 75 to 80 lbs. per in., machine test 12 in. per min.[1]

Cementing. It was found early in the development that seams could be made 100 per cent in strength without the application of sewing and taping. The sewing however is required because the cement becomes soft at a high temperature which allows a seam slippage if the sewing is omitted. The threads are depended upon to hold the seams during the period of cement softening. When the temperature is reduced, the cement becomes hardened and is as strong as originally. The present tests on cement require that the temperature be held to 115° F. plus or minus 5° and that it should withstand the required load for not less than 24 hours without failure.

Taping. Taping is required to insure gas tightness of the seams because the sewing punctures the gas film of the fabric, also to protect the thread from wear. Where seams are exposed to the gas directly, an additional tape of greater width is cemented over the narrower tape. All taping is biased in order that it may stretch with the envelope.

---

[1] Complete tables giving the strength and permeability characteristics of rubberized airship fabrics are included in Part III of the volume "Free and Captive Balloons" of the Ronald Aeronautic Library. The tables referred to give data regarding each layer of cloth and rubber comprising the fabrics.

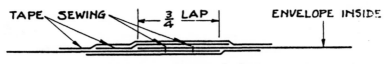

LONGITUDINAL GAS TIGHT SEAM.

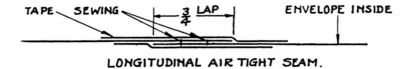

LONGITUDINAL AIR TIGHT SEAM.

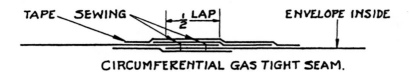

CIRCUMFERENTIAL GAS TIGHT SEAM.

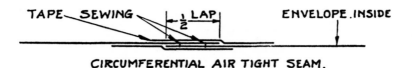

CIRCUMFERENTIAL AIR TIGHT SEAM.

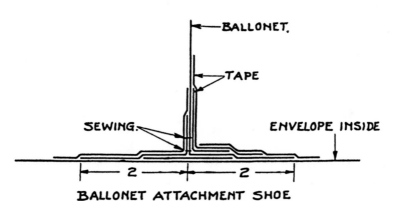

BALLONET ATTACHMENT SHOE

Figure 7. Seams and Ballonet Attachment Shoe

Dark lines appear on the edges of the tape as it stretches which has been mistaken for seam slippage but in reality it is due to the actual narrowing of the bias tape as it stretches.

Standard Seams. Figure 7 illustrates the standard seams in use at present for nonrigid airships. All longitudinal seams have a ¾-in. lap, with sewing spaced ¼-in. apart; either the lock or chain stitch is used with 6 or 8 stitches per in. The inside and outside tapes are 1½ in. to 1⅝ ins. in width. An additional tape 2⅜ in. in width is cemented to the inside for gas-tight seams. This tape overlaps the edge of the narrower tape equally. The narrower tape both inside and out overlaps the fabric edges by ⅝ in.

The circumferential seams differ from the longitudinal seams in that the lap is only ½ in., and that the width of the narrower tape is 1⅛ in., and of the wide tape 1⅝ in. The reduction of the width of the circumferential seam is due to the longitudinal envelope stresses being less than the circumferential stresses. Reduction in seam width produces a material saving in weight.

The foregoing applies to envelope seams. The ballonet seams are identical with the envelope air-tight seams with the exception that the sewing is omitted. Sewing is not considered necessary as the ballonet is not under great stress.

All inside tapes are non-aluminized whereas the outside tapes are aluminized.

Weights. On page 34, the seam weights are tabulated for the use of the designer.

Tailoring. The envelope of a nonrigid airship is tailored to overcome the permanent deformation produced by the forces of internal pressure and weight acting upon it. The process consists of cutting out "pie-shaped" vertical strips from either the top or the bottom of the envelope or both.

TABLE 2—SEAM WEIGHTS

Type	Wt. Fabric oz. per sq. yd.	Wt. Seam lbs. per linear yd.
Ballonet Seam..................................	8.5	.073
Ballonet Shoe..................................	8.5	.074
Envelope Seam, Gas-tight, Circumferential.........	13.4	.0808
Envelope Seam, Air-tight, Circumferential.........	11.4	.05214
Envelope Seam, Gas-tight, Longitudinal............	13.4	.129
Envelope Seam, Air-tight, Longitudinal	11.4	.078

The width of the strips has been standardized to a maximum of 3 in.

The theoretical determination of the deformation of the envelope from which it is possible to determine the proper amount and location for tailoring, will not be dealt with here; it is set forth fully in Report No. 16 of the National Advisory Committee for Aeronautics (1917) by Haas and Dietzius as translated from the German by Professor Karl K. Darrow.

For the comparatively small nonrigid airships so far produced in this country, the proper amount of tailoring has been determined by one or more of the following methods: by observations on the form of the first airship of any new series upon which corrections may be based; by comparison of the bending moment curves of similar types of airships; or by water model tests showing the amount of deformation to be overcome.

Ballonet

Historical. The ballonets of the first practical airship to be constructed in America, the Goodyear F, 77,000 cu. ft., sister ship of the Navy B, 84,000 cu. ft. airship, were ovoidal in form and were suspended from the top of the envelope by means of patches and ropes, one being located in the

nose and the other one-fourth of the envelope length from
the tail of the airship.

This type of bailonet proved impracticable for the following reasons: Excessive fabric weight; internal rigging
which was difficult to install and inaccessible to inspection
adjustment, and maintenance; inflation difficulties caused
by gas pressure on folded fabric which produced excessive
strains on the suspension, at times causing it to break away.

Form. The ovoidal form was superseded by the diaphragm. In this type the underside is formed by the envelope and the upper side by a diaphragm duplicating
the portion of the envelope enclosed. The diaphragm is
attached to the inside of the envelope along the "ballonet
intersection line." The problem is to design the diaphragm
so that on deflation of the ballonet, the diaphragm fabric
will lie evenly upon the envelope beneath.

With the ballonet located in the *nose* of the envelope,
the diaphragm is designed as a duplication of the envelope
patterns beneath (see Figure 8).

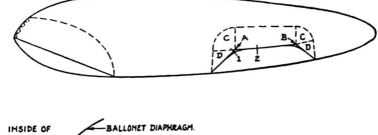

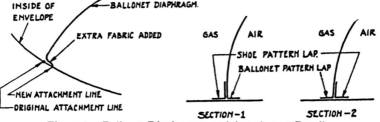

Figure 8.   Ballonet Diaphragms and Attachment Details

The *rear ballonet,* not being in the tail where the section of the envelope diminishes rapidly, the middle of the intersection line is made on an element of the envelope; this part of the ballonet approximates a cylindrical section when inflated. The ends consist of sections approximating conical and spherical wedges (C and D respectively, in Figure 8). The cylindrical and conical sections duplicate the envelope patterns beneath, the spherical section being added to allow this type of construction to assume its inflated position.

As the envelope fabric stretches about 4 per cent beyond its original dimension in a transverse direction due to internal gas pressure, it is necessary to allow this much *excess fabric* in the diaphragm in order to prevent straining the attachment line when the ballonet is deflated.

In order to prevent the ballonet attachment from loosening at points A and B (Figure 8), it is necessary to round the intersection line at these points, adding fabric for shaded areas (right and left hand of this area required as will be seen by a study of Figure 8, lower left sketch), and interchanging position of "ballonet pattern laps" with "shoe pattern laps" at the location of the new attachment line (Figure 8, lower right).

Attachment. The attachment of the ballonet to the inside of the envelope was originally made by means of a sewed and taped seam. Taping applied on the outside of the envelope to cover the stitching, entailed considerable labor as the aluminum proofing had to be removed by buffing. The present type of attachment, known generally as the "shoe construction" (Figure 7), is a cemented seam, thereby reducing labor considerably; it has proved very satisfactory having withstood several years of service tests.

Number. Two is the usual number of ballonets. As it is desirable to trim the ship by means of the ballonet, two ballonets are preferable to a single ballonet. However, the single ballonet has been used successfully, in the smaller ships as the Pony Blimp *A*, *AA* and *AB*, and with the questionable success in the Navy *J* and Army *MA* airships.

The *single ballonet* with transverse partition has not been entirely successful owing to the difficulty in designing the partition so that it will fold evenly on the bottom of the envelope when deflated, without producing excessive strains at the junction of its shoe with the main diaphragm shoe. Even with this difficulty eliminated there remains the resistance of the partition to unfolding when the inflation is on one side of the partition with the other side deflated. This resistance is sufficient to produce rupture in the partition, causing a concussion due to the rush of air through the rupture from the inflating side to the deflated side.

This type of ballonet has been made to work successfully in the Army *TC* airships by taking the precaution to have a little air in the deflated side of the partition, say 1,000 cu. ft., during inflation of the other side of the partition.

Contrary to popular opinion, considerable degree of trim can be obtained, with the single ballonet equipped with the partition. With the *TC* airship the maximum range of trim from the condition of forward ballonet empty and rear ballonet 85 per cent full to the reverse condition, was found to be 12½°.

Location of the center of volume of the ballonets should be directly over the center of gravity of expendable weights in order to effect the trim of the airship the least when ballonets are kept evenly full.

In the early stages of development the ballonets were located as far apart as it was possible to get them in order to obtain the greatest degree of trim. That arrangement, however, produced excessive tail droop owing to diminished lift over the control surfaces. Furthermore, this arrangement caused the airship to be very sensitive in trim as might be expected.

Therefore ballonets are located as close as it is possible to get them, allowing for the air damper valves and air ducts in the envelope.

Nose Stiffening [2]

To avoid the necessity for very high internal pressures, nose stiffening is provided (see Plate V). It is obvious that without nose stiffening the inside pressure necessarily would be greater than the dynamic pressure. At 60 M.p.h. this pressure on the nose at the center line of the ship would be 1.75 in. of water, and the internal pressure when diving at 30° would have to be 3.1 in. of water in a ship 200 ft. in length. This pressure would not take care of gusts, accelerations of the ship, changes of internal pressure due to surging of the gas and other departures from still air standard conditions.

The problem therefore consists in determining the proper length and strength of the battens such that the algebraic sum of all the air and gas pressures acting on the rigid portion of the nose shall be directed forward or that the longitudinal component of the gas pressure shall be greater than the longitudinal component of the external air pressure; and that the moment of the external forces at the nose end of the batten is equal to that of internal or supporting forces. The following is an example to illustrate the method of design.

Problem. To determine the length and size of nose battens for an 80,000 cu. ft. nonrigid airship with the following factors given:

[2] See also Chapter XVI of this volume for nose stiffening of semirigid airships.

(Official Photograph, Air Corps, U. S. Army)

Plate V.   Nose Stiffening

Maximum air speed.........45 M.p.h.
Form of airship given on Figure 9.
Table 3, Pressure Distribution Data for Angle of Pitch of 0°.
Table 4, Pressure Distribution Data for Angle of Pitch of 9°.
Internal Envelope Pressure, 1.1 in.

(a) Plot the intensity of pressure curve from Table 3 for about 20 per cent of the length of the envelope.

(b) Assume the number of battens to be 12 and determine the batten spacing L which multiplied by the width of station W is the area assumed to be supported by the batten.

(c) *External loads:* These are obtained by multiplying the pressure curve ordinate at each station by the area previously obtained for that station which result is the station load in pounds per impact pressure. The moments of these external loads are then obtained and integrated and finally multiplied by the impact pressure. This impact

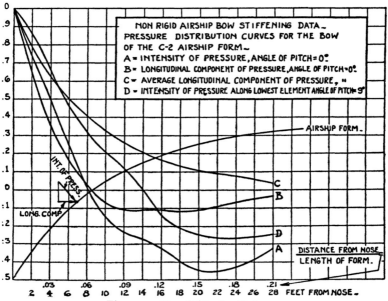

Figure 9.   Bow Stiffening Data

TABLE 3—PRESSURE DISTRIBUTION DATA FOR C-2 FORM
(Angle of Pitch, 0°)

p/q	x/l	p/q	x/l
1 00	0	− .21	.3713
.63	.0215	− .17	.4430
.15	.0498	− .14	.5265
− .22	.0844	− .10	.6092
− 35	.1231	− .09	.6920
− .45	.1630	− 08	.7752
− .33	.2052	− .02	.8574
− 25	.2878	.03	.9380
		.17	1.0000

TABLE 4—PRESSURE DISTRIBUTION FOR C-2 FORM
(Values of p/q Angle of Pitch 9°)

x/l	φ						
	0°	30°	60°	90°	120°	150°	180°
.0	.882	.854	.792	.833	.869	.847	.893
0215	.803	.844	.574	.514	.364	.331	.332
0498	.401	.435	.166	.085	− .112	− .160	− .223
0844	.016	.036	− .229	− .278	− .461	− .479	− .516
.1231	− .153	− .099	− .334	− .368	− .503	− .508	− .519
.1630	− .249	− .216	− .416	− .418	− .509	− .499	− .467
.2052	− .237	− .202	− .364	− .383	− .449	− .417	− .389
2878	− .214	− 168	− .325	− .321	− .368	− .291	− .285
.3713	− .178	− .146	− .319	− .277	− .270	− .204	− .200
.4430	− .220	− .157	− .281	− .254	− .252	− 196	− .138
5265	− .213	− .167	− .249	− .226	− .251	− .129	− .098
.6092	− .182	− .132	− .255	− .203	− .197	− .120	− .082
6920	− .168	− .129	− .255	− .171	− .168	− .071	− .037
.7752	− .185	− .154	− .245	− .145	− .122	− .070	− .036
.8574	− .148	− .093	− .178	− .075	− .066	− .012	+ .014
.9380	− .143	− .068	− .058	.066	.024	.022	− .021
.9750	.093	.138	.038	.116	.075	.097	.068
1.0000	.114	.155	.074	.122	.081	.098	.126

Explanation of Symbols

p = Pressure at point on model
q = Impact pressure
x = Distance from nose to plane perpendicular to axis through point on model
l = Length of model
φ = Angle between plane of tube and vertical
φ = 0° when tube is lowest   φ = 180° when tube is highest

pressure is assumed to be produced by a wind velocity 15 M. in excess of the maximum speed of the airship in order to take care of gusts. This assumption results in an impact pressure of 9.7 lbs. per sq. ft. which is multiplied by the summation of moments for each station, the number of stations being selected as 10.

(d) *Internal loads:* The supporting areas as noted in paragraph (b) above are multiplied by 5.7 lbs. per sq. ft. which is the pressure equivalent to an internal pressure of 1.1 in. of water. This product, which is the supporting load, is then used to determine the moment of the supporting load about the zero station. The integration of these moments gives a result at station 10 which is approximately equal to the summation of the moments of the external load as noted in the previous paragraph and shown in Table 5.

(e) *The length of these battens* is therefore determined as approximately 10 ft. This length should be checked against the curve of average longitudinal component of pressure to satisfy the conditions requiring that the algebraic sum of all the air and gas pressures acting on the rigid portion of the nose shall be directed forward. The ordinates of the curve of *average longitudinal component of pressure* is obtained from the intensity of pressure curve for the angle of pitch of zero degrees by determining the longitudinal component of the pressure at various points along the envelope curve as indicated in Figure 9, from which is determined by integration the *average longitudinal component of pressure* desired. The ordinate of this curve at station 10 on the batten, when multiplied by the impact pressure of 9.7 lbs. per sq. ft. gives the air pressure in lbs. per sq. ft. normal to the cross-section of the envelope which should not exceed the gas pressure of 5.7 lbs. per sq. ft. in order to prevent cupping in of the nose of the envelope.

TABLE 5—NOSE STIFFENING DATA
(Internal and External Loads)

Station	Dist. btw. Sta. ft.	Dist. along Batten ft.	R. ft.	L. ft.	W. ft.	Ordinates Pressure Curve lbs./sq. ft. I.P.	Station Load lb. I.P.	External Loads				Internal Loads		
								Moment about Sta. 0	Σ Moment	Σ Moment × 9.7		Support lbs.	Moment about Sta. 0	Σ Moment
0	1	0	.75	.79	.5	.880	.35	0	0	0.0		2.25	0	—
1	1	1	1.58	1.65	1	.875	1.44	1.44	1.44	13.96		9.40	9.40	9.40
2	1	2	2.42	1.26	1	.865	1.09	2.18	3.62	35.12		7.18	14.36	23.76
3	1	3	3.33	1.74	1	.850	1.48	4.44	8.06	78.18		9.91	29.73	53.49
4	1	4	4.08	2.13	1	.815	1.73	6.92	14.98	145.40		12.14	48.56	102.05
5	1	5	4.92	2.57	1	.755	1.94	9.70	24.68	239.40		14.65	73.25	175.30
6	1	6	5.75	3.01	1	.685	2.06	12.36	37.04	359.29		17.16	102.96	278.26
7	1	7	6.50	3.40	1	.610	2.07	14.49	51.53	500.84		19.40	135.80	414.00
8	1	8	7.17	3.75	1	.545	2.04	16.32	67.85	658.15		21.38	171.04	585.04
9	1	9	7.88	4.12	1	.485	2.00	18.00	85.85	832.75		23.48	211.32	796.36
10	1	10	8.54	4.47	.5	.405	.90	9.00	94.85	920.05		12.70	127.00	923.36

(f) *Strength of batten.* As further indicated on Table 6, the resultant load, shear, partial moment, and total moment are obtained for each station of the batten. With a load factor which should not be less than 3, the stress for any particular type of cross-section selected may be determined.

TABLE 6—NOSE STIFFENING DATA

(Bending Moments)

Station	(−) Ext. Load lbs.	(+) Int. Load lbs.	Resultant Load	Shear	Partial Moment	Total Moment
0	3.40	* 16.42 ⎫ 2.25 ⎰ 18.67	+ 15.27	+ 15.27	∞	∞
1	13.97	9.40	− 4.57	+ 10.70	+ 15.27	+ 15.27
2	10.57	7.18	− 3.39	+ 7.31	+ 10.70	+ 25.97
3	14.56	9.91	− 4.65	+ 2.66	+ 7.31	+ 33.28
4	16.78	12.14	− 4.64	− 1.98	+ 2.66	+ 35.94
5	18.82	14.65	− 4.17	− 6.15	− 1.98	+ 33.96
6	19.98	17.16	− 2.82	− 8.97	− 6.15	+ 27.81
7	20.08	19.40	− .68	− 9.65	− 8.97	+ 18.84
8	19.78	21.38	+ 1.60	− 8.05	− 9.65	+ 9.19
9	19.40	23.48	+ 4.08	− 3.97	− 8.05	+ 1.14
10	8.73	12.70	+ 3.97	− 0.0	− 3.97	− 2.83

* Load of 16.42 lbs. = reaction at nose to satisfy requirement that $V = 0$.

Rip-Panels

Purpose. The rip-panel is designed for use in emergency or forced landings. As its name implies, it consists in ripping or tearing a panel from the gas cell, thus permitting a rapid deflation of the gas, an operation which obviously should take place close to the ground with the ship in full descent. The correct procedure in this operation is a subject for piloting which is beyond the scope of this volume.

Historical. The original panel consisted of a narrow, grommeted slit about 8 in. in width and 15 ft. in length, narrowing toward the nose. This was covered on the

interior of the envelope with a strip of parallel fabric which
was secured in place by cementing and sewing. One end,
which overlapped the slit about a foot, tapered away forming a lip to which a toggle was secured for attaching the
rip-cord. The rip-cord was then led in the direction of
the slit to a fairlead located so as to give a vertical lead to
the car, the cord passing out of the envelope through a
gas-tight gland. The rip-cord was secured about 12 in.
from the toggle end of the rip-panel and then at intervals
between this point and the fairlead to smaller patches,
enough slack being allowed between these points to avoid
a possible premature starting of the panel. The panel was
reinforced against splitting at either end by lacing across
the slit with cord through an eyelet arrangement along
the edges of the grommeted slit. This type of rip-panel
did not prove successful, probably owing to slow velocity
at which the gas would be expelled through this obstructed
opening.

A type of panel very similar to the one at present in use
was then developed which followed the original in general
design except that the strip of parallel fabric remained a
part of the envelope during the process of ripping. The
toggle and rip-cord were attached to a strip of bias fabric
that was cemented to the upper surface of the parallel
fabric strip, dipping through the parallel fabric at one end.
A pull on the rip-cord tore the bias strip through the parallel
strip down the entire length of the panel.

This was later followed by a type designated as the
"cheese cutter" rip-panel which was first developed for use
in the coastal ships of the Royal Air Force, Great Britain.
This type, similar to the one previously developed, replaced
the bias fabric ripping strip with a flexible steel wire, secured
to a toggle-patch cemented to the parallel strip about one
foot from its end. This wire was secured at intervals along

the panel in a manner to provide slack throughout the length. The end which dipped through the parallel strip was secured to a male eyebolt with a circular flange, screwing through an opening in the panel into a flange female eyebolt on the under side of the strip. Rubber washers were introduced to make a gas-tight joint. The rip-cord was made fast to the female eyebolt from where it was led in a manner similar to the types previously described, to a second gas-tight joint of male and female eyebolts on the rip-panel. The operating end of the rip-cord was then secured to the latter female eyebolt. The eyebolt glands were torn through the fabric of the envelope and rip-panel by a pull on the cord which resulted in the flexible steel wire splitting the fabric strip. In this type of rip-panel the cord lacing between the grommet edges was omitted.

In American airship practice at the beginning of the World War, the type of rip-panel adopted was a duplication of the present observation balloon type. This consisted in a series of reinforced elliptical openings in the envelope which were covered on the gas side by a wide panel, cemented and sewed with a single row of stitching along the outer edges of the panel. This type of panel was very difficult to operate owing to the resistance encountered in separating the panel from the envelope, which was cemented for a width of about 1 in. along the edge. This resistance would increase to an excessive, almost inoperative point, due to air vulcanizing which inevitably takes place during the exposure encountered in flights. This type of panel was further unsuccessful owing to the restricted flow of gas through these comparatively small openings. This restriction was so great as to cause one of the early small types of nonrigids built for the United States Navy, to be carried for a distance of $\frac{1}{2}$ m. or more after the panel had been completely ripped.

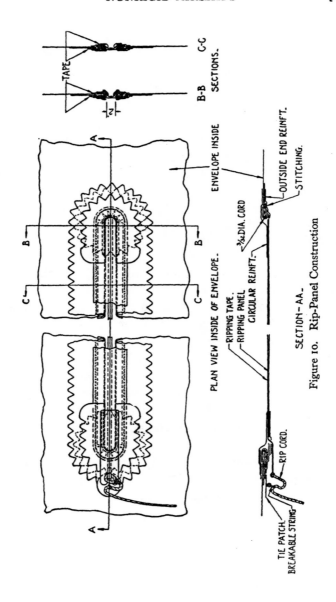

Figure 10.   Rip-Panel Construction

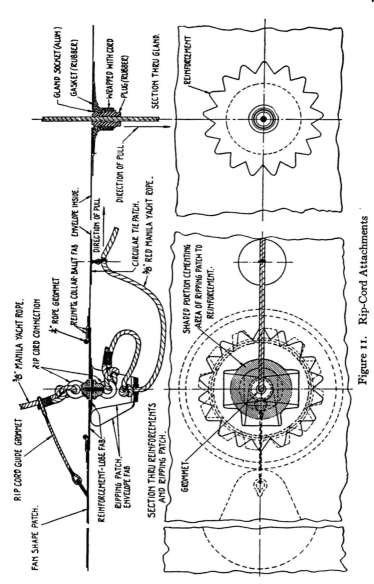

Figure 11.　Rip-Cord Attachments

The type of rip-panel likewise known as the "cheese cutter," finally adopted in the United States, is described below.

Construction. The cheese cutter type of rip-panel, as now in use, is shown on Figure 10. A long slot about 2 in. in width is made in the envelope, the edges being reinforced with extra fabric and the ends with fabric turned back and cemented over a cord. The latter reinforcement is made in order that the panel when slit will not tear the fabric of the envelope at the end of the slot. The panel itself differs from the fabric of the envelope, being made of 2-ply straight fabric instead of 3-ply bias. This type of fabric is used so that when a tear in the panel is started it will continue in a straight line and require a very moderate pull to operate it—not over 40 lbs. This panel is cemented to the envelope and sewed with a double row of stitching which is covered with tape on the inside and outside of the envelope to prevent gas diffusion.

The ripping strip is usually made of strong tape about $\frac{1}{2}$ in. in width with a cover of rubberized fabric cemented around it. This unit is cemented along the center of the entire length of the straight ply rip-panel fabric on the outside of the envelope, passing through this panel at the starting end. The rip-panel is slit for about an inch where this ripping strip passes through, for the purpose of reducing the resistance to start the rip. This slit is covered on the outside by a reinforcing patch to prevent leakage of gas.

The rip-cord, which is $\frac{3}{8}$ in. diameter rope, is joined to the ripping strip and continues, through properly located guide patches, around the interior of the envelope, emerging through a rip-cord gland (Figure 11) from which it is led to a suitable location within reach of the pilot. To prevent the rip-cord from starting the rip-panel prematurely, and from whipping around and thereby becoming knotted inside the envelope, it is secured with breakable cord at proper intervals to small patches that are cemented on the inside of the envelope along the shortest distance from the ripping strip to the rip-cord gland. The lower end of the rip-cord is always dyed red.

Location. A rip-panel should be located at the highest point of the envelope in order to provide for a rapid escape of gas. The position of the panel with reference to the axis of the ship has been the subject of considerable controversy between the advocates for the longitudinal position and those for the transverse position.

The advocates for the transverse position, in which the panel extends at right angles to the gore lines over the top of the envelope, point out that this position prevents the panel from taking a zigzag path which is characteristic of the panel located longitudinally, owing to the alternate biasing of the envelope patterns by rings. However, failures have never resulted from zigzagged rip-panels, although this condition could be overcome by alternating the bias fabric by gores.

The longitudinally located rip-panel is considered advantageous from an operating standpoint. Since the control lines can be arranged to operate more positively than in case of the rip-panel located transversely. Furthermore, the fabric tension being greatest in the transverse direction, will cause the rip-panel to flare open upon ripping. In the case of the transversely located rip-panel, there will be a tendency to obstruct the flow of gas due to buckling action on the envelope caused by the positive bending moment which causes the nose and tail to rise.

The following data show the practice followed in the latest training type airships of the United States Army:

TABLE 7—RIP-PANEL POSITIONS

Airship	Volume	Number Rip-Panels	Distance from Nose	Length
TC......................	200,000	2	$\begin{cases}31\% \\ 66\%\end{cases}$	21 ft. 21 ft.
TA......................	130,000	2	$\begin{cases}29\% \\ 64\%\end{cases}$	15 ft. 15 ft
TE......................	80,000	1	19%	20 ft.

CHAPTER IV

SUSPENSIONS

The means by which the car of a nonrigid airship is attached to the envelope will be discussed in the following paragraphs.

Object. The primary object in the design of the car suspension that is brought out in the progressive development of the various types of suspension, is two-fold; first, to reduce the head resistance to a minimum and second, to bring the car as close to the envelope as possible, thereby reducing hangar height and bringing the line of thrust closer to the center of resistance.

Types

The Astra-Torres and Parseval types of suspension, having been discussed in Chapter I, will not be repeated here. The reader is referred to the Handbooks on the "Coastal" and "C-Star" Airships, by the Airship Department of the British Admiralty, May 1918, for a complete detailed description of the Astra-Torres suspension, which is now considered obsolete.

Net. The net that was placed over the entire envelope was the earliest form of suspension. This type became obsolete owing to its high resistance, weight and complication. However, it is still used on free balloons, as aerodynamic resistance is hardly a factor to be considered in this case compared to its convenience and simplicity in connection with the suspension of the basket.

Band. This type of suspension which was used in the

Navy A and the first airships of the Navy B series, consisted briefly of splitting a main suspension rope from the car into two, four, eight or sixteen parts so as to reduce the load at the final attachment to the envelope to a stress which it is approximately capable of carrying. This attachment consisted either of a toggle enclosed in a flap of fabric which is sewed on through the envelope similar to the present Type R observation balloon suspension, or of a crow's-foot of webbing similar to the Navy Type M observation balloon suspension. These attachments were spread out along the balloon equidistant from one another in order to distribute the stresses as uniformly as possible over the surface of the fabric. The system was complicated, heavy, and subject to frequent breakages owing to the numerous small cords and attachments. The most serious objection to this type of suspension was the enormous air resistance produced by it, which has been quoted as being over four times what would be anticipated from the envelope alone.

Catenary. Figures 12 and 13 show the construction of one of the loops in the catenary suspension and the method of laying it out. This type has been used extensively by the French in their Zodiac airships and by the Italian, modified in detail, notably for the observation balloons, Type AP, and also adapted to their semirigid airship suspensions. This type of suspension attachment, when properly designed and applied, has a very neat appearance, but owing to the difficulty of design and application, it has not been generally adopted in America, being replaced by the rope finger type which has met with singular success in nonrigid airship construction. Furthermore, the catenary suspension is heavier than the rope finger type.

Patch Attachments

Eta patch. The patch developed by the British Admiralty known as "Eta" is shown on Figure 14. It consists

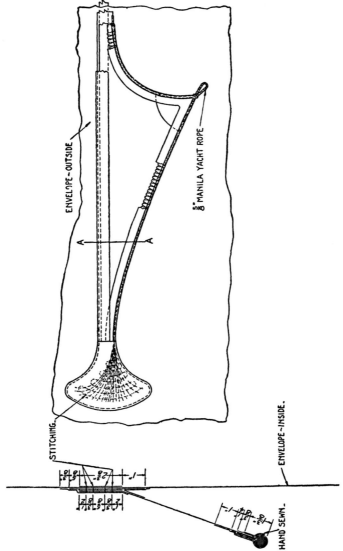

Figure 12.   Catenary Type Patch

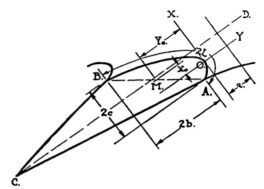

Figure 13.   Catenary Diagram

1. To construct catenary AOB
2. Given AC and BC lines of suspension
3. Bisect ∢ ACB giving bisector CD which is assumed ⊥ and ‖ to X and Y axes
4. By construction determine the component distances 2C and 2B ⊥ and ‖ to CD
5. Assume length 2L of catenary so that its maximum offset from chord AB is approximately
   ¼ the chord length
6. By reference to Mark's Hand Book determine X_0 and Y_0, coordinates of the mid-point M
   so that the lowest point O is located
7. With O as origin, plot AOB from formula—

$$Y = \alpha \left[\cosh\left(\frac{X}{a}\right) - 1 \right]$$

of a steel ring having several strips of silk or cotton webbing
passed through it and sewed onto the envelope together
with a piece of fabric forming a suitable covering.   This
patch has been found to be very light and strong.   Its principal objection lies in the partial concealment of the steel
rings in the folds of the fabric, which makes impracticable
the inspection of deterioration of the fabric at this point
due to corrosion of these steel rings.

Rope finger patch.   (Figure 15).   The standard suspension
patch for nonrigid airships in the United States since 1918
is the rope finger type.   The principle of this patch is
that instead of distributing the stress through the fabric
by means of a multiplicity of divided and subdivided cords,
the stress is led directly to the envelope where it is distributed on the surface of the fabric itself.   The process of
constructing this patch is discussed in Chapter VIII,

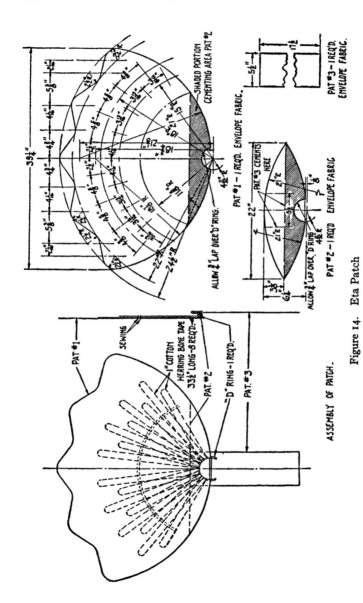

Figure 14.   Eta Patch

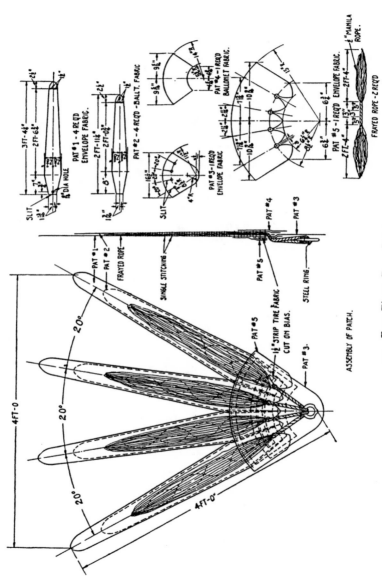

15. Four-Finger Rope Patch

page 122. For car suspension this patch has four fingers, whereas for fin suspension the use of the two-finger patch is the usual practice. In case of the four-finger patch, the line of direction of the suspension load should bisect the two inner fingers. As experiments have indicated that these two fingers carry the greatest amount of suspension load the line of direction of this load can be varied from the center line of one pair of outer fingers to the other pair of outer fingers. Therefore, this permits the movement of the car between the limits of permissible change in direction of the suspension load; thereby constituting a very important advantage of this type of patch over any patch or suspension attachment previously described. In practice, however, to vary the direction of the suspension load considerably from the center line of the two middle fingers is considered poor design. Figures 18 to 21 inclusive, indicate various types of patches in use and include various sizes of rope finger patches designed for the loads indicated, which loads were the results of exposure tests under varying temperatures from 75° to 110° F.

Horseshoe patch. This patch, shown in Figure 16, was designed and patented by J. R. Gammeter, Process Engineer of the B. F. Goodrich Co., of Akron, Ohio, in 1918, for the Navy C airship. It was made of Gwilliam threads laced radially around the Bowden cable and imbedded in a rubber mold. There were three disadvantages of this type of patch which made it impracticable for application as car suspension attachment for nonrigid airships:

(a) A decrease in the fabric tension in a direction normal to the bisector of the V formed by the patch cable, below that of the component of stress of this cable normal to the bisector, would cause wrinkling in the envelope fabric resulting in a change in form of the patch from the true circle to that of an ellipse, thus causing the load to be con-

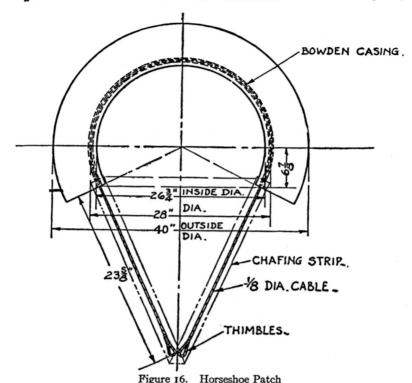

Figure 16. Horseshoe Patch

centrated in the upper portion of the patch, producing its
early failure.

(b) The line of direction of the suspension cable was
required to be coincident with the bisector noted in the
foregoing paragraph, or in other words, to the center line
of the patch. A slightly eccentric load would cause deformation of the patch, resulting in wrinkling and con-
sequent lowering of efficiency. It was evident that this
requirement could not be met in practice.

(c) The weight of this patch as compared with the rope
finger patch was excessive.

This horseshoe patch was tried on the first Navy *C*

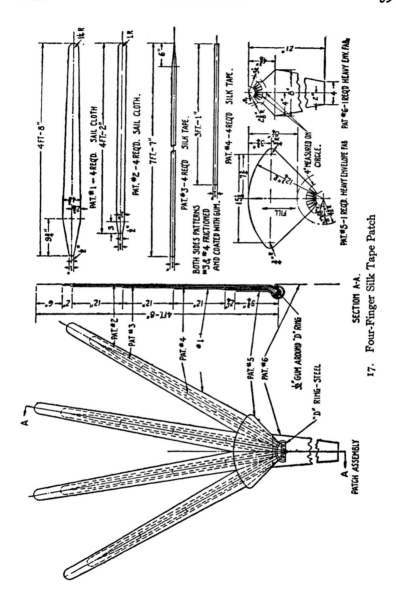

17. Four-Finger Silk Tape Patch

envelope produced by the B. F. Goodrich Co., but was later replaced by the rope finger type of patch before acceptance of the ship by the Navy.

SKETCH	STRENGTH-LBS.	WEIGHT-LBS.	DESCRIPTION.	USE & REMARKS.
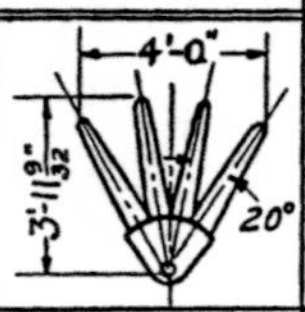	2000	1.85	4 FINGER ROPE PATCH.	TC CAR SUSPENSION. " GRAB LINE UNIT.
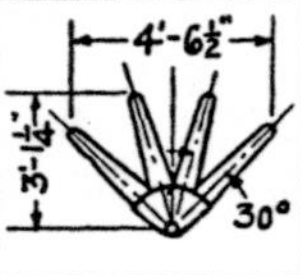	1800	1.41	4 FINGER ROPE PATCH	TA GRAB LINE TC "　　"
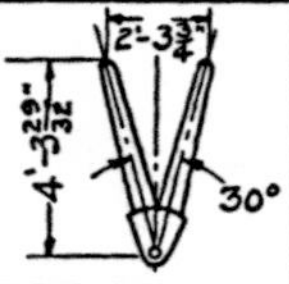	1800	.91	2 FINGER ROPE PATCH	TC NOSE BRIDLE.
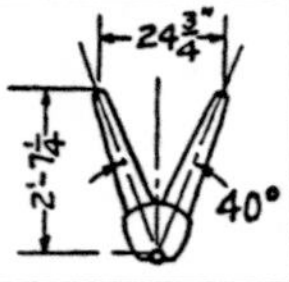	1000	.42	2 FINGER ROPE PATCH	TA } FIN { SUSPENSION TC } { SURGING. TA NOSE BRIDLE.
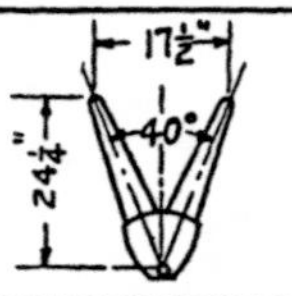	500	.22	2 FINGER ROPE PATCH	TC SCOOP SUSPENSION.
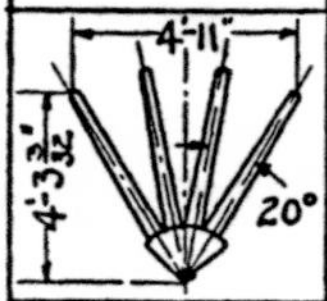	2000	1.02	4 FINGER SILK TAPE PATCH.	CAR SUSPENSION.

Figure 18.　Schedule of Patches

Silk tape patch. In 1919 the silk tape patch shown in Figure 17 was produced by the Goodyear Tire & Rubber

Co. to replace the rope finger patch, claiming the following advantages over the latter.

SKETCH	STRENGTH-LBS.	WEIGHT-LBS.	DESCRIPTION.	USE & REMARKS.
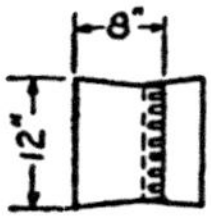		.26	LACE PATCH	TA FIN BASE.
	1000	.22	CIRCULAR BULLS-EYE PATCH.	RIP CORD GUIDE.
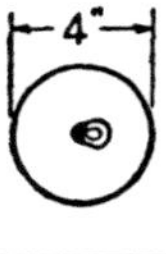	250	.02	CIRCULAR ROPE LOOP PATCH.	PLUMB-BOB. BREAKABLE STRING. RIPCORD TIE PATCH.
	500	.15	CIRCULAR ROPE LOOP PATCH.	CONTROL.
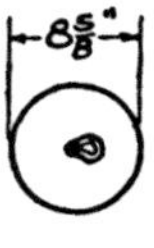	500	.08	CIRCULAR ROPE LOOP PATCH.	RIP CORD SUSP'N.
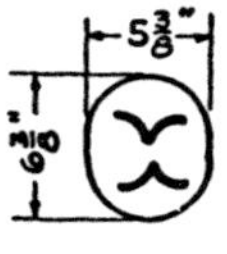		.035	ROPE TIE PATCH	BOWDEN CASING.

Figure 19.　Schedule of Patches

Weight.　The silk tape patch weighed approximately .6 lb. less than the rope patch, for the 2,000 lb. size.

Elasticity.　It was evident that the rope finger patch

was not sufficiently elastic, especially when applied in the direction of the fill thread of the fabric, which stretches

SKETCH	STRENGTH-LBS.	WEIGHT-LBS.	DESCRIPTION.	USE & REMARKS.
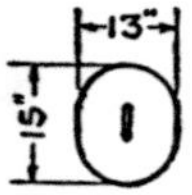 13" × 15"	1250	.28	ROPE LOOP PATCH	TC FIN BASE
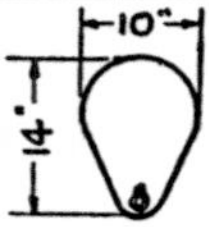 10" × 14"	1000	.13	FAN PATCH.	TC RIP CORD GUIDE.
 5"		.025	1 GROMMET PATCH	VALVE LINE GUIDE.
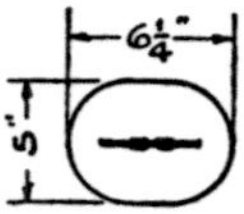 6¼" × 5"		.036	2 GROMMET PATCH	VALVE LINE GUIDE.
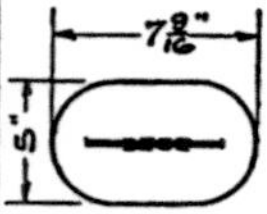 7⅞" × 5"		.053	4 GROMMET PATCH	VALVE LINE GUIDE
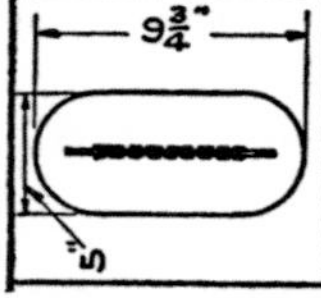 9¾" × 5"			9 GROMMET PATCH	VALVE LINE GUIDE.

Figure 20. Schedule of Patches

considerably more than the warp thread. The silk tape patch was claimed to have about twice as much stretch as the rope patch, approaching more closely the average

stretch of the fabric.   This property would produce a more
even distribution of the load.   The test indicated the foregoing contention to be correct in that the silk tape patch
would hold a greater number of pounds for a considerably

SKETCH	STRENGTH-LBS	WEIGHT- LBS	DESCRIPTION	USE & REMARKS.
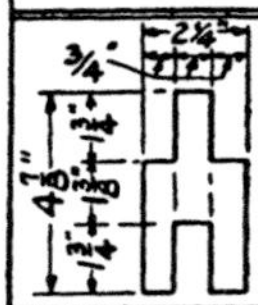		.005	TUBE FASTENING	MANOMETER TUBE
	450	.07	CIRCULAR BULLS-EYE	TA-CONTROL LINES.
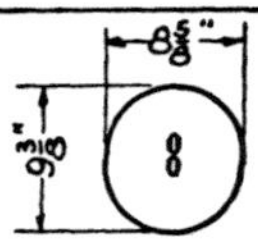	450	.10	DOUBLE LINE BULLS-EYE	TC-CONTROL LINES.
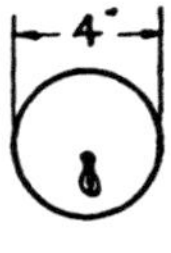	200	.018	ROPE LOOP	TA AIRLINE INTERSECTION.
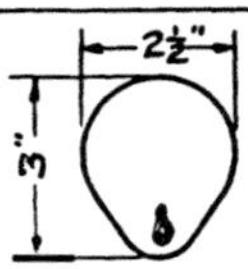	100		FAN PATCH	WATER MODEL.

Figure 21.   Schedule of Patches

longer time than the rope finger patch when tested under
the same conditions.

Uniform strain. An even distribution of load was further
produced by the longer fingers and the more perfectly
stepping down of the tape in the fingers, both factors

tending to carry the load out over a larger surface of the envelope.

Appearance and resistance. It is evident that this type of patch would present a smoother and neater appearance and therefore offer less resistance than the rope finger patch with the bulky mass of rope underneath.

A feature of this type of patch is the elimination of sewing in it. The silk tape is frictioned with rubber that is cured together and to strips of sail cloth.

Design of Car Suspensions

Car position. The car should be light in weight and placed as close as possible to the envelope for the three-fold purpose of bringing the thrust line nearer the center line of resistance, reducing car weight to a minimum, and reducing the required hangar vertical clearance. In nonrigid airships designed in America it has been found practicable to determine the location of the car within the following limits: the maximum propeller pitch clearance to be 30 in. and the minimum to be 24 in. from the surface of the envelope.

Martingales. The fore-and-aft guys shown in Figure 22, designated as martingales, should be provided to prevent the car from swinging forward when nosing the airship down and from swinging backward when nosing the airship upward, and also to resist the thrust.

Anti-rolling guys. One or more pairs of suspensions should be crossed to prevent the car from falling over sideways. These guys are unnecessary when the car suspensions are attached at the top of the car. When engines are installed on outriggers on the car, anti-rolling guys should be attached on the outward edges of the outrigger. The tension in these latter guys should be kept at a low figure; not to exceed 50 lbs. when in the hangar.

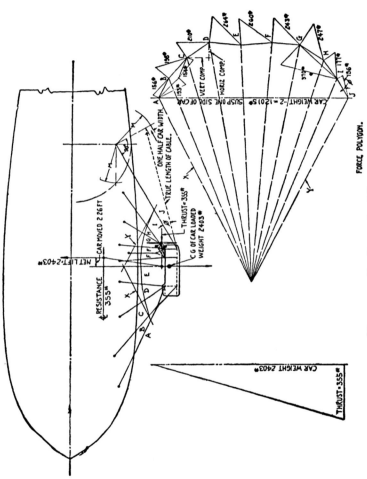

Figure 22. Car Suspension Diagram

Number of cable suspensions. In selecting the proper number of suspensions, two factors should be kept in mind: first, that a large number of ropes increases the resistance, and second, that a small number of ropes tends to poor distribution of the load on the envelope. With reference to attachment to the car, it is preferable to use fewer main suspension wires and more bridles than the reverse. The spacing of these attachments on the car should be closer near heavy weights such as engines, fuel systems, and tanks for water ballast.

Position of attachments on the envelope. As the tension immediately under the attachments is considerably less than that above them, there is a tendency for the fabric to bulge out to meet the attachments. The attachments should therefore be located below the tangent formed by the suspension to a circular envelope, in order to prevent the cable lines from cutting into the envelope after leaving the attachments. In practice a distance of 2 or 3 ft. below the tangent points is satisfactory where a plane passing through a pair of opposing suspension lines, is nearly perpendicular to the axis of the envelope. At other positions, for example, at the fore-and-aft points, the limiting location down on the envelope should be such that the deviation of the suspension line from the tangent plane should not exceed 20°.

Cable stresses and fore-and-aft positions of car. Figure 22 shows a graphical determination of the cable stresses in the car suspension and of the car in the fore-and-aft direction. For cable stresses, the reader is referred to N.A.C.A. Report No. 115, by C. P. Burgess. The tensions in the cable should be selected so that the force polygon and funicular polygon closes, thereby satisfying the conditions for static equilibrium, which is that the sum of the horizontal components of the tension is zero, and that the sum of the vertical component equals the net lift, and the sum of the moments about the center of gravity is zero. Other conditions to be kept in mind in selecting the car suspension tensions are that they should be chosen so as to produce as small a bending moment in the envelope as practicable and that the weight of the car should be taken by wires as nearly vertical as possible, since the incline wires receive heavy loads when the airship inclines up or down. Another condition of minor importance is that the bending moment in the car should be small.

The suspension diagram shown on Figure 22 shows the tensions in the vertical longitudinal plane. Therefore, a correction for the angularity of the cable to that plane will be necessary to find the actual tension in the cable. In order to counteract the strong couple produced by the thrust of the propellers and the resistance of the airship, it will be necessary to place the car with its center of gravity forward of the center of lift and thus produce an opposing couple. This is shown graphically in the diagram by drawing in a vector representing the thrust of the propellers. This thrust is taken for 80 per cent of maximum speed which is considered the cruising speed at which the airship should fly level. Therefore the closing line represents the resultant of net lift and propeller thrust. Then if a line is drawn from a point where the center of resistance crosses the center of net lift, downward and parallel to this line of resultant, it will pass through the center of thrust at a point abreast of the correct position for the center of gravity of the car.

Center of resistance. The suspension diagram (Figure 22) is for the *TE* Airship of 84,000 cu. ft. capacity. The following data were used to determine the center of resistance and its magnitude shown on the diagram.

(a) From Table 42, page 206, of L. Bairstow's "Applied Aerodynamics," the resistance of the envelope is 35 per cent of the total resistance of the airship.

(b) The resistance coefficient C of the envelope is .0111, C being expressed by the following equation:

$$C = \frac{gR}{\rho V^2 \text{Vol.}^{\frac{2}{3}}} \qquad (6)$$

Where:

g = 32.2 ft./sec./sec.
R = Resistance in lbs.
V = Vel. ft./sec.

Vol. = Volume in cu. ft.

ρ = Density of air lbs./cu. ft. taken as .076 in the following.

(c) The velocity of the airship is expressed by the following equation:

$$V = \left(\frac{73.546 \times F \times E \times \text{Hp.}}{C \times \text{Vol.}^{\frac{2}{3}}}\right)^{\frac{1}{3}} \qquad (7)$$

Where:

F = Ratio of resistance of envelope and airship = .35 as noted in paragraph (a) above

E = Propeller efficiency = .62

Hp. = Horsepower (½ power) = 50, which corresponds to 80 per cent of full speed, considered the normal cruising speed at which the ship should fly level

V = Vel. in M.p.h.

Therefore

V = 33.5 M.p.h.

(d) From the foregoing and from Bairstow data referred to in paragraph (a) the values on page 69 are derived.

Angle of trim. The position of the car thus determined fixes the *angle* the airship should *trim* when fully loaded. This angle is expressed by the following equation:

$$\alpha = \tan^{-1} \frac{a}{d} \qquad (8)$$

α = Angle of trim in degrees

a = Horizontal distance of the center of gravity of the airship from the center of buoyancy (C. B.) as determined below

d = Vertical distance of center of gravity, (C. G.) of airship below center of buoyancy

TABLE 8—RESISTANCE FACTORS

Part	Resistance		Moment Arm Dist. from Env. Axis ft.	Moment lbs. ft.
	Per Cent of Hull	lbs.		
Envelope....................	35	124.2	0	0
Car........................	16	56.8	25.5	1,448
Rigging....................	21	74.6	19.5	1,455
Surfaces...................	28	99.4	0	0
Resultant..................	100	355.0	8.19	2,903

Table 9 gives the schedule of weights and moments for determining the center of gravity of hull.

Table 10 gives the schedule of weights and moments for determining the center of gravity of car.

Table 11 gives the calculations required to determine the angle of trim.

Center of net lift.

Center of buoyancy (C. B.) is   60.33 ft. aft of nose

Gross lift 80,000 × 1.05 × .055 = 4,620 lbs.

Therefore distance center of net lift aft of nose is:

$$X = \frac{4,620 \times 60.33 - 150,074.2}{2,403} = 53.34 \text{ ft.}$$

which is indicated on Figure 22.

$$\textit{Angle of trim} = \alpha = \tan^{-1} \frac{60.33 - 59.44}{9.84}$$

$$= \tan^{-1} .0905$$

$$= 5° \ 10'$$

Note: Horizontal arm for car (reference Figure 22) = 53.34 − 2.26 = 51.1

TABLE 9—CALCULATIONS FOR HULL CENTER OF GRAVITY

Item	Weight lbs.	Horizontal		Vertical	
		Arm ft.	Moment ft./lbs.	Arm ft.	Moment ft./lbs.
Envelope.................	1,290.0	64.25	82,889.5	0	0
Ballonet, etc.	243·0	51.5	12,514.5	8.5	2,065.5
Air Lines................	8.5	54.5	463.2	16.0	136·0
Nose Bridle..............	4.5	3.5	15.7	0	0
Nose Stiffening...........	52.0	3.5	182.0	0	0
Handling Line Unit—For'd .	14.3	22.5	321.7	13.0 ⎫	325.0
Handling Line Unit—Aft..	10.7	77.5	829 2	13.0 ⎬	
Rip-Panel and Cord.......	10.0	25.0	250.0	14.4	144.0
Pressure Tubes........ . .	7.5	45.5	341 2	17.0	127.5
Car Suspension...........	100.0	52 0	5,200 0	13.0	1,300.0
Fin Suspension...........	50.0	110.0	5,500.0	0	0
Valves:					
Gas..................	25 6	44.0	1,126 4	2.5	64.0
Air—Forward..........	20.2	28.0	565.6	16.0	323.2
Air—Rear.............	20.2	74.6	1,506.9	15.5	313.1
Control Lines............	38 0	90.0	3,420.0	12.7	484.5
Scoops and Check Valves..	17.0	61.5	1,045.5	16.5	280.5
Appendices............. ⎧	2.25	17.0	38.2	14.0	31.5
⎩	2.25	90.25	203.0	14.0	31.5
Top Stabilizer............	53.0	110.0	5,830.0	0	0
Top Streamline...........	3.0	116.25	348.7	0	0
Bottom Stabilizer.........	57.0	110.0	6,270.0	0	0
Horizontal Stabilizer.......	114.0	110.0	12,540.0	0	0
Rudder.................	29.0	117.5	3,407.5	15 5	449.5
Elevators...............	45.0	117.0	5,265.0	0	0
	2,217.0	67.69	150,074.2	26.8	5,955.8

Moments taken about nose and axis of envelope.

TABLE 10—CALCULATIONS FOR CAR CENTER OF GRAVITY

Item	Weight lbs.	Horizontal		Vertical	
		Arm ft.	Moment ft./lbs.	Arm in.	Moment in./lbs.
Car Body Structure.......	252.0	6.6	1,664.0	26.75	6,741.5
Controls.................	50.0	5.2	261.5	16.5	825.0
Fuel System.............	63.5	11.0	699.0	6.5	413.0
Outrigger	56.8	11.2	638.2	3.8	216.5
Electric System..........	70.7	5.7	401.3	19.45	1,375.0
Ballast Tank.............	44.0	7.75	341 0	29.5	1,300.0
Instruments.............	25.0	5.5	137.5	6.0	150.0
Drag-Rope..............	35.0	.75	26.5	21.0	735.0
Pyrene.................	13.0	6.15	80.0	18.0	234.0
Power Plant............	452.0	....	5,802.0	−1.5	−679.0
Passengers (2)...........	392.0	4.0	1,568.0	11.0	4,312.0
Pilot...................	196.0	6.25	1,225.0	11.0	2,156.0
Mechanic...............	196.0	8.5	1,666.0	11.0	2,156.0
Gasoline................	282.0	11.0	3,102.0	18.0	5,070.0
Oil....................	40.0	11.0	440.0	2.0	80.0
Ballast.................	235.0	7.75	1,821.0	29.5	6,930.0
	2,403.0	8.27	198,730.0	13.3	32,015.0

Moments taken about nose of car for horizontal and about top longeron for vertical.

TABLE 11—CALCULATIONS FOR ANGLE OF TRIM OF AIRSHIP

Item	Weight lbs.	Horizontal		Vertical	
		Arm	Moment	Arm	Moment
Hull........................	2,217	67.69	150,074.2	2.68	5,955.8
Car........................	2,403	51.1	122,800.0	24.85	59,750.0
Helium.....................	2,060	60.33	124,200	0	0
	6,680	59.44	397,074.2	9.84	65,705.8

CHAPTER V

CAR

Structure. The strut and wire type of construction has practically been relegated to the past. The semi-monocoque car body (see Plate VI) has replaced the earlier type owing to its characteristics of a cleaner design, a firm outer surface that serves as a measure of protection to the occupants, and withstands rough usage compared with the strut and wire frame covered with fabric; also a more permanently rigid body requiring no maintenance adjustment of the wire bracing. The present type of wooden semi-monocoque car bodies are covered throughout with birch plywood. An all-metal semi-monocoque car is now under construction, which promises a material saving in weight.

The present cars are not provided for complete protection to the pilot from the elements. Winter tops or closed tops have been tried with satisfactory results and it is anticipated that future cars will be at least partially enclosed. The points to be kept in mind in designing a closed type are light weight and means of quick egress in case the necessity arises for the occupants of the car to abandon it.

Adjustment principles. *The minimum distance of the propeller tip to the ground* should be such that the propeller circle will clear the ground when the car is rolled 15 degrees.

For location, suspension and envelope clearance reference is made to these subjects as they appear under "Suspension Design."

The distance from the nose of the car to the ground should be such that with the car resting on its nose and landing bumper, the angle it makes with the ground should not be less than 10 degrees.

The angle of clearance made by the line drawn from the *lower edge of the rudder* to the lowest point on the car with the ground should not be less than 7 degrees.

Fuel system.[1] To reduce the compressive forces produced by the horizontal components of the car suspension, the fuel tanks have been suspended from the envelope in several designs. Notable among these are the Class *D* and the Army *A*-4 airships. The fuel tanks were also suspended inside the gas chamber, being inserted in gas-tight envelope recesses similar to the Navy *E* type airship. The principal objection to these methods of installation of fuel tanks are as follows:

> Excessive weight due to multiplicity of tanks and length of fuel line.
> Inaccessibility for inspection and maintenance.
> Difficulty of determining the gasoline level.
> Inaccessibility for refueling.

The present practice is to install the fuel systems completely in the car (see Plate VII). In this location pumps are needed to raise the fuel the required amount above the carburetor. The pressure system in which a high pressure was maintained on the fuel level has been replaced by the gravity system in which a gravity tank of about 5 per cent of the fuel capacity is installed, the fuel being raised from the storage tank to this level by means of wind-driven pumps. This system bids fair to be replaced by a suction system in which the suction pump is located on and driven by the engine. By means of pressure relief valves the pressure head on the carburetor is maintained constant. This system has proved very satisfactory on airplanes and is now being tried on nonrigid airships. The vacuum system in which a Stewart vacuum tank is used, similar

[1] A discussion of fuel systems for airships appears in volume "Aircraft Power Plants," Ronald Aeronautic Library.

to an automobile installation, has been used with success on the *OB*-1 airship and is being installed on the *TE* airship.

All fuel tanks are equipped with fuel discharge valves which at present are identical with the water ballast valves

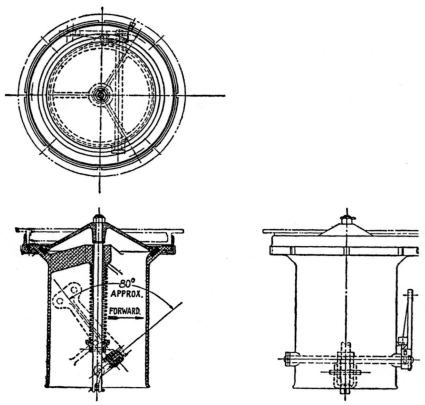

Figure 23. Water Ballast Discharge Valve, 4-Inch Type

previously described. These valves are for the purpose of using fuel as emergency ballast. (See Figures 23 and 24.)

All fuel tanks are constructed from aluminum sheet, which construction is supported by many years of satis-

Plate VI.   Semi-Monocoque Car Body for *TC* Airship

Plate VII.   Installation of Fuel Tanks in *J*-1 Airship Car

factory performance. The remainder of the fuel system is practically in accordance with standard airplane practice.

Engine outriggers. In twin-engine airships where the engines are mounted on the outside of the car, they are supported on a transverse platform familiarly known as the *outrigger*. In the *TA* airship design this outrigger serves as an air scoop (see Plate VIII). On the Navy

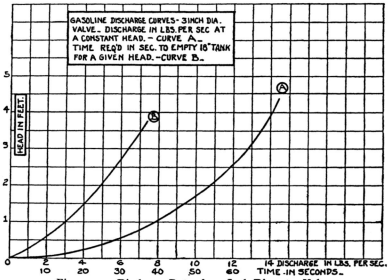

Figure 24.   Discharge Rates for 3-Inch Diameter Valve

Class *C* and *D* airships these supports were entirely of tubular construction, steel tubes being used throughout. A later design of the *C* car made by the Goodyear Tire & Rubber Co. was the first to bring out the cantilever type of construction in which the main structural members were two parallel box type beams built up of plywood webbing and spruce capping.   These beams were set transversely across the top longeron of the car and interbraced by longitudinal and diagonal sub-beams, the whole being covered on the top and bottom with plywood. This structure appeared very satisfactory for the first ships of this design, but later it was improved by knee braces of tubular construction for the purpose of reducing the amplitude of vibration that was reported as being quite severe in some cases. This bracing entirely eliminated the vibration. The *engine beds*, formerly of box type construction, were later changed to solid beams as the plywood beams would not withstand the vibration. Ultimately the outrigger design is tending toward the combination of the continuous cantilever beams knee-braced on their outer edges with the tubular type of construction. Steel tubes are best suited for the purpose of bracing, owing to the feasibility of welding attachment lugs thereto.

Drag-rope stowage. The most satisfactory location for the drag-rope stowage is the nose end of the car just forward of and clear of the pilot control. The base of this stowage slopes downward and outward so that the rope will rest against the doors. The stowage should be accessible from the pilot seat in order that the pilot may forcibly eject the rope in case it should stick upon operating the release catch of the doors. The end of the drag-rope is secured to the drag-rope bridle and to the quick release clip which is described in Chapter IX.

Landing gear. The landing gear that is considered most satisfactory for nonrigid airships is the pontoon type so called, which is a cylindrical bag with hemispherical ends made of rubberized tire-duck fabric. This is attached to a cradle which is secured directly to the bottom of the bulkhead, formed to receive it as in the present *TA* and *TC* airship cars, or the cradle may be attached to a superstructure consisting of struts, wire-braced to the bottom of the car, in order to increase the ground clearance for the car.

Plate VIII. *TA* Engine Outrigger Showing Air Stack

(Official Photograph, Air Corps, U. S. Army)

Pontoons. The specification for the 19-in. diameter pontoon used on the *TC* airship car is as follows:

Pontoon to be constructed to withstand a maximum internal pressure of 10 lbs. per sq. in. without evidence of failure and a pressure of 5 lbs. per sq. in. 5 days without evidence of leakage.

Two layers of 17¼ oz. tire duck fabric to be plied together, the fabric having been frictioned on both sides and coated on one side with 1 ply of gum, the gauge of which is such that 8 plies equal 16/64 in. in thickness. An inner layer of gum 3/32 in. in thickness is applied. All seams are covered with gum strips ¾ in. in width.

The 17¼ oz. tire duck has an ultimate tensile strength of 185 lbs. per in. and is in accordance with the Bureau of Standards Circular No. 115.

Problem. The foregoing specification was based upon the following factors:

(a) Total weight of car 7,600 lbs. distributed over two pontoons the total cylindrical length of which is 104 in., giving a unit loading of 73 lbs. per in.

(b) A load factor of 4 is assumed, as the structure of the car was designed to withstand a load factor slightly greater than 5. This assumption is made in order that the pontoon will fail prior to the over-stressing of the car structure.

(c) The vertical velocity for landing was taken at 8 ft. per sec., equivalent to free fall from a 12 in. height.

The problem is to determine the *maximum internal pressure* to which the pontoon should be subjected. The kinetic energy to be absorbed by the landing gear or pontoon is,

$$E = \frac{Wv^2}{2g} \tag{9}$$

If the car comes to rest after a motion of x ft., the work done by gravity on it is Wx, and the total energy stored in the pontoon is:

$$\text{Work} = W\left(x + \frac{v^2}{2g}\right) \qquad (10)$$

The average force in the pontoon is equal to half the maximum F given by the following equations:

$$\tfrac{1}{2}\,Fx = W\left(x + \frac{v^2}{2g}\right)$$

$$F = W\left(2 + \frac{v^2}{xg}\right) \qquad (11)$$

Therefore,

$$x = \frac{v^2}{g\left(\dfrac{F}{W} - 2\right)} \qquad (12)$$

and the load factor $\dfrac{F}{W}$ being given above as equal to 4, the deflection is found to be 12 in. or 1 ft.

Assuming that the pontoon takes the form of an ellipse in cross-section, the *final internal pressure* to resist the force F, from which may be calculated the *maximum tension* of the fabric is determined:

Reference Marks' "Mechanical Engineer's Handbook," the perimeter of ellipse equals,

$$\pi\,(a + b)\,k \qquad (13)$$

which is equal to $\pi 19$, the perimeter of the pontoon section when not depressed.

Therefore,

$$\pi 19 = \pi\,(a + b)\,k$$

Where b the semi-minor axis is equal to $3\tfrac{1}{2}$ as deduced from the deflection $x = 12$ in.

Whence

$$k = \frac{19}{a + 3.5} \qquad (14)$$

In which a and k being unknown are determined by plotting m and k from values given in the reference above noted (Marks), which are:

m = 0.1   0.2   0.3   0.4   0.5   0.6   0.7   0.8   0.9   1.0
k = 1.002 1.01 1.023 1.04 1.064 1.092 1.127 1.168 1.216 1.273

and m from equations (14) and (15)

$$m = \frac{a - b}{a + b} = \frac{a - 3\frac{1}{2}}{a + 3\frac{1}{2}} \tag{15}$$

from the intersection of which is determined a value for k satisfying both relationships; the value of a is therefore found to be 13.9 in.

With the cradle designed to support the pontoon the full length of the major axis ($2a = 27.8$ in.) and the load per inch of pontoon length being $73 \times 4 = 292$ lbs., *the final and maximum internal pressure,*

$$p = \frac{292}{27.8} = 10.5 \text{ lbs./sq. in.}$$

from which the tension occurring at the extremities of the major axis of the elliptical section is,

$$T = pr$$

Where

$$r = \frac{b^2}{a} = .89 \text{ in.}$$

Whence

$$T = 9.3 \text{ lbs./in.} \tag{16}$$

Assuming adiabatic expansion, the *initial internal pressure* occurring in the undeflected pontoon is determined from the following relation:

$$P_1 V_1^{1.4} = P_2 V_2^{1.4}$$

Where

$$P_1 = 10.5, \ V_1 = \pi ab = 152.8, \text{ and } V_2 = \frac{\pi}{4} 19^2 = 283.5,$$

Whence

$$P_2 = 4.43 \text{lbs./sq. in., and } T \text{ from (16)} = 84.5 \text{ lbs./in., the } \textit{maximum tension.}$$

From the foregoing evidently the material selected for the pontoon is considerably over-strength, as the strength of the fabric for constant load is about

$$185 \times .90 \times 2 \times .60 = 200 \text{ lbs. per in.,}$$

the strength doubled being taken as 90 per cent of the machine strength for single-ply, and constant load strength as 50 per cent of machine strength, the latter being that obtained at a speed of jaw separation of 12 in. per minute. However, the ultimate strength of the fabric would be reached at a pressure of 10.5 lbs. per sq. in., the maximum required for landing, when the pontoon is not deflected, and as such a pressure is liable to be realized under changing atmospheric pressure it would be advisable to install a pressure relief valve set to blow off at 10.5 lbs. per sq. in.

The foregoing analysis does not consider the stretch of the fabric which approximates 20 per cent under maximum load.

Elevator and rudder controls. *Rudder controls* may be either the wheel and drum type, the stirrup type, or the foot-bar (airplane) type. Of these the latter, for fixed station control, is favored for small ships up to 130,000 cu. ft. For larger ships the load becomes too great for rudder bar or stirrup control. This load depends on the mechanical advantage permissible from the layout and on the length of rudder horn. The maximum angular movement of the rudder should be from 17° to 20°.

Elevators are controlled by a handwheel mounted in the vertical longitudinal plane either on the side of the car or between the altitude and direction pilot when both occupy the same cockpit. For each degree of angular movement of the rudder, the angular movement of the handwheel should not be less than 9° or 10° for satisfactory control. A smaller ratio would produce fatigue on the pilot. A hand and a foot brake should be installed so that the elevator wheel may be clamped at any desired position, for use on long flights.

The *cables* in the control systems should be 7 x 19 extra flexible steel aircraft cable. All control sheave grooves and grooves in drums should fit the cable radius snugly to prevent flattening of the cable and resultant fraying of the same. Where bends occur, control sheaves should be used and every consideration should be given in the design to minimize the friction of operating controls.

Emergency rudder controls or "jury rigs" are required in order to maintain directional control when the main controls fail. This consists of an additional pair of lines connected to the rudder horns and terminating in stirrups or other form of convenient handgrip located so as to be easily accessible from the rear cockpit. The leads should be as direct as possible to eliminate friction, and the arrangement should be such as to function with the least amount of effort.

CHAPTER VI

MANEUVERING CONTROLS

Control Surfaces

The purpose of this chapter is to present an analysis of experience in control surface design as applied to nonrigid airships. The form of surfaces and the overhung balance, which has been the prevailing American practice, is illustrated in Figure 2 and Plate IX; these also show the new paddle type counterbalancing that has proved successful for rigid airships. The streamline internal brace type of structure has been developed in preference to the externally braced king-post surfaces which latter was the type most extensively used in recent years by the French and English as exemplified in the Zodiac and the *C*-star ships produced respectively by these countries.[1]

An investigation was made by the writer to derive satisfactory data for determining areas and locations of control surfaces of the cruciform type for nonrigid airships. Figures 25, 26 and 27, also Tables 12 and 13 show data resulting from this investigation.

The data collected cover characteristics on American built ships that were known to control satisfactorily, such as the Navy *H* towing airship later known as the Army *OB*-1 airship, the Army *A*-4 airship, the Navy *J* airship and the Navy *C* and *D* airships. The *ZR*-1 was included as a check owing to exhaustive wind tunnel tests having been conducted to support the contract design.

[1] The reader is referred to the Navy Department, Bureau of Aeronautics, Technical Note No. 116, "Notes on Balance Control Surfaces," by Lieut. Walter F. Diehl, U. S. N., dated June 15, 1923.

Plate IX.   Overhang and Paddle-Type Control Surface on Experimental *TC* Airship

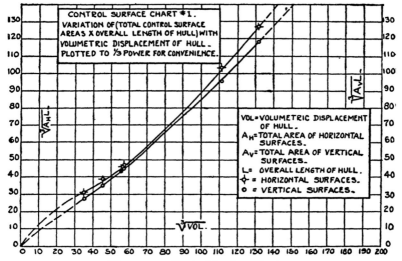

Figure 25. Control Surface Chart

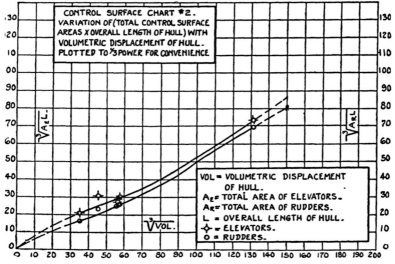

Figure 26. Control Surface Chart

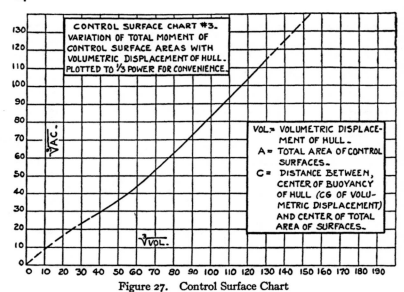

Figure 27. Control Surface Chart

The curves (Figures 25, 26 and 27) resulting from the investigation, represent the following relationships:

$$\text{Vol.} = f(AL) \tag{17}$$
$$\text{and Vol.} = f(AC) \tag{18}$$

    Vol. = Volumetric displacement of hull
      A = Area of control surface
      L = Overall length of hull
      C = Distance between center of buoyancy and center of total area of surfaces

These are believed to form a satisfactory basis for the determination of areas and locations of control surfaces of the cruciform type. The formulas are substantiated by comparing performance data from certain American airships; poor controllability is found where the curves indicate it.

From these curves, A can be determined, Vol. and L being given; then substituting in the product AC from curves for equation (18) determines the value for C. It is interesting to note that values for airship R-80 fall very nearly on the curve on Figure 25. These values were determined from British Report R and M No. 541 on Wind Tunnel Tests of the R-80 Airship Model, which gave a total of 3,611 sq. ft. while the chart indicates a total of 3,563 sq. ft., which is a difference of 48 sq. ft. or 1.3 per cent. These curves are further substantiated as follows:

It appears that the movable surfaces of the A-4 airship are too large, an indication borne out by statements from pilots that the movable surfaces are larger than necessary. Likewise, the Zodiac airship is indicated as over-surfaced, thus corroborating various prevalent opinions.

TABLE 12—CONTROL SURFACE DATA FOR NONRIGID AIRSHIPS

Airship	Total Areas (sq. ft.)					Vol. cu. ft.	L ft.	C ft.
	Vertical	Horizontal	Rudder	Elevator	Total			
OB-1	228	328	48	96	556	43,030	93 85	32
A-4....	262	346	84	168	608	95,000	162	60
J	462	492	85	122	954	174,880	168	70
C....	460	495	85	120	955	181,000	196	77
D	460	495	85	120	955	190,000	198	78
* ZR-1	2,401	2,966	489	576	5,367	2,289,861	680 15	290

NOTE: Areas include balanced portion
    Vol. =Volumetric displacement of hull
    L   =Overall length of ship
    C   =Distance between center of gravity of volumetric displacement and center of total area
        of surfaces
* ZR-1 data added for check.

TABLE 13—CONTROL SURFACE DATA FOR NONRIGID AIRSHIPS

Airship	Chart I		Chart II		Chart III	All Charts
	$\sqrt[3]{A_vL}$	$\sqrt[3]{A_hL}$	$\sqrt[3]{A_rL}$	$\sqrt[3]{A_eL}$	$\sqrt[3]{AC}$	$\sqrt[3]{Vol.}$
OB-1	27 76	31 34	16 51	20 81	26 10	35 04
A-4.	34 88	38 27	23 87	30 10	33.10	45.63
J	42 66	43 56	24 26	27 37	40 60	55 92
. ...	44 84	45 95	25 54	28 65	41 90	56 57
D	45 00	46 11	25 63	28 75	42 10	57 50
* ZR-1	118 00	126 30	69 20	73 20	116 00	131 80

* ZR-1 data added for check.

The Army Military $M\,A$, known to be unstable, is shown by these curves to be under-surfaced.

The previous statement also applies to the Pony Blimp AA.

Experience has indicated that for training airships where inexperienced pilots are concerned, the areas obtained by the foregoing data should be increased from 5 to 10 per cent.

The maximum loadings which control surfaces have been required to stand have been 10 lbs. per sq. ft. for fixed surfaces and 6 lbs. per sq. ft. for the movable surfaces. This requirement has been satisfactory for ships propelled up to 60 m.p.h. The weights have been kept down to a maximum of .5 lb. per sq. ft. Surfaces of this weight have been tested to withstand a loading of some 15 to 18 lbs. per sq. ft.

Scoops, Air Dampers and Ducts

Air scoops with their ducts and dampers are for the purpose of conveying and controlling air to the ballonets from the propeller blast produced by the airship engine propellers. Figure 28 shows the arrangement of the standard scoop and air damper valve, to the latter of which are connected the air ducts leading to the ballonets, as used on nonrigid airships of the TA and TC design. The diameter of the scoop is 15 in. and the radius of the air duct, of semicircular form, is 12 in.

On the early airships constructed in America, the air ducts were located on the outside of the envelope, being laced thereto. This arrangement obviously increased the resistance of the airship and was found to be heavier and less practical than the present type which is located internally. It was thought by the earlier designers that to place the air lines insides of the envelope would cause them to become shut off by the weight of the ballonet fabric. This apprehension was overcome by flaring out the end of the

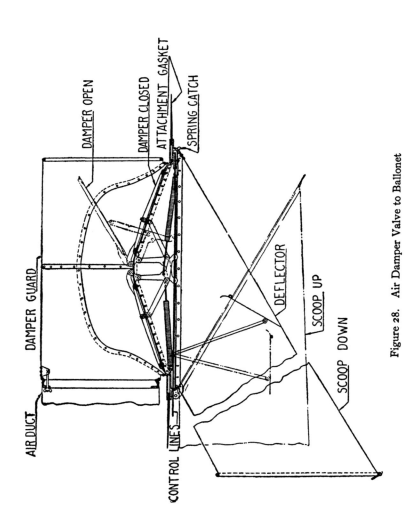

Figure 28.   Air Damper Valve to Ballonet

air line entering the ballonet and designing the ballonet so that its folds would not lay beyond the ballonet shoe.

In the *TA* airship the scoops are replaced by an air duct leading from the center of the engine outrigger to the envelope, the damper being placed on top of the outrigger. Entrance of the air blast is made on the forward end of the outrigger within the propeller circle, the air passages continuing through the outlet where the air damper valve is located. Non-return flaps are hung in the air lines in the outrigger to prevent the air from one side of the outrigger passing out through the other side in case one engine only is operating. An accordion is placed in the air line from the outrigger to the envelope to allow for the variation of the distance from the car to the envelope caused by the change of pressure in the envelope.

Provision is made for drawing scoops close to the envelope when not in use, thereby reducing the resistance to the airship. Ordinarily, one scoop has been provided for each engine, thus requiring two independent air duct systems in the envelope. A recent attempt was made on the *TC*-6 airship to combine the two air ducts in the envelope into one thereby using only one air damper valve. This system did not prove a saving in weight as anticipated.

The control lines for the air damper valves consist of 3/32 in. 6 x 7 flexible aircraft cable. The 7 x 7 cable has proved unsatisfactory as not being as flexible as the 6 x 7.

Air friction in air ducts. In Aircraft Technical Note 142 of the Navy Department, Bureau of Construction and Repair dated April 5, 1919, Capt. F. M. Rope, of the R.A.F., recommends that the velocity of air in the ducts be kept below 50 ft. per sec. to avoid excessive kinetic losses.

From Kent,

$$h = \frac{L\,v^2}{K\,d} \tag{19}$$

Where

h = Head in inches of water
L = Length in feet
v = Velocity in feet per second
d = Diameter in inches
K = Constant = 13,120

From tests conducted on "Coastal" airship air ducts Captain Rope recommends the value of 14,600 for K (being transposed from millimeter and hydraulic mean depth units).

With further reference to Kent,

$$Q = 0.6245 \frac{hd^5}{L} \tag{20}$$

in which Q = Quantity of air in cu. ft. per sec.

Automatic Valves

Requirements. Following are the requirements for the ideal automatic airship valve. The figures in the margin indicate the relative merits of these requirements which form a fair basis for comparison of airship valves:

Ruggedness, durability	10
Accessibility for inspection and repair	8
Easily installed and removed; valve holes used as manholes	7
Light weight	7
Simple and cheap, the minimum number of parts	10
Manual positive control	7
Automatic positive control	7
Gas-tight, from no pressure up to popping point	7
Warning device to indicate failure of any part	3
Minimum aerodynamic resistance	3
Valve to open with decreasing tension and vice versa	6
Easily operated manually	3
Fool proof	3
Minimum danger from electrostatic charge	3
Water-tight, to prevent water getting into envelope	3
Minimum number of adjustments	10
Protection from fabric which might interfere with working of valve parts	3

Present standard type.[2]   The standard airship valve
now in use in the United States is the Goodyear 18 in.
automatic type as shown by Figure 29.   This valve was
invented by A. G. Maranville, assignor to the Goodyear
Tire & Rubber Co.; it is protected by U. S. Patent No.
1,384,268, dated July 12, 1921.   The principal features of
this valve are as follows:

The knob on the outside is for adjusting the pressure
which can be varied between limits of 20 and 60 mm.   All
moving joints in this valve are equipped with ball bearings.
The valve stem is also equipped with adjustable roller
bearings, further to reduce the friction of the moving parts.

Spring tension.   The lever system is so designed that it
gives a decreasing tension on the valve which aids in the
maintenance of the constant volume and pressure in the
envelope.

The *emergency closing device,* otherwise known as the
positive closing device, is to prevent the possibility of the
valve sticking open.   The positive closing cord is distinct
from the opening cord.

Gaskets.   The lip type gaskets used in this valve make
it very sensitive on opening and closing.   The valve is
attached to the envelope by a special molded gasket that
insures a good fit.   The valve is held in place by a clamping
ring with wing-nuts.

Static Wiring.   All parts of the valve are electrically
connected; the connection between the clamping ring and
inner frame being made by the wing-nuts and bolts.   A
flexible wire connection is made between the dome and
frame.

Leakage.   The valve is tested in a vertical position for
air leakage.   This leakage does not exceed 8 cu. ft. per 24
hrs. under a water pressure of 1 in.

[2] Types of balloon valves are described and illustrated in the volume "Free and Captive
Balloons," of the Ronald Aeronautic Library.

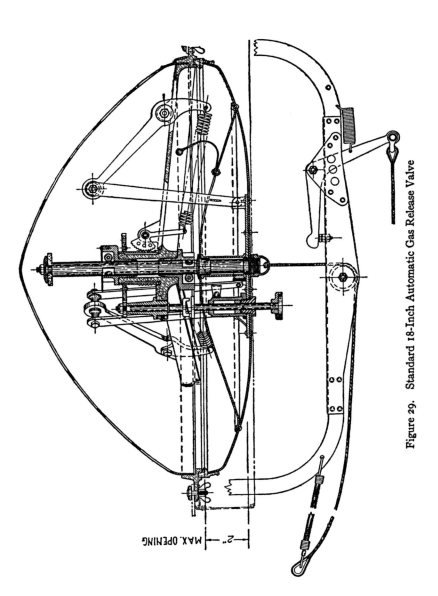

MAX. OPENING |—2"—|

Figure 29.   Standard 18-Inch Automatic Gas Release Valve

Weight. The weight of the valve is approximately 16 lbs.

Shipping Trunk. Each valve is shipped in a specially constructed trunk which protects it from rough usage. The trunks contain instructions for installation and spare parts.

Acceptance test. These valves are given the following test before being packed for shipment or use:

Valves shall be tested with air in testing tank in a vertical position. This presupposes the most adverse condition under which a valve is placed on an airship.

The testing is as follows:

> Valve set at 1 in. water pressure—tested to blow at .2 in. above.
> Valve checked for leakage at 1 in. water pressure.
> Valve set at 2.5 in. water pressure—tested to blow at .2 in. above.
> Valve checked for leakage at 2.5 in. water pressure.
> Valve set at 1.5 in. water pressure—tested to blow at .2 in. above.

Tests for leakage to last for 15 minutes at each pressure given above. Leakage must not exceed 1/12 cu. ft. during the 15 min. period (⅓ cu. ft. per hr.).

New type valve. A new type of valve has been invented by J. R. Gammeter of the B. F. Goodrich Co., which though still in the experimental stage, has promise of being a very satisfactory valve. This valve is shown by Figure 30. A brief description of the major differences from the present standard valve as previously described follows.

The spring mechanism is designed to give the same loading at all pressure settings. A change in pressure of .1 in. of water is claimed to be sufficient to operate the valve in any position whether horizontal, top, bottom, or vertical. Considerable friction is eliminated as compared with the standard type of valve by having the center stem ride on rockers.   This should result in the sensitivity to the change in pressure quoted above.   The method of mounting the valve in the envelope is simplified in that a molded gasket is provided which is cemented to the envelope and has the

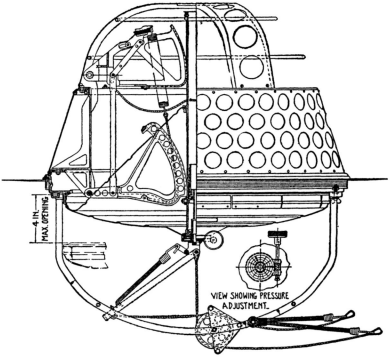

4 IN.
MAX. OPENING

VIEW SHOWING PRESSURE
ADJUSTMENT.

Figure 30.   Goodrich 20-Inch Gas Valve

valve inserted therein.   Should this prove to be a satisfactory and positive means of mounting the valve in the envelope, ease of installation and a saving of weight will have been obtained.

Using aluminum alloy casting the weight of the valve is 21 lbs., while with magnesium alloy casting, it is 17.6 lbs. The diameter of the valve is 20 in.   The valve at present is furnished with the following pressure ranges: Valve on bottom, minimum .4 in., maximum 2.2 in. of water; valve on side, minimum, .9 in., maximum, 2.7 in. water; valve on top, minimum, 1.4 in. maximum, 3.2 in. water. The maximum opening of the valve is 4 in.

The leakage, when tested with gas and valve set .1 in. of water below blow-off, was 2.4 cu. ft. in 24 hrs. at a pressure of 1.4 in. of water. At a pressure of .3 in. below blow-off, the valve is practically 100 per cent leakproof. The foregoing is based on a test with the valve in a vertical position, i.e., the disc is in the plane of the vertical. With the valve in the horizontal position, the leakage is less.

Valve testing. Figure 31 shows an airship valve-testing apparatus designed and constructed by the Naval Aircraft Factory, Philadelphia. This apparatus is for testing airship valves for leakage and blow-off at various gas pressures.

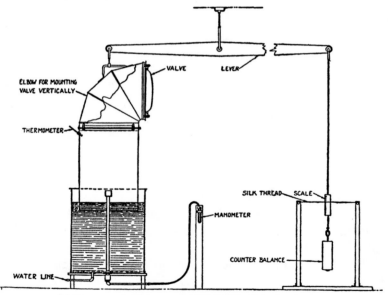

Figure 31. Arrangement of Valve Testing Apparatus

As shown, this apparatus is similar to a gasometer with a suitable counter balance, a thermometer, a manometer, and deflection scale. The thermometer is for the purpose of taking the temperature of the gas during a leakage test. It is inserted in a rubber stopper which is placed in the hole provided for it. The manometer is removable by removing the rubber stopper for the purpose of filling or exhausting the gas chamber. The change in position of the movable tank as shown on Figure 31 is measured on the scale graduated so as to read the drop of the tank directly in inches. Two silk threads, each stretched with a rubber band, are used for reference lines.

The apparatus is shown with the elbow for testing the valves in a vertical position. For a test in the horizontal position, the valve is put in place on top of the vertical tank after removing the elbow. The method used to make an air-tight joint between the elbow and the vertical tank comprises a rubber gasket pressed firmly between two ⅛ in. wires backed up by a metal ring and a wooden clamping ring.

Blow-off test. The valve is mounted in the vertical or horizontal position as desired and the gas is let in the test tank through the manometer connections as noted in the above. Sufficient gas must be admitted to the tank to expel completely all air through the valve. By manipulation of the weights on the balancing arm, the gas pressure is maintained constant during blow-off. The valve is regulated by its adjusting screw so that it holds tight at say .5 in. water pressure and opens at .7 in. of water pressure, blowing off at slightly higher pressures. The time required for the tank capacity to blow off through the airship valve is obtained with a stop watch. From this and knowing the capacity of the tank, the blow-off of the valve in cubic feet per minute may be obtained.

Leakage test. The valve is placed on the apparatus in the same manner as in the previous test. With the lever arm in the horizontal position at the start of the test, the gas pressure is regulated at the desired pressure and readings of the temperature and the drop in the test tank are recorded hourly. The leakage in 24 hrs., which is the standard of comparison, may then be determined. Should gas be used in the test, Cetus lubricating oil to a depth of $\frac{1}{4}$ in. should be used on top of the water in the test tank to prevent absorption of the gas in the water as well as prevent saturation of the gas with water vapor.

Discharge rate tests. McCook Field Serial No. 2,583 on the subject of Tests and Valves for *RS*-1 Airship, reports the discharge rates of the Goodyear 18 in. and 28 in., and Gammeter 20 in. airship valves under various conditions of valve setting, internal pressure, air velocities over the valves, deflectors "on" and "off," etc. The research was carried out under the general supervision of the author for the Lighter-than-Air Section and M. A. Smith of the Propeller Branch, the work being directed by D. Adam Dickey of the Propeller Branch, the author of the report.

The general arrangement of the tests is shown on Plates X and XI. A 5,000 cu. ft. supply balloon with a nose airballonet to maintain rigidity against the propeller blast, was supported so that it could be adjusted and secured in any desired position. The arrangement permitted almost any internal pressure for any delivery within the operating range of the equipment and certainly exceeding the range required for nonrigid airships.

The characteristics of only the Goodyear 18 in. and Gammeter 20 in. airships valves will be recorded here. These are nonrigid airships valves whereas the Goodyear 28 in. valve is primarily and at present a semirigid airship valve.

The discharge rate for the Goodyear 18 in. valve is expressed by the following formula:

(Official Photograph, Air Corps, U. S. Army)

Plate X.   General Arrangement for Tests of Airship Valves

Plate XI.　Blower and Metering Equipment for Tests of Airship Valves

$$Q = 1,044 \times O\sqrt{H_i} \qquad (21)$$

and for the Gammeter 20 in. valve, by the formulas

$$Q = (1,296 - 89.1 \times O)O\sqrt{H_i} \text{ (Deflector off)} \qquad (22)$$

and $\quad Q = (1,231 - 97.7 \times O)O\sqrt{H_i} \text{ (Deflector on)} \qquad (23)$

Where $\quad Q$ = Air delivery in cu. ft. per min.

$\qquad O$ = Valve opening in inches

$\qquad H_i$ = Internal pressure of bag in inches of water

Comparing sensitiveness of these valves at 1.5 in. internal pressure which is normally used in flight, the Goodyear 18 in. valve reaches its maximum discharge rate of 2,630 cu. ft. per min. at .8 in. above the valve setting, whereas the Gammeter valve discharges its maximum rate of 5,070 cu. ft. per min. at .55 in. above setting. At 50 per cent maximum discharge rate, the Goodyear valve requires about .7 in. rise of internal pressure as compared with .05 in. for the Gammeter 20 in. valve.

Valve setting. The conditions that govern the pressure limits are:

Pressure should not be less than that required to maintain a rigid envelope beam against buckling or wrinkling of the envelope. For ships of 200,000 cu. ft. capacity, this pressure is about .5 in.

The pressure should not be lower than that required or determined by the nose stiffening design.

The increase in pressure for head of helium is .0105 in. per ft. Under the discussion of nose stiffening, it was determined that an internal pressure of 1.1 in. of water was required at the axis of the *TE* airship envelope. This was for an air speed of 45 M.p.h. approximately, the nose battens being designed to take care of the additional pressure due to gusts assumed to have a velocity 15 M.p.h. higher. Consequently the pressure required at the manometer in the car, which is 23 ft. below the axis of the envelope, will be 1.1 minus .0105 × 23 = .86 in.

The pressure on the ballonet valve is equal to the pressure of the gas at the top of the ballonet when full. Therefore with full ballonet, the pressure on the ballonet valve is greater than that on a valve located at the same elevation in the envelope.

Keeping the following conditions in mind in addition to the requirements that the valve should be set as low as possible in order to insure the factor of safety of the envelope as high as possible, the valve settings for the *TE* airship are determined as indicated on Figure 32: (a) descent angle

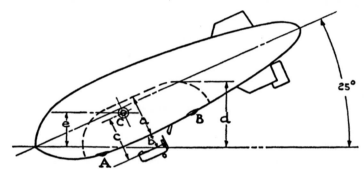

TABLE OF VALVE PRESSURES AND SETTINGS.

CONDITION	VALVE	PRESSURE AND SETTING.
1. NOSE DOWN 25° 45 M.P.H.	A B	1.1 + (32 × .0105) = 1.44"
	C	1.1 + (16.25 × .0105) = 1.27"
2. HORIZONTAL FLIGHT 45 M.P.H.	A B	.86 + (26.5 × .0105) = 1.13"
	C	.86 + (21 × .0105) = 1.08"
3. VALVE AIR AUTO- MATICALLY BEFORE GAS VALVES BLOW.	A B C	CONDITION (1) SET TO HOLD AT 1.45" CONDITION (1) SET TO HOLD 1.4" AT VALVE AND 1.15" AT CAR

DIMENSIONS:— a = 19.75 FT.   d = 32.00 FT.
              b = 6.75 "   e = 16.25 " .
              C = 21.00 "

Figure 32.   Valve Settings for Type *TE* Airship

of 25 degrees, ballonet full; (b) level flight, full speed with ballonets full.

Blowers [3]

Blowers are required for an airship when the pressure at the mouth of the air scoop is below that required for safe flight. Such a condition exists when the airship is being towed or when going at a low speed, as when hovering over an object, or when landing at sunset, or when the engine has failed. The capacity of the blowers is determined from the conditions of the problem presented. The usual capacity is from 1 to 2 per cent of the envelope volume.

Three sources of power for driving blowers have been tried in this country. They are:

Hand-driven—as in the Navy Class D airship.
Direct drive off of the engine—as in the Military (MA) airship.
Independent engine or electric motor—as in the Zodiac (RN-1) and the U. S. MB respectively.

The Navy Class B airship was equipped with a small gasoline engine of motorcycle type developing approximately 2 hp., driving a multivane blower made by the B. F. Sturtevant Co. through a V-belt or clutch. The housing and hangars were made of aluminum.

For power-driven blowers the propeller type has been the most satisfactory and most efficient.

The U. S. MB blower was designed to have a maximum delivery of 1,800 cu. ft. of air per min. against a static head of ¾ in. of water. The design, construction and tests were conducted at McCook Field, Dayton, Ohio. The blower as shown by Figures 33 and 34 delivered 1,800 cu. ft. per min. under static head of .7 in. of water when running at 3,600 r.p.m. and absorbing approximately .26 hp. The pressure,

[3] Formulas relating to horsepower and delivery of blowers are given in the volume "Balloon and Airship Gases," of the Ronald Aeronautic Library.

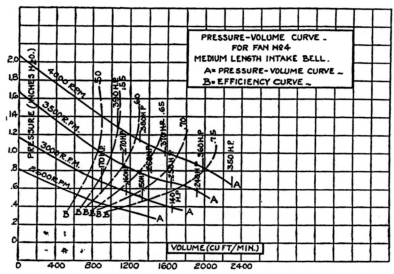

Figure 33.   Pressure-Volume Curve for 12-Inch Blower

volume, efficiency and power curves are shown on Figure 33. The fan was made from .122 in. duralumin. The plan-form of the fan was sawed out of a flat piece of metal, each blade being twisted to the proper angle at the 3, 4, 5 and 6 in. radii, and filed down to the proper sections at these radii. A complete report of the tests is set forth in Serial No. 2,270 by the Engineering Division, McCook Field, Dayton, Ohio, dated January 11, 1924.

The high delivery required of this blower was based on the requirements of hauling down the U. S. *MB* airship, with engines removed, at the rate of 1,000 ft. per min.

'Figures 35 and 36 show the pressure-volume curves, and the design of an airship blower which will deliver 10,000 cu. ft. per min. under a static pressure of approximately 1 in. of water and have a speed range up to 3,600 r.p.m. from idling speed. The maximum power absorbed is 7.5 hp. at a delivery of 12,320 cu. ft., the static pressure being

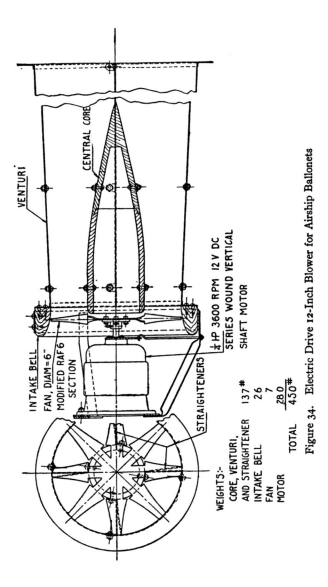

CENTRAL CORE

VENTURI

¼ HP 3600 RPM 12 V DC
SERIES WOUND VERTICAL
SHAFT MOTOR

INTAKE BELL
FAN, DIAM = 6"
MODIFIED RAF 6
SECTION

STRAIGHTENERS

WEIGHTS:-
CORE, VENTURI,
AND STRAIGHTENER   137#
INTAKE BELL   26
FAN   7
MOTOR   28.0
TOTAL   450#

Figure 34.   Electric Drive 12-Inch Blower for Airship Ballonets

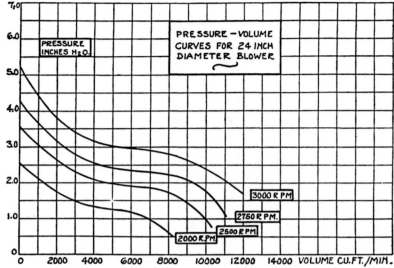

Figure 35.   Pressure-Volume Curve for 24-Inch Blower

2.44 and the r.p.m. being 3,340. The weight of the rotor is 4.3 lbs. and the total weight of the blower including fan, venturi and shaft is 20 lbs.

Ballast

Water is now used for ballast exclusively in preference to sand. The reason for this preference is that the water is more positive in action, therefore more easily controlled; it is more easily supplied, being a more universal substance than sand; and it is cleaner to handle.

The capacity of water ballast tanks varies from 4 to 7 per cent of the gross lift of the airship.

Figures 23 and 24, respectively, show the standard 4 in. water ballast valve now in use, and the discharge curve for a 3-in. valve of the same design. The discharge rate of this valve is estimated to be 15 lbs. per sec. as an average rate of discharge in emptying a tank with an initial head of 3 ft.

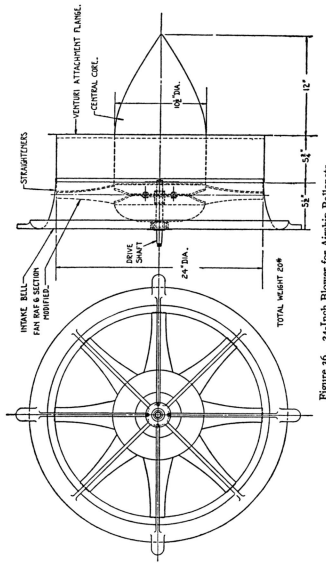

Figure 36.   24-Inch Blower for Airship Ballonets

Considerable difficulty has been experienced in getting a leak-proof valve. The most satisfactory material for seats for these valves has been found to be Acco cork.

CHAPTER VII

INFLATION AND HANDLING EQUIPMENT

Inflation Equipment

Appendix. Appendices, or inflation sleeves and deflation sleeves, commonly called, are located as indicated on Figure 2 for the purpose of inflation, deflation and purging of the gas in the envelope. Where only one sleeve is supplied, as in the smaller ships, it is located amidships. Figure 37 shows the design of the standard inflation or deflation sleeve for nonrigid airships. It is 10½ in. diameter for connection to the hangar tubing.

Inflation connector. To make the connection between the inflation appendix and the hangar inflation tubing, a metal or fibre sleeve is commonly used to which the appendix and tubing are connected at opposite ends by means of elastic cord commonly referred to as the "elastic inflation tube type." The metal tubing is tapered at each end whereas the fibre tubing is beaded on each end to prevent the tubing from being accidentally disengaged.[1]

Recently a connector has been developed which promises to be very satisfactory having the requisite gas tightness, obtained in the old type noted above, and the additional feature of being quickly and easily attached or detached; it is shown in Figure 38. This connector is made of three parts; the two outer rings are permanently attached, one to the appendix, and the other with the elastic cords to the inflation tubing. These are brought together with the

[1] Safety rules relating to the inflation of airships and the transfer of gases from cylinders or holders, are set forth in the volume of the Ronald Aeronautic Library entitled "Balloon and Airship Gases."

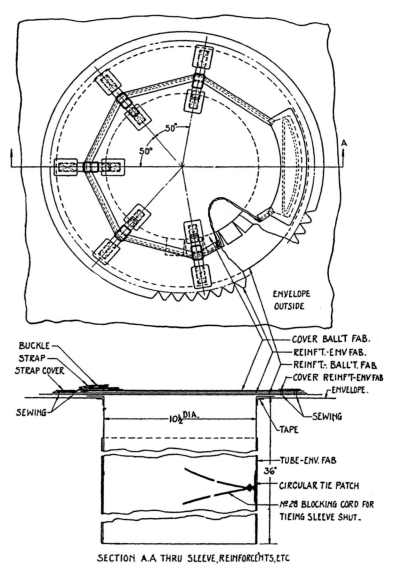

SECTION A.A THRU SLEEVE, REINFORCEMENTS, ETC

Figure 37. Appendix Construction for Airship Envelopes

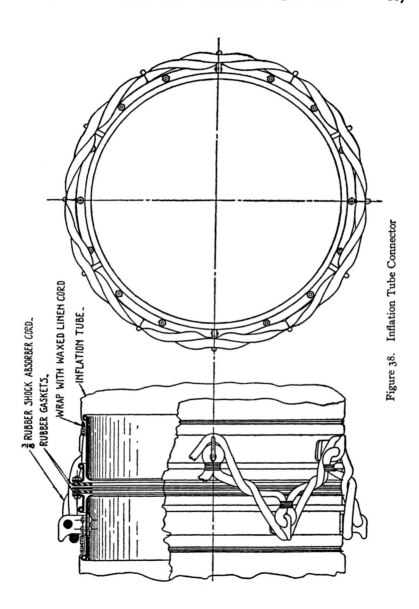

Figure 38.   Inflation Tube Connector

rubber disk inserted between them, this disk being mounted permanently between flanged rings which serve as guides for lining up the two outer rings so that their metal edges will meet directly opposite each other on the rubber disk. The elastic cords are then snapped over the lugs which bind the whole together much in the same manner as the heads of a drum are held.

Inflation net—*Cotton seine mesh type.* Figure 39 (a) shows the type and construction of an inflation net which up to a recent date, has been considered standard for nonrigid air-

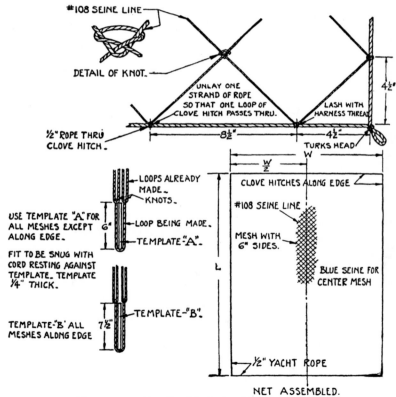

Figure 39a.   Details of Inflation Net Construction

Plate XII.   Webbing Type of Inflation Net

ships.   This net was designed for use on the Navy Class C and D airships and has been adopted for the TC airships.

The width of the net is determined from the following:

$$W = D \left(1 + \frac{\pi}{2}\right) + 20 \qquad (24)$$

Where D = Diameter of airship envelope

It is necessary that the net extend below the bottom of the envelope about 10 ft. on each side.

In length the net should extend to the forward edge of the top fin with enough material to extend beyond the nose a distance equal to the radius of the envelope.   An empirical formula for the length is

$$L = .045 \text{ Vol.}^{\frac{2}{3}} + \frac{D}{4} \qquad (25)$$

Where   Vol. = Volume of envelope
         D = Diameter of envelope

It is essential that the net extend beyond the nose as the center of bouyancy being forward tends to nose the bag out of the net, the latter rolling back rapidly.

Cotton webbing type.   The cotton seine mesh net is being replaced by the cotton webbing type which is shown on Plate XII.   The principal advantages of this type of net are:

Low maintenance cost
Greater durability
Greater strength
Less wear on envelope

Two-inch cotton webbing with an ultimate strength of 1,000 lbs. is used.   The meshes are 30 in. x 48 in., joined with 9-cord linen, the corners being reinforced with three loops of the cord as shown on Figure 39 (b).   This Figure is the design of a net for the TA and TC type airships, or ships ranging from 130,000 to 210,000 cu. ft.; the rows of

"D" rings allow for the variation in adjustment required
by the range in size.

Mooring and Handling

General. As the mooring and handling of airships will
be covered in another volume of the Ronald Aeronautic
Library, a description is given here only of special devices

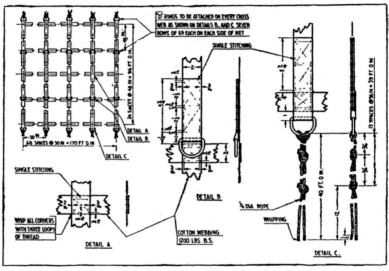

Figure 39b.   Details of Inflation Net Construction

developed for nonrigid airships and the arrangement of
handling lines on the envelope.

As indicated on Figure 2, the majority of the handling
lines are located forward of the car, it being necessary to
arrange the handling crew in this manner so as to pivot the
ship into the wind, in which direction its resistance is the
least, therefore the vertical components of the loads on the
handling lines which tend to crash the ship to the ground
are minimized.

At the pivot point, a group of 4 finger patches radiating

from the junction point of two handling lines, is located as shown on Figure 2, page 6. This group of patches is located on the lowest element of the envelope.

The drag-rope bridle, item 31 on Figure 2, is joined to the drag-rope which latter is joined to the quick release clip as shown in Figure 43. The clip serves as a junction of the drag-rope to the car from which it is snubbed when the drag-rope is first released to the handling crew. After the forward velocity of the ship is checked, the quick release clip is operated by the pilot thus breaking the connection to the car and transferring the load to the envelope.

Emergency handling gear for small nonrigid airships. Special equipment was developed owing to the general difficulty and risk involved in bringing an airship into or out of a hangar by the method of using large handling crews. The advantages gained, therefore, by this method of handling small nonrigid airships herein described are: the economic feature of money saved in ground crew; less structural damage; and the ability to launch an airship from a hangar under the condition of severe cross-winds, which ordinarily would prohibit exit maneuvering by the method of using only the handling crew.

Figure 41 is a sketch of the arrangement of the equipment used in this method of handling small nonrigid airships. The ground lines act as flexible cable-ways on which ride two or more snatch blocks. The operation of launching an airship in a cross-wind is as follows:

With the bow of the airship to the door, the windward handling lines of the airship are secured by taking a half hitch about the hooks of the two snatch blocks riding on the windward ground cable; then with the majority of the crew on the car, the airship is rushed out into the cross-wind, the detail on the after windward line easing off roundly after the tail of the ship has cleared the doors, thus per-

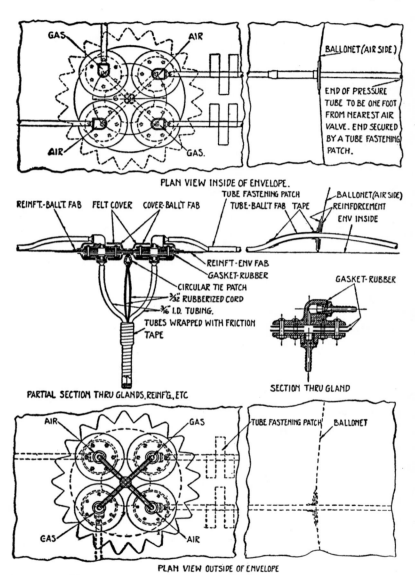

Figure 40.   Construction of Pressure Tube Gland Unit

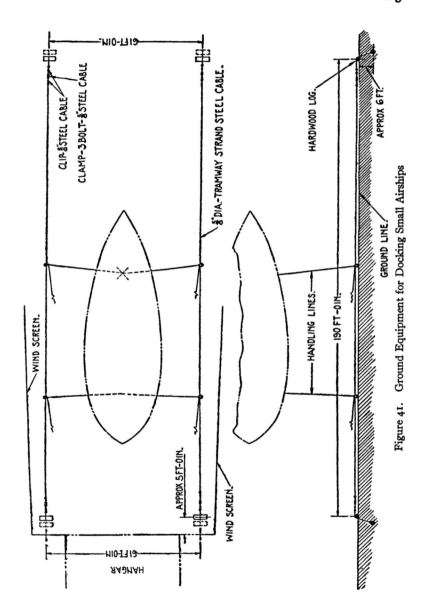

Figure 41.   Ground Equipment for Docking Small Airships

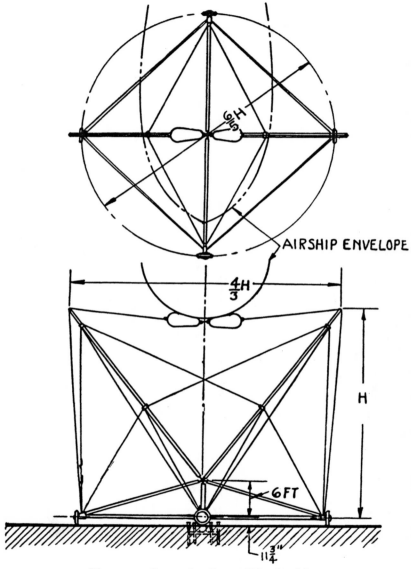

Figure 42.   Suspension Type of Mooring Mast

mitting the airship to nose into the wind riding on the forward lines.

Portable mooring mast—suspension type. Figure 42 shows the general assembly of this equipment, which was developed owing to the previous unsatisfactory performance of airships moored at the nose. This type of mast, which moors the airship at a point between the nose stiffening and the car suspension, is considered to have the following advantages:

> Flexibility; permitting the airship to weave to and fro without exerting any severe strain due to sudden gusts of the nature produced by the rigid type of nose mooring masts.
>
> Increased stability of mooring owing to ability of attaching in the line of action of the center of resistance of the airship. This latter will have the effect of reducing the strain due to aerodynamic couples.
>
> Reduced height, which naturally reduces aerial obstruction, a desirable feature for landing fields.

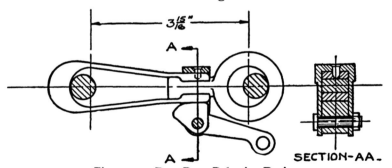

Figure 43.   Drag-Rope Releasing Device

From the sketch it will be seen that the mast is of tubular construction with steel wire cable bracing, mounted on wheels so that it can be turned readily to proper position with respect to the wind direction. This mast was successfully used for mooring the U. S. *MB* airship during the

Gypsy Moth project in the New England States in the summer of 1923.

Constant pressure system. This system which is shown in Figure 44, is for the purpose of maintaining the pressure in the airship envelope, constant and as low as possible. Obviously the system is applicable only while the ship is in a hangar. High-sustained pressures have a detrimental

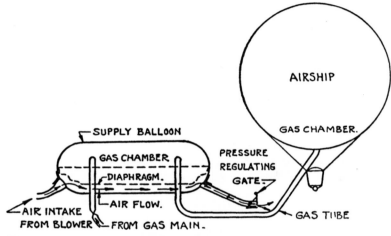

Figure 44. Equipment for Maintaining a Constant Low Pressure of Gas in Docked Airships

effect on envelope fabric, as clearly brought out in an article entitled, "Effect of Envelope Pressure on Airships," by R. H. Upson, Chief Aeronautical Engineer of The Aircraft Development Corporation, Detroit, Michigan, in the December 15, 1919 issue of *Aviation*.

A supply balloon of 5,000 cu. ft. capacity is interposed between the gasometer and the airship so that the airship internal pressure will at all times be governed by the supply balloon pressure. The supply balloon pressure is regulated by the pressure of air in its ballonet, which in turn is maintained by a continuously-running constant-speed motor-driven blower, as shown. The regulating gate at the air outlet is for the purpose of setting the pressure for the system. A "no current" signal should be placed in the electric circuit to indicate to the operator or warn him in case the power should be interrupted. It will be seen that with this arrangement, as the airship gas contracts the gas in the supply balloon is forced into the airship without loss of pressure owing to the slow velocity of flow. When the gas in the airship expands, the supply balloon absorbs the excess volume of gas without appreciable increase in pressure. The supply balloon should be doped heavily to avoid leakage.

CHAPTER VIII

CONSTRUCTION AND INSPECTION

Inspection of Fabrics

General. *Cloth.*[1] The raw cloth is generally inspected at the textile mill, and if recently inspected there, inspection at the rubber proofing plant should not be necessary, other than sufficient tests to identify the material. Cloth received from storage or purchased on the open market without previous inspection should be examined carefully in order to prevent defective material from being proofed, where the defect frequently will be unnoticeable until failure.

Aluminum. Particular attention should be given to the copper content and fineness of the powdered aluminum, that the requirements of the specification for this material are met.

Rubber proofing. Some manufacturers object to process inspection of rubberized fabric on the grounds that the actual composition and preparation of the proofing are still more or less secret processes. It is necessary, however, to follow the process through the manufacturing operation to see that the requirements of the specification in regard to material and method are complied with. Special attention should be given to the elimination of water soluble materials in the outside proofing of envelope fabrics. The inspector should familiarize himself with the different grades of rubber since only the harder and non-resinous rubber should be used for proofing this type of fabric. The fineness of the

[1] More complete information regarding raw cloth and rubberized fabrics for airships is given in Part III of the volume "Free and Captive Balloons," Ronald Aeronautic Library.

pigments used should be determined, and if lumpy the dough or cement should be strained.

Visual inspection. All fabrics should be inspected over a light table. The inspector should constantly watch the fabric as it passes over the bank of lights. The visual inspection of fabrics is made for two classes of defects: (1) raw cloth imperfections; (2) fabric imperfections.

These defects may again be subdivided into: (a) places to be marked for cutting out entirely; (b) places that may be repaired by a patch.

Raw cloth defects. All defects in raw cloth manufacture that weaken the cloth should be marked for cutting out. The following imperfections weaken cloth:

> Broken warp or filler threads.
> Thin threads.
> Places where a slub has been removed and the threads have
> > been broken.
> Pin holes, etc.

Generally speaking, the only imperfections of cloth manufacture that render it necessary to patch the rubberized fabric are slubs, heavy places, knots, and other slight imperfections of weaving that may tend to make the cloth unduly thick at any point, thereby lessening the coating of rubber. These places should be marked for patching.

Fabric defects.

> Hard wrinkles, torn spots, places stretched owing to poor
> > doubling, etc., should be marked for cutting out.
> Pin holes, bare spots where the rubber coat has not been
> > properly applied, thick or thin places in the coating, etc.,
> > should be patched.
> The width of the laps on the bias should be carefully noted.

Inspection of Construction Operations

General considerations.

All construction operations should be inspected to determine that each airship is satisfactorily built in all particulars.

No rejected material should be used where it would cause an apparent weakness in the part.

A progress chart should be kept to check closely each stage of manufacture.

Outline of construction processes. *Cutting.* Care should be taken that the extreme edge of the selvedge, which very often is slightly bare, should not be incorporated in the panels.

Cementing. The surface of the cloth to be cemented should be washed with a felt pad immersed in solvent. Cement should be applied in the following manner to obtain the greatest adhesive qualities:

The cement receptacle should remain covered to prevent loss of solvent. Should the cement become thick due to unavoidable loss or a thinner cement be desired, solvent naptha or benzol may be added. Cement that has been thinned should stand 24 hrs. before being used.

As far as service conditions permit, cementing should not be done in wet weather or when the humidity is high. Cement in which large globules of water are found should be discarded.

Unless unavoidable, the cementing operation should not be done in direct sunlight.

The surface of the cloth to be cemented should be washed with a felt pad immersed in a solvent, allowing the surface to partially dry before the cement is applied.

Where aluminized fabric is to form a union between two parts, the aluminum proofing must be removed by some suitable process that will not injure the fabric beneath or remove the rubber coating under the aluminum. This aluminum must be removed from the entire surface that is to be cemented, allowing $\frac{1}{8}$ in. beyond the edge of the object which is to be cemented thereto (tape, patch or other accessory). After the aluminum proofing has been removed, the surface is cleaned with a felt pad that has been immersed in a solvent and then squeezed out. Upon completing the union of the parts, the buffed-off aluminum which appears exposed beyond the edges of the part is covered with aluminum cement applied with a soft brush.

Stringy cement should not be used.

Two or three coats of cement should be applied; each coat drying at least 15 min. before the addition of another coat; the last coat should dry ½ hr. The cement shall be thoroughly dry before the two surfaces are stitched together.

The cemented surfaces are placed together and rolled with a stitcher to remove trapped air, etc.

Excess cement around the edge of the seam or patch may be removed with the felt swab or destroyed with fine talc or soapstone. Either must be used sparingly.

Stitching. Eight stitches to the inch is regarded as standard practice and either lock or chain stitch may be used. Judgment should be exercised in interpreting this practice, as a large number of stitches in a given area punctures the fabric enough to weaken it, whereas too few stitches produce a seam of insufficient strength under conditions of high temperature when the cement becomes softened, thus allowing parts under stress to slip.

The inspector should educate the sewing machine operators that the best work is obtained by running the machine slowly and stitching straight. When breaks occur in the thread, the stitching should be started 1 in. behind the point of rupture. The stitching should not be unraveled as this leaves holes in the fabric through which the gas may permeate. Where stitching pulls beyond the edge of the fabric, such places should be taped. All stitching should be cemented and taped.

Taping and reinforcing. The cement that is applied for taping should cover a greater surface, say ⅛ in. beyond the width of the tape. As the gas permeates very considerably at the seams, every effort should be made by the inspector to insure that there is a pure, smooth coat of rubber between the tape and the seam. Tape should be applied to the seam without stretching after slightly moistening with a felt pad immersed in solvent. The tape should then be heavily rolled down.

Patches.[2] The method of making rope patches is described in the following paragraphs.

(a) Cut the rope to finished length and serve as indicated by Figure 15 at the point where fraying out of the fibers is to start.

(b) Separate the fibers and comb out with the fingers. An awl may be used in this process, but care should be taken not to break the fibers. It is recommended that at least one-third of the fibers be combed out in order to prevent an excessive bunching of the fibers for the fingers.

(c) The frayed out portions of the rope fingers, should then be laid on the table and the cement soaked in with stubby brushes. The cement may otherwise be poured over the rope fingers and the operator's fingers run through the fibers to spread the cement evenly.

(d) The fingers are then formed to a templet made for that purpose.

(e) A period of 12 hrs. drying should then follow.

(f) Operations (c), (d) and (e) should then be repeated for the other side of the rope fingers.

(g) The foregoing operations should be repeated three times.

(h) It is important to have enough cement. Should inspection reveal that the cement has not soaked through to the root of the frayed-out section, additional cement should be applied at this point in the operations.

(i) The rope fingers should be rolled thoroughly on both sides.

(j) The cemented finger should then be thoroughly dried.

(k) The fabric coverings are applied with three coats of cement.

(l) A fiber stitcher should be used for rolling the fabric and rope fingers together. Manufacturers at present use metal stitchers.

[2] Rubberized fabrics suitable for making patches, are described in Part III of the volume 'Free and Captive Balloons," Ronald Aeronautic Library.

(m) The patch is now ready for sewing and aging. This aging should extend over a period of at least 10 days.

Inspection of accessories. The following suggestions are noted for the inspector's guidance in connection with the inspection of envelope accessories:

(a) Ropes should be tested for strength, size, general texture and pliability.

(b) The long splice should be used when ropes are to go through a block and tackle, otherwise the short splice is just as efficient.[3]

(c) The steel cable must be tested for strength from time to time, and should consist of seven strands of 19 wires. The terminals are required to be spliced on this cable. In cases where 7 x 7 cable is used, the wrapped and soldered terminal is the practice.

.(d) All metal parts should be examined for smoothness and should be wrapped with burlap to prevent injuring the envelope.

(e) Gas and air valves should be tested for leakage and to insure that they open with a specified tension.

Completed inspection. When the envelope is completed it should be inflated with air and entered by the inspector. With the aid of light held on the outside of the envelope he should examine every panel for pin holes, patching those found. Judgment should be used as to the number of patches allowed per panel, keeping in mind that numerous patches temporarily strengthen the fabric, but that they become detached when exposed for any length of time to the weather. The outside of the envelope should be inspected for general contour, which should be smooth, and for correct cementing of seams. Insecure cementing on seams can be detected by vigorously rubbing the thumb against the edge of the tape where poor cementing is suspected. If poorly cemented,

[3] Properties of cordage are tabulated in Part II of volume "Free and Captive Balloons," Ronald Aeronautic Library.

the tape will readily come away from the envelope. Pinched or bunched places in the seam denote undue stretching of the panels while they are being joined and weaken the envelope considerably.

After being satisfied that seams on the top of the envelope and as much of the side as can be seen are good and that those places which are to be patched are marked, the envelope should be rolled over and the other half examined.

Leakage. Finally the envelope should be left fully inflated for 24 hrs. to insure the inspector that there is no leakage. All openings are closed by covering with pieces of fabric, and the envelope is then air-inflated until the pressure of ½ in. of water is obtained. If at the end of 24 hrs. a drop in the pressure of not more than ¼ in. has occurred, taking into consideration changes in temperature and atmospheric pressure, the envelope is acceptable for service.

Packing

Prior to the rolling of the envelope for packing, all metal parts should be covered with burlap or similar material in a manner to afford adequate protection to the envelope.

The envelope is spread out on ground cloths so that the lower surface between the suspension points is thoroughly stretched. The envelope is then carefully folded lengthwise along the meridian seams in the manner of an accordion so as to avoid folding the panels. This operation should be conducted so as to avoid any possible damage to the envelope.

A light-weight soft cloth cover should be wrapped around the envelope before putting it into the canvas packing case.

The packing case should be constructed of 17¼ oz. tire duck rubberized to approximately 31 oz. per sq. yd.

The envelope thus packed is placed in a strong wooden packing box.

Wooden packing boxes, strong and durable enough to insure their contents against damage in shipment should be provided for the car surfaces.

Valves and all accessories should be boxed or crated so as to protect them adequately from damage in shipment.

CHAPTER IX

ERECTION, INFLATION AND RIGGING

Preparation of floor to receive envelope. Floors should be thoroughly cleaned of all foreign material. Ground cloths must be dry and oil removed as the oil is liable to soak through and injure the airship fabric. The floor is then covered with clean tarpaulins overlapping 3 ft. and covering a surface with length and breadth equal to that of the envelope deflated.

Envelope Inspection

Laying out and inflating. The envelope is unrolled along the length of the ground cloth starting at a point about 20 ft. from one end of the cloth. The envelope is then stretched so that the lower part between the suspension patches is flat on the cloth. When the envelope is completely unfolded, all openings are closed except one in which is introduced the inflation sleeve from the blower.

Exterior inspection. A thorough inspection is then made and all repairs deemed necessary from this inspection are made at once. The inspection is made to discover weak spots in panels and seams, particular attention being given to stretching, creeping, bad sewing or cement. All fabric fastenings such as suspension patches, suspension bands, or fin adjustment patches, are inspected separately.

Interior inspection. Entrance is made through the valve opening, care being taken not to injure this opening in any way. Flash lights or electric search lights are used for interior inspection.

Envelope. A careful inspection of the envelope should be made for possible defects found in the manufacture of fabric, rubber film, sewing or taping; these are marked with chalk and immediately repaired.

Rip-panels. Special care should be taken in adjusting the rip-panel and line with breakable twine connections so that one patch breaks loose at a time.

Leakage test. The leakage test is then conducted similar to the method described in Chapter VIII.

Inflation and Rigging of Envelope

Air deflation. The envelope is rolled simultaneously from nose and tail so as to force all air toward the center and out through the side valves. Care must be taken to see that no air is contained within the ballonets during the process of rolling, thus preventing abnormal air pressures which are liable to puncture the ballonet. After the air has been forced out, which may be assisted considerably by the use of a blower, attaching the suction side to the deflation sleeve, the gas valves should be inserted to prevent air being sucked into the envelope during the process of unrolling. Care should be taken during unrolling that these valves are supported in a manner, by special rack or other arrangement, to prevent them from becoming damaged against the floor. When completely spread out, the top center line of the envelope should be uppermost and coincident with the longitudinal center line of the ground cloth.

Inflation net. The inflation net should be spread out and thoroughly inspected for any defects such as broken strands which are liable to cause the net to start tearing during inflation. The net is then rolled at right angles to the blue strip through its center, after which it is placed at the nose of the envelope at right angles to the envelope

axis following which it is unrolled to a point where the leading edge of the upper fin is to be attached. Sandbags are
distributed along each side of the envelope and hooked
onto the net, stretching it tightly across the envelope.
Loose ends of the net are then tucked under the sides of
the envelope to prevent tangling during inflation. There
should be a sufficient number of sandbags distributed to
counteract the lift of the gas, with an extra supply for
emergency use. Three canvas bands about 2 ft. in width
are placed across the envelope at regular intervals. These
are heavily weighted down by sandbags.

Surfaces. Horizontal surfaces are brought into place,
buckled to the envelope and rigged to the top suspension
patches. Blocks and tackles should be used to support
the surfaces from the hangar roof trusses so that they may
be raised during the inflation. The top vertical stabilizing
surface is similarly attached. Adjustments of the cables
are necessary during the process of inflation.

Gas inflation. Inflation should be so controlled as to
prevent any tendency of the gas to surge or roll; very dangerous conditions are liable to result even to the extent of
causing the envelope to break away from the net. Inflation
is usually begun at the nose, and as it proceeds, each row
of sandbags is removed successively toward the tail of the
envelope. Care should be taken to keep the envelope on an
even keel during this inflation; for if the nose or tail of the
envelope should be allowed to get too high, the inflation
net is liable to start rolling, thus allowing the envelope to
slip from under it. Distribution of the sandbags should be
in accordance with the distribution of net lift to prevent
any undue straining of the fabric.

Attaching accessories to envelope. The nose stiffening,
air valves, the lower vertical fins, rudder, and control lines,
are attached in an order that will eliminate the necessity

for complicated scaffoldings, and wherever possible, installations should be made by the riggers from the floor.

Attaching car. The car is placed on a cradle which is mounted on skids or rollers to facilitate moving it to any desired position. The engines are installed and all connections made ready for tests with the exception of the propellers. The car is then brought in under the center line of the envelope and leveled by using spirit levels and plumb-bobs. The envelope is then placed so as to be in exact position relative to the car as required by the design; the vertical distances from the envelope to the nose and tail of the car, and the horizontal distance to a transverse seam usually are given.

The car suspension cables are then attached to the car fittings, all turnbuckles being fully engaged with the exception of about two threads showing on each end. The cables are adjusted to take out slack. The envelope is allowed to rise by lowering the sandbags on each side of the net the distance of approximately 1 mesh. The position of the car in relation to the envelope is rechecked; pressure in the envelope is maintained constant during the process of rigging. This pressure should be the ordinary flying pressure. The tensions of the car suspension cables are then adjusted in accordance with diagram furnished with the airship. Special precaution should be taken in tightening the clamps. See that the last clamp is tightened first, the middle clamp second and the clamp next to the thimble last, in order that each clamp should take the proper strain and tension on the cable. If this is not done, the cable will slip through clamps and become damaged. Care should also be taken that nuts on the clamps are not drawn too tight as the threads are liable to be stripped during an excessive tension.

With the envelope completely rigged and the car fully

loaded to the design capacity, the ship is then releveled until plumb-bobs hanging from the nose, tail, and from the maximum width of the horizontal meridian (or widest element), are just clearing the floor.

Aligning horizontal surfaces. Three plumb-bobs are attached to each horizontal surface, one from the leading edge, one from the outer edge, and one from the rear point of the surface adjacent to the envelope. The two horizontal surfaces are then leveled by adjusting the stay cables so that all these plumb-bob lines are of the same length as those attached to the envelope. Adjustments are made by pulling up on the 1/16 in. aircraft cord cotton-center flexible lacing cable. Each loop of this cable should be tied separately so that in case one strand is broken the next will not become loose.

Vertical surfaces. The top and bottom surfaces are aligned by hanging plumb-bobs beside them and centering until the plumb-bobs on each side of the surface are just clearing.

Elevator and rudder control cables. Control surface installation is considered one of the most important parts of the erection of the airship, as any defect is liable to cause a wreck of the airship. The sheaves should be thoroughly lubricated to enable free movement of the surfaces. Shock absorbers are provided in each control line for the purpose of taking up all the slack.

Tail-droop. Tail-droop tends to incline the ship downward at the nose as the surfaces are attached along the widest element, thus producing positive angle of incidence to the line of flight which results in an aerodynamic load being exerted upward at this point. This pitching moment may be counteracted by lowering the leading edge and raising the trailing edge of the surfaces by means of the adjustments provided.

Removing the net. Upon completion of the rigging of the airship, the net may be removed. The best way to do this is by suspending block and tackle from the roof, attaching it to the net, and lifting it clear of the envelope as it is rolled. Care should be exercised that the envelope is not injured or chafed by dragging the net over it, also to see that the net does not foul the valves or the rigging. The rolling of the net is accomplished by placing a man on top of the envelope and holding him in position by block and tackle suspended from the roof. An extension ladder is also placed on each side of the envelope; each end of the net being supported by a ladder.

Trim of airship. The trim of the ship is determined with the car loaded as required by the diagram furnished with the airship and by allowing the ship to be freely suspended in the hangar. Simultaneous readings of the plumb-bob lines at the nose and tail of the envelope are then made, together with reading of the ship's inclinometer. The angle, whose sine is the difference between the bob-line lengths divided by the length of the airship, should agree with the ship's inclinometer reading; the car top longeron line, the axis of the ship, and the inclinometer "o" line, all being parallel. The angle thus determined should be that specified in the design. Throughout the whole alignment operation, the ship must be kept at flying pressure and with ballonets equally full.

Valve adjustments. The valves should be gauged before they are mounted on the envelope and should also be checked on the ship by putting the latter under suitable pressure before attempting a trial flight. A valve should open under the tension exerted on its control which is equal to the pressure times the area of the valve disk. This value, in grams, is equal to $\frac{R_p}{10}$. To test the point of opening, a sheet of cigarette paper is inserted between the seat and flap. This should slide under very slight tension. After placing the valve in its assigned position in the envelope, an extra manometer is placed in the car at the same height as the manometer used during the flight. Then the pressure is brought up to the point at which the valve should open. A hydrogen leak detecting apparatus [1] is used to ascertain whether the valves leak. The one practical method of verifying the tightness of a valve consists of placing the open eye in the immediate proximity.

Drag-rope. In order to insure preservation, the drag-rope should not be coiled when wet or muddy, but should be left spread out to dry and then carefully brushed before coiling. The use of a drum, made for the purpose, facilitates the coiling of drag-ropes as it enables a regular rolling and tension throughout the operation.

Parachutes. Chutes should be packed at least once each week. Whenever a chute has been exposed to dampness it should be hung up and dried thoroughly before using again. A parachute should always be packed under the personal supervision of the one who is to use it. Individual, self-containing parachutes should always be packed by the user.

Inspection prior to flight. This inspection should be conducted under ordinary flying pressures.

Envelope. An inspector should be placed on the top of the envelope, suspended by block and tackle, to determine if any parts had been chafed during erection and to thoroughly inspect the rip-panel and top seams for the following defects:

> Apparent condition of cement.
> Creeping of panel.

[1] Instruments for detecting gas leakage are described in "Aircraft Instruments," a volume of the Ronald Aeronautic Library.

Mildew.

Moisture.

Hydrogen leaks along edges of panel and seams of the envelope.

The *rip-cord* must be maintained in first class condition at all times, as an injury of any kind, or defect in the material, is liable to result in disaster should a forced landing be required in which the rip-panel would be used. Inspection should be made where the cord passes through a gland in the envelope. Where the connection is made by means of lugs, inspection should be made for gas tightness.

Surfaces. The following points should be observed in the inspection of surfaces:

Alignment.

Proper amount of lacing cord in suspension lines.

Turnbuckles to be locked.

Shackle pins to be keyed.

Proper tension in the suspension lines.

Control cables, for broken strands.

Proper bearing lubrication.

Proper tension in the shock absorbers.

All terminals properly secured.

Valves. Valves should be rechecked for proper adjustment. Air valves to open at least $\frac{1}{2}$ in. lower than the gas valves. Control wires should be thoroughly inspected for positive connections and damaged material. A very light coat of oil should be given these cables to prevent rust.

Suspension patches. All patches should be inspected for creeping, cement, mildew, and damaged rope. Care should be taken that the cable attached to the patch is riding at the proper angle for which the patch was placed on the envelope. The cables should be inspected to determine their condition and should be given a light coat of boiled linseed oil or light lubricating oil to prevent rust.

Each suspension cable should be rechecked to see that it is carrying the proper tension as specified by the design diagram.

Car.   Inspection of the car should cover the following points:

> Structure; including fittings, woodwork, bracing. Wooden parts which have become oil-soaked should be replaced.
>
> Controls; the control wires from the pilot's seat to the valves, engines, control surfaces, water ballast, drag rope, etc., should be in first-class working order.
>
> Installations; the electrical installations should be tested for grounds, crosses, continuity, conductivity. No changes should be made in installations without due regard to fire hazard involved, proximity of moving parts, and proximity of instruments which might be affected by the flow of current. Instruments should be checked for accuracy.

Power plant.[2]   The engine should be warmed up gradually until the temperature is at least 60° C. It must be remembered that when the engine is cold the oil is thick and there is danger of a cavitation in the oil line if the engine is speeded up. Continued running with open throttle on the ground will cause overheating. The throttle should never be suddenly opened or closed unless it is absolutely essential. If the throttle is jerked closed, valves that are running at cherry red heat will cool suddenly and warpage will result. During running of the engines the following items should be checked:

> Tachometers, oil pressure gauges, temperature gauges, fuel feed gauges.
>
> That all cylinders are firing properly; that there are no knocks in engines.
>
> Vibration due to improperly balanced propellers.
>
> Loose connections for gasoline, oil, and water.
>
> Valve and ignition timing.

[2] Characteristics of engines suitable for airships are set forth in volume "Aircraft Power Plants," of the Ronald Aeronautic Library.

Valve clearances.

Carburetor; for proper functioning of valves, floats, etc.

Starters and generators for tightness of electrical connections and that they function properly.

Radiator connections and water pumps.

Upon completion of the run, all spark plugs should be removed and clearances of the points tested.

CHAPTER X

HYDROSTATIC TESTS

Introduction. The method of determining the deformation of airship envelopes by experimentation on water filled models in practice has proved completely satisfactory as evidenced by comparison of the deformation thus obtained with the original. This method was first used by the Italians as described by Captain Crocco in the periodical *La Technique Aéronautique* for June 1, 1911. The model envelope is made of the same material as the full size airship envelope. The size is such that when filled with water, the tensions at various points on the model are equal to those at the corresponding points of the full size airship envelope. These experiments could also be performed by submerging an air filled model in water, however there would be the inconvenience of making the measurements under water.

It is obvious that such a method, being practical, is an important factor in the design of airships, in determining in advance whether the proposed shape will be all that is expected of it from the viewpoint of form and balance, thereby eliminating the expense which might otherwise result from guesswork applied to the design of an airship if constructed without this preliminary step.

Object. The general purpose of the water model is to to determine the following points:

> Increase in volume due to fabric stretch.
> Amount of tailoring required to produce a form symmetrical to the horizontal axial plane, and to produce uniform stresses.

Effect of resistance, thrust and control surface reaction.

Static stability at various pressures.

Center of buoyancy.

Practical load distribution, when considering other requirements of the design, which will produce the least amount
of deformation.

Limits in trim produced by the control of air in ballonets.

Location of suspension patches to prevent chafing of lines
on envelope.

Maximum and minimum safe pressure.

Minimum factor of safety.

Overall dimensions for housing.

Theory [1]

Pressure, tension and geometric relations.   The internal
(P_i) and external (P_a) pressure vary according to the law
(see left side diagram of Figure 45):

$$h = \frac{P_o^4}{\gamma_o^7} \log_e \frac{P}{P_o}$$

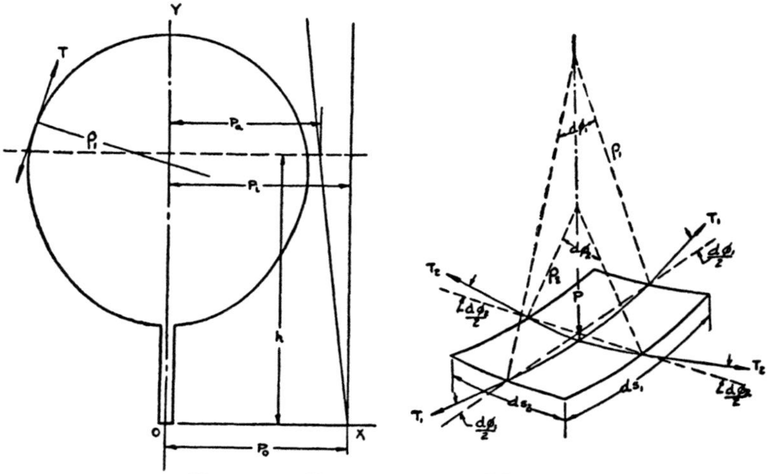

Figure 45.   Hydrostatic Test Diagrams

[1] References: N. A. C. A. Report No. 16 (1917), and Technical Note No. 87, March, 1922;
also Technical Note No. 1, Bureau of Aeronautics, United States Navy, by J. C. Hunsaker.

where P_o is the atmospheric pressure at any definite level and γ_o is the weight per cubic foot of the gas at the same level. This may be replaced with the linear equation, as very small heights are dealt with:

$$P_o - P = h \cdot \gamma_o \qquad (26)$$

or

$$h = \frac{P_o - P}{\gamma_o}$$

OX is drawn to represent the plane where the two pressure curves intersect, that is where $P_i = P_a$. (For a spherical balloon the lower end of the appendix terminates in this plane.)

At any point of the ship's envelope there are two radii of curvature ρ_1 and ρ_2 corresponding to the two principal directions of an element of the fabric, i.e., respectively perpendicular to the envelope axis and in the meridian plane at an angle of α with the axis. The relation between pressure P, tensions T_1 and T_2 and radius of curvatures ρ_1 and ρ_2 of the element is (see right side diagram of Figure 45):

$$Pds_1 \cdot ds_2 = 2T_1 \sin \frac{d\phi_1}{2} ds_2 + 2T_2 \sin \frac{d\phi_2}{2} ds_1 \qquad (27)$$

where

$$P = P_i - P_a$$

Since the sine of an infinitely small angle is equal to the angle and

$$\rho_1 d\phi_1 = ds_1$$
$$\rho_2 d\phi_2 = ds_2$$

we have

$$P\rho_1 d\phi_1 \rho_2 d\phi_2 = T_1 d\phi_1 \rho_2 d\phi_2 + T_2 d\phi_2 \rho_1 d\phi_1$$

whence by cancelling $(d\phi_1 \cdot d\phi_2)$,

$$P \cdot \rho_1 \cdot \rho_2 = T_1 \rho_2 + T_2 \rho_1$$

or

$$P = \frac{T_1}{\rho_1} + \frac{T_2}{\rho_2}$$

and

$$T_2 = \frac{\pi \rho_1^2 P}{2\pi \rho_1 \cos \alpha} = \frac{\rho_1 P}{2 \cos \alpha} \qquad (28)$$

Therefore

$$T_1 = \rho_1 P \left(1 - \frac{\rho_1}{2\rho_2 \cos \alpha} \right) \qquad (29)$$

Thus we have defined the relations between tensions, pressures, and radii of curvature for any point on the original envelope surface. The same relation holds for the water-filled model. With the model made on a scale equal to $\frac{1}{n}$ that of the original, the relation between the radii of curvature for corresponding points for similarity of forms must be

$$\rho' = \frac{1}{n} \rho \tag{30}$$

where the primed quantity refers to the model.

Hence,

$$\frac{T_1'}{T_1} = \frac{\rho_1'}{\rho_1} \cdot \frac{P'}{P} \left(\frac{2\rho_2' \cos \alpha - \rho_1'}{2\rho_2' \cos \alpha} \right) \left(\frac{2\rho_2 \cos \alpha}{2\rho_2 \cos \alpha - \rho_1} \right)$$

$$= \frac{P'}{P} \cdot \frac{1}{n} \cdot n \cdot \frac{1}{n}$$

$$= \frac{P'}{P} \quad \frac{1}{n} \tag{31}$$

Similarly $\frac{T_2'}{T_2}$ is proved $= \frac{P'}{P} \cdot \frac{1}{n}$

By definition

$$P' = (P_o' - h'\gamma_i') - (P_o' - h'\gamma_a') = h' (\gamma_a' - \gamma_i')$$
$$P = (P_o - h\gamma_i) - (P_o - h\gamma_a) = h (\gamma_a - \gamma_i)$$

Therefore

$$\frac{T'}{T} = \frac{1}{n} \frac{h' (\gamma_a' - \gamma_i')}{h (\gamma_a - \gamma_i)} = \frac{1}{n^2} \frac{(\gamma_a' - \gamma_i')}{(\gamma_a - \gamma_i)}$$

Since similarity requires that $h' = \frac{1}{n} h$

$$n^2 = \frac{T}{T'} \frac{(\gamma_a' - \gamma_i')}{(\gamma_a - \gamma_i)}$$

Scale of water-filled model. The scale of the model is thus determined where the value is assigned to the ratio of $\frac{T}{T'}$. As the problem is to make the model out of the same fabric as the large envelope, the ratio of $\frac{T}{T'} = 1$ and we obtain

$$n^2 = \frac{\gamma_a' - \gamma_i'}{\gamma_a - \gamma_i} \qquad (32)$$

where $\gamma_a - \gamma_i$ is the lifting power of the gas per cubic foot, which is dependent on temperature, absolute pressures, the humidity of the air, and purity. Contrarily, $\gamma_a' - \gamma_i'$ is more constant since the density of water (γ_a) varies but slightly, and density of air (γ_i') is negligible in comparison with water.

Substituting values in (32)

$$\gamma_a' = 62.4 \text{ lbs. per cu. ft.}$$
$$\gamma_i' = .076 \text{ lbs. per cu. ft.}$$
and $\gamma_a - \gamma_i = .055$ lbs. per cu. ft. for helium
$$n^2 = \sqrt{1,135} \text{ whence } n = 33.7$$

Therefore the ratio of linear dimension of the model to the original is $\frac{1}{33.7}$.

Conversion factors. The following factors, based on the foregoing theory are given for reference to show the relation between the water-filled model and full size helium airship, where $n = 33.7$.

Item	Model	Full-Size Airship
Linear Dimensions	1	33.7
Volume	1	38,250
Gross Lift	1	33.7
Fabric Tension	1	1
Fabric Stretch	1	33.7
Pressure (Inches of Water)	33.7	1
Pressure (Head of Fluids)	1	33.7
Bending Moments	1	1,135
Stresses on Suspension Lines or Other Tension or Compression Members	1	33.7
Diameter of Tension and Compression Members	1	5.8
Diameter of Members under Pure Bending	1	10.4

Weight of parts on full size airships = 33.7 × counter

weights.   Weight of model must be accounted for in addition.

One pound of water is equivalent to 613 cu. ft. of helium gas.

Equipment

Model.   Including envelope suspension and car the model is constructed $\frac{1}{n}$th the size of the original,   the same fabric being used in the model envelope as used in the original, care being taken to arrange the patterns so that the warp and fill of the various plies of fabric are laid in the same directions as in the original.   It will be impractical to do this throughout as the right and left bias are alternated in rings in the full size envelope whereas it is necessary to make the model of gores only, due to its diminutiveness. However, it is essential that the warp threads of the straight ply be circumferential, as in the full size envelope, and that the gores alternate right and left bias.   The number of gores is reduced in order to make the strengthening due to the seams stand in the same ratio to the strength of the seamless fabric as in the large envelope.

The reduced weight of the envelope may be compensated by one of two methods: either by introducing an air sack extending the entire length of the model of such a capacity that the weight of water displaced by it equals the reduced weight of the envelope, the cross-sections of the sack being designed so that the distribution along the axis of the envelope approaches as closely as practicable that of the reduced weight of the envelope; or by counterbalancing with a weight equal to this reduced weight of envelope, the counter-weight being applied to the envelope by a band along the side elements as shown by Figure 46 and Plate XIII.   The latter method   is considered the more practicable and reproduces an envelope cross-section which is nearer correct than that produced with the sack as it distributes the reduced envelope weight along the surface of the model.

In large models, of 200,000 cu. ft. ships or over, the weight of the model envelope acting in the opposite sense to that desired, should be annulled by counter-weights,

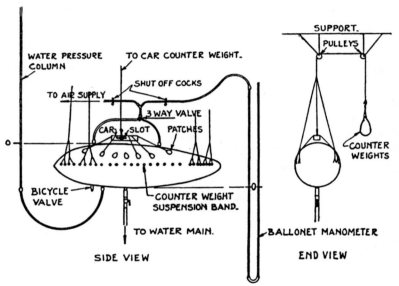

Figure 46. Hydrostatic Test Diagram

which in the case of the lever system of counter-balancing, can be effected by means of riders that can be moved along the levers.

For *car suspension* a suitable type of patch is shown on Figure 21.   The lines should be preferably of cable or rods with means of adjusting length and tension.

The model car should have suspension attachment points located exactly to scale; screw eyes may be used for attaching suspension lines.   A slot should be located longitudinally in the model for the insertion of a bolt for attach-

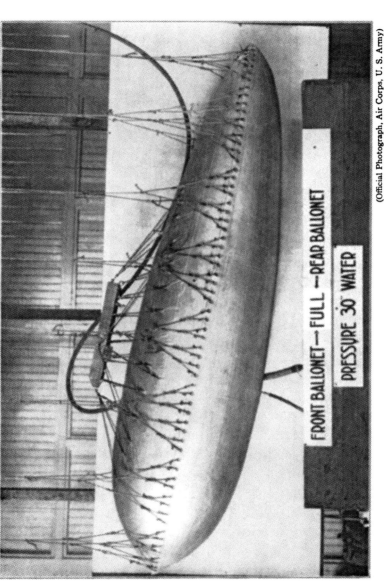

FRONT BALLONET—FULL —REAR BALLONET

PRESSURE 30° WATER

(Official Photograph, Air Corps, U. S. Army)

Plate XIII.   Installation for Water Model of *TC* Airship

ment of the car counter-weight. The slot is for the purpose of controlling the position of the car center of gravity.

The nose stiffening, envelope accessories, and control surfaces are all counter-weighted from the band used for counter-weighting the envelope.

An appendix of suitable size should be provided for filling or emptying the model of water. Bicycle valves should be located in the top and bottom and in the ballonets for admitting or letting out air or water and for manometer tube connections.

Apparatus for test. Ordinarily the following items are required:

1. A suitable frame or other means of support for the model and counter-weights; the model itself should be supported clear of obstructions so as to be accessible for adjustments, measurements, manipulations, observations, and photographs.

2. A system of counter-balancing. The lever system is the lightest and has lowest frictional resistance though it is not adaptable to large changes in inclination of the model as the fulcrum points are usually fixed. The pulley system as indicated on Figure 46 has been satisfactory, the friction being as low as 1 per cent of the model weight.

3. Water manometers; a straight tube for measuring pressures in the water compartment of the model and a U-shaped manometer for measuring ballonet air pressures.

4. Water and air connections.

5. Measuring instruments, such as, steel tape and large calipers. The latter which is for measuring the diameter may be supplemented by an "adjustable" template that is, an open frame with radiating rods that may be adjusted radially so that the form of any cross-section of the envelope may be plotted.

6. Counter-weights, usually sandbags; lead shot how-

ever is preferable because of its greater specific weight thereby reducing the space required.

7. Photographic equipment.

8. Inflation net for large models.

Procedure

Design and calculation. In the design of the rigging that is attached to the envelope band, the bridles should concentrate at as many points as practicable considering the bulk and arrangement of the counter-weights. The distribution of the counter-weights is then determined to agree with the hull weight curve. The location and magnitude of the car weight is then determined, for the degree of loading required.

Assembly. The model is first air-filled to a small pressure and checked with the design for agreement as to size and form. It is then weighed and filled with water in the inverted position, the water level coming to the envelope bottom (or the top side of the model), and counter-weighted in accordance with the calculations, the volume being checked by the total amount of counter-weight required, any deductions or additions being made at the car.

The manometer tube for ballonets is then filled to the zero level (i.e., to the envelope bottom) and the straight pressure tube is connected to the envelope; the datum line being established at the same level as the manometer zero level.

The model is kept filled to flying pressure, which in inches of water is n times the pressure of the original, for several days, adding water as required from day to day until the maximum stretch of the fabric is reached.

Observations. In general, the observations to be made are:

1. Increase in volume due to stretch. Multiply weight in pounds of water added by $n \div$ lift of gas per cu. ft. to obtain this increase in cu. ft.

2. Effect of propeller thrust, resistance and control surface loading, which may be applied with a net or by means of patches and bridles properly placed.

3. Lowest pressure that will prevent buckling.

4. Pressure where wrinkling starts.

5. Location of wrinkles, and what redistribution of weights would improve condition?

6. Change in tension of car suspension under conditions (2) and (3), that is, with respect to dangerous tautness or looseness. Should they be readjusted at different pressures?

7. Any twist in envelope due to unequal fabric strains.

8. Effect of different ballonet inflations, combining same with angles of pitch.

9. Measurements of longitudinal sections to determine lengths and contours of top, bottom and side elements in the meridian planes of these elements, and to determine the curvature of the planes of the elements.

10. Measurements of the transverse sections, by means of the calipers and template previously described, to determine diameters, circumferences, contours and distance vertically to the car.

11. Bursting pressure from which may be determined the strength of the fabric. Inasmuch as the strength of the fabric is increased by the moisture, this pressure will be in excess of that which would obtain under flying conditions. Pieces of the original fabric from which the model was constructed should be tested under standard conditions and also after soaking in water the length of time during which the water model was tested. This should be checked with the strength of samples taken from the bursted model and against the tension calculated from the bursting pressures. From these tests a factor is determined, which applied to the model bursting pressure will determine actual bursting strength.

CHAPTER XI

PREDICTION AND ANALYSIS OF HELIUM NON-RIGID AIRSHIP PERFORMANCE

As the analysis of airship performance is covered in the volume "Airship Design" of the Ronald Aeronautic Library, only actual figures of helium airship performance are tabulated for reference and further study as to their relationship.

The total fixed weight including mechanics and minimum crew, reserve and take-off ballast, are considered to be governed by the following general law, as derived by Umberto Nobile, in N.A.C.A. Technical Note No. 63, "The Employment of Airships for the Transport of Passengers," dated August, 1921:

$$P = \alpha V^{1/3} + \beta V^{2/3} + \gamma V + \delta V^{4/3} \qquad (33)$$

where V is the volume in cu. ft. and

$$\beta = \beta' + \beta'' v^3$$
$$\gamma = \gamma' + \gamma'' v^2$$

where v is the velocity in M.p.h.

The coefficient of utilization ρ, is defined as

$$\rho = \frac{fV - P}{fV} \qquad (34)$$

in which f is the lifting force of gas in lbs. per cu. ft. The useful lift is:

$$\phi = fV - P \qquad (35)$$

Table 14 lists the component parts of the airship and the coefficients in equation (33).

Table 15 gives the useful lift ϕ and coefficient of utilization as expressed in equations (34) and (35) over a range of volumes from 50,000 to 500,000 cu. ft. and velocities of 45, 55, and 65 M.p.h.

146

Table 14—Weight of Various Parts of Helium Nonrigid Airship in Function of Volume and Speed
(Vol. in cu. ft., and speed in M.p.h.)

Parts	Proportional To	Weight lbs.	$\alpha V^{1/3}$	$\beta V^{2/3}$		γV		$\delta V^{4/3}$
				β'	$\beta'' v^2$	γ'	$\gamma'' v^2$	
1. Envelope, Including Ballonets, Rip-Panels, etc., Not Otherwise Itemized	$V^{4/3}$	3,151						2.56×10^{-4}
2. Gas Valves	$V^{2/3}$	40		.0114				
3. Gas Valve Controls	V	10				4.75×10^{-6}		
4. Air Valves and Dampers	V	155				74.0×10^{-6}		
5. Air Valve Controls	$V^{4/3}$	4						$.00325 \times 10^{-4}$
6. Nose Stiffening	$V v^2$	77					$1.26 \times 10^{-7} v^2$	
7. Control Surfaces and Lines	V	672				320×10^{-6}		
8. Car Suspension	V	212		.3		101×10^{-6}		
9. Power Plant and Support	$V^{2/3} v^3$	1,873			$.34 \times 10^{-6} v^3$			
10. Controls	$V^{4/3}$	59						$.048 \times 10^{-4}$
11. Landing Gear–Pontoons	V	100				47.6×10^{-6}		
12. Electrical	V	263				125×10^{-6}		
13. Car Structure and Instruments	$V^{4/3}$	1,051						
14. Crew: Mechanics	$V^{2/3} v^3$	400			$.0725 \times 10^{-6} v^3$			
Minimum	$V^{1/3}$	400	6.75					
15. Reserve and Take-off Ballast	V	810				386×10^{-6}		
			$\alpha = 6.75$	$\beta' = .3114$	$\beta'' = .412 \times 10^{-6} v^3$	$\gamma' = .01058$	$\gamma'' = 1.26 \times 10^{-7}$	$\delta = 2.571 \times 10^{-4}$

Note: Above Coefficients are derived for TC Airship where $V = 210,000$ cu. ft. including fabric stretch and $v = 54$ M.p.h.

TABLE 15—VARIATION OF USEFUL LIFT (ϕ) AND COEFFICIENT OF UTILIZATION (ρ) WITH SPEED AND VOLUME

Volume cu. ft.	Vel. = 45 m.p.h.		Vel. = 55 m.p.h.		Vel. = 65 m.p.h.	
	ϕ lbs.	ρ %	ϕ lbs.	ρ %	ϕ lbs.	ρ %
50,000	573	20.9	154	5.6	.....	...
100,000	1,478	26.9	842	15.3	.....	...
150,000	2,363	28.7	1,524	18.5	218	2.6
200,000	3,191	29.0	2,173	19.7	565	5.1
250,000	3,992	29.0	2,811	20.4	965	7.0
300,000	4,700	28.5	3,353	20.5	1,268	7.7
350,000	5,451	28.3	3,971	20.6	1,659	8.6
400,000	6,073	27.6	4,446	20.4	1,921	8.8
450,000	6,769	27.4	5,006	20.2	2,274	9.2
500,000	7,332	26.7	5,457	19.8	2,502	9.1

PART II

SEMIRIGID AIRSHIPS

By

W. WATTERS PAGON

Mem. Am. Soc. C. E.; Member Special Committee on Design of Navy Airship *ZR*-1 and Army Airship *RS*-1

CHAPTER XII

DISCUSSION OF SEMIRIGID AIRSHIPS

General

There is an extensive series of types of airships (about 70 built in Italy alone) that do not come into either the nonrigid or the rigid classes. They are known under the comprehensive name of *semirigids*. Several factors have led to the development of such ships.

The lower elements of an airship envelope are subjected to less longitudinal gas pressure tension than the upper ones, hence the envelope has more tendency to buckle here under negative bending moment, than at the top under equal bending in reverse direction. The inclined suspenders —if used—which support the car or cars, exert considerable longitudinal compression on the lower fabric of the envelope, especially if the car is close hung, which adds to the gas bending effect. Hence, either the loads of ballast, fuel, etc. must be so disposed as to cause positive initial— "static"—moment; or the gas pressure must be made high enough at the bottom to avoid such buckling; or a keel must be provided to serve as a means of reinforcing the lower elements of fabric; or a combination of methods must be employed.

Aside from the local compressive forces due to car suspension, the several cars produce groups of concentrations of load causing high local bending moments. Keels of the continuous trussed type, if used, serve to distribute the loads to all the vertical envelope suspenders in a manner similar to the action of a stiffening truss of a suspension bridge (see plan of Basenach type, *M*-IV). Articulated keels (see page 154) are somewhat trussed by the car suspenders, so that they act similarly. But this analogy fails in one respect; namely that the envelope has in itself considerable bending strength and stiffness, whereas the bridge cable has only very small rigidity.

It has been considered that there is an intermediate region where the length of ship is too great for economical design in the nonrigid type, and yet it is not great enough to justify a full rigid frame. In this field the semirigid class is appropriate. It cannot be clearly defined nor its limits fixed in the present state of knowledge, although one expert has limited it between 150,000 and 1,500,000 cu. ft. There are however, some authorities who doubt that such a region exists, or at any rate that there is real economy, in the broad sense, in ships of semirigid type. Only experience and time will solve the question.

A further argument for a keel lies in the better action of the steering controls. Should there be any material change in the lower profile length of the envelope due to bending, it can readily be seen that the control wires from car to rudders and elevators would slacken, perhaps enough to offset the take-ups, leaving the control surfaces somewhat without restraint. A keel largely eliminates this slackening. It also more or less stiffens the fins in case of loss of gas, in certain designs.

In *Aviation*, December 15, 1919, R. H. Upson ably shows the advantage of low stresses in the envelope fabric. Aging in the rubber film is more rapid when under tension —allowing leakage—and a fabric continuously under strain will fail at lower stress than if unstrained. For instance, a fabric with a fatigue factor of 2.8 will momentarily sustain 2.8 times as much load as if under continuous tension. Upson claims that the only safe rule is always to maintain as low a pressure as is practicable.

A further advantage lies in a characteristic that is inherent in a low pressure ship; namely, that at low pressures there is sufficient variation of volume with small change of pressure to make the ship quite insensitive to rise and fall.

Wind resistance is diminished by reducing the number of car suspenders.

With much of the stiffness of the rigid, the semirigid is cheaper, quicker and easier to construct, to inflate and deflate, and to repair.

The purpose of Part II of this volume is to treat only of ships of this semirigid class, and of the means that have been adopted to stiffen the envelope where its strength and stiffness are least.

Historical Development

In nonrigids it is not practical to suspend the cars from the bottom of the ship because distention of the envelope would result. Hence numerous suspenders are brought either to "patches" or to a "suspension band," located at such height on the envelope that the suspenders are tangent to it, and produce only shear on the connection. (See Basenach M - III.) On smaller ships good distribution of load can be attained.

In a lecture in the Hall of the National Association of Italian Engineers and Architects, in February 1922, Col. G. Arturo Crocco attributed the origin of the semirigid to Renard's *France*, which had external framing separate from the envelope. The Lebaudy type was a step in the development with a frame under the central length of the envelope, conforming to its shape.

In Italy, the home of the semirigid, there was early felt the need of some sort of stiffening for the lower fabric. This was first met by providing two lines of steel tubular columns fastened to the envelope, braced apart with tubular struts, and provided with diagonal wires (see Types P and M). Such columns must fit the envelope profile when in any condition of inflation, hence they were divided into short lengths and connected by ball and socket joints. Keels of this type will be referred to herein as "articulated"; although a trussed keel with members joined by ball connections is, in the common meaning of the word, also articulated. The suspenders carrying the car weight, and the fore-and-aft wire braces carrying the propeller, wind and inclined gravity thrusts, are connected to the joints of these columns. Thus all (longitudinal) tangential components are resisted directly by the columns and the fabric is relieved of this duty. For negative moments also the envelope is reinforced in the region where longitudinal gas tension is low. It should be noted that the weight of cars will maintain a tension in the suspenders, and hence to a certain extent the keel is thereby trussed and the columns held to a definite conformation, but should there be marked deformation of the envelope it is possible that some suspender may be made inactive, whereupon the columns will be held in position only by their fastenings to the fabric, i.e., in the last analysis by the gas pressure and fabric tension. Hence such keels may still become truly articulated, in the sense used herein. But in a later design having two cars, fore and aft (see Type A, Figure 58), there is an overlapping of the respective suspension systems, and even a rigid strut between the two cars, so that the degree of trussing of the keel columns is increased. Cables sewed to the fabric and looped between connections at the joints transmit the lift to the suspensions.

In order to resist not only the car suspensions, but also the bending forces, the Società Leonardo da Vinci adopted a scheme of entirely different character. They provided a keel of triangular cross-section (see Forlanini Type, Figure 65), having three longitudinal lines of articulated columns braced in the three planes by crossed wires and rigid struts. The internal suspensions, secured to the fabric, were brought together at a common longitudinal axis, and from this the lift of the gas was transmitted by diagonal cables to the top joints of the keel frame. Thus a true rigid keel was obtained, concealed within the envelope. This system employs a number of longitudinal, porous, silk diaphragms, having different lateral inclinations, which serve as suspenders as well. By reason of the number of these diaphragms it is possible to draw in the envelope so that it is contained within a circular outer cover, which is inflated with air from a nose scoop to maintain its shape.

The Stabilimento di Costruzione Aeronautiche have utilized also a triangular keel (usually external) but have employed not more than 3 internal lines of suspension. These lines are nearly on the central vertical plane and each consists of a series of steel cables rising from the top keel joints, (and bottom joints as well, in the *Roma*) or from bridles above the axis of the ship, and connecting to a "catenary band" which is made fast to the fabric. The catenary band consists of a fabric diaphragm of small depth having sewed to its lower edge a rope, looped between suspender connections into short catenaries that serve to distribute the concentrated loads to the envelope nearly as a uniform load.

Where a central suspension is used, the envelope assumes a shape somewhat like that of the cardioid, but the ratio of height to width varies greatly with the inflation pressure as shown in the theory. Where numerous suspenders are used, the change of shape is largely confined to the local alteration of the fabric between suspenders, although the height-width ratio still varies somewhat.

The Parseval Company have recently been experimenting with a type which approximates more nearly to the Zeppelin. They propose (see Parseval Type, Figures 66 and 67) a complete peripheral net enclosing and fastened to the envelope, which differs, however, from the Zeppelin in that an ineffective transverse bracing of wires is used. The bracing still allows the net to deform laterally to a great extent and change its cross-sectional shape with varying inflation pressure in the envelope. Substantially, therefore, this provides metal reinforcement to all parts of the envelope and reduces the fabric to the rôle merely of a gas container. It is claimed that bending deflection of such ships is almost nil, although none have been built so far.

The Basenach type, sometimes called Gross, or Gross-Basenach, was developed in Germany before the World War; four ships, M-I, M-II, M-III, and M-IV, were built. Larger, redesigned ships have been planned since the war, but not built. The keel was suspended below the envelope and was straight at first, with rigid trusses hinged at two points in the M-I. The post-war design contemplated incorporating the keel with the envelope in a manner similar to the Italian designs.

During the war the largest Italian ship, according to Colonel Crocco, had a capacity of 18,000 cu. m. (635,000 cu. ft.) in contrast with 60,000 cu. m. (2,120,000 cu. ft.) for the German ships of rigid type. After the war the T-34 was built of Usuelli type by the Costruzione with a capacity of 34,000 cu. m. (1,200,000 cu. ft.) and sold to the United States as the *Roma*.

Materials

Semirigids differ from nonrigids to a marked degree only in the presence of metal framing and in that the fabric is subjected to lower inflation pressure. Hence the fabric may be of less strength or lighter material, or conversely for the same strength its life is increased.

The fabric [1] is discussed later for each class of ship. The keels that have been built by the Italian companies have all been of thin tinned steel tubing. The thickness varies with the required strength in the various members.

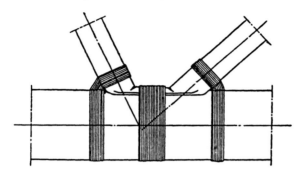

Figure 47a.   Construction of Italian Keel Girder

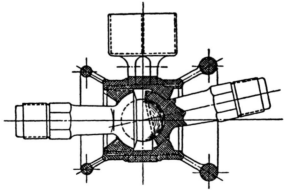

Figure 47b.   Italian Method of Forming Keel Joint

The diameter is less subject to change because of the need for stiffness against buckling. Bracing is seized to the tubes and then soldered (see Figure 47), and the columns and transverse struts are sweated into ball and socket joints

---

[1] Fabrics suitable for the envelopes, partition diaphragms, keel covers, and other parts of semirigid airships, are described in Part III of volume "Free and Captive Balloons," of the Ronald Aeronautic Library.

designed for the tension and compression to which the columns are to be subjected. Diagonal wires are made fast in eyes formed in the joint pieces.

In the United States Army Airship *RS-1*, recently built, the keel is composed of duralumin columns and steel wires. The columns are bulged outward toward the center of length for increased stiffness and strength. They are made of thin sheet metal pressed cold into segmental channels of the type of the now extinct Phoenix column, but with a longitudinal bulge in addition. The channels are riveted together and the assembly entered into steel castings, to which they are riveted. The castings are of ball-and-socket type similar to those of the Italian ships, with eyes for the bracing wires. The transverse struts are made without bulge, but otherwise like the columns. From numerous tests a series of standard columns and joints have been made, each of which is used for a given range of stresses.

Theory of Shape of Envelope

The longitudinal profile of an airship owes its form largely to aerodynamic considerations. Whatever the type, the wind resistance must be reduced to a minimum, consistent with strength. Where the fabric alone resists all bending it is true that the transverse section must be of a size to resist bending stresses and deflections, hence the nonrigid may in general have a lower elongation ratio; i.e., ratio of total length to maximum diameter. In semirigids the keel may assist sufficiently to permit of an increase in this ratio. But having determined the maximum diameter to give the required lift and strength, the longitudinal profile is completed on an aerodynamic basis (see Military and Forlanini Types). During the war the Italian ships were built for lightness, but in later designs wind resistance of envelope and suspensions has been considered.

The Società Leonardo da Vinci has based its envelopes

upon the surface generated by the revolution of a curve composed of two cubic parabolas whose common axis is normal to the axis of the envelope at the maximum diameter. Military types have been based on a sine curve (see page 162). All have been guided by previous ships and wind tunnel tests on models.

The transverse cross-section has generally been developed by the use of water models as described in Chapter X of this volume.

In Italy Col. G. Arturo Crocco has shown [2] that the form of a cylindrical envelope, subjected to gas pressures increasing vertically as a linear function from a known minimum value at the lowest element, is the same as that of the "elastica," or linear beam, subjected to bending moments linearly proportional to the perpendicular distance from a fixed line. Using this conception he contrived a mechanical device which employs a thin steel spring, held at each end by a pair of thumb screws. The form may then be traced on paper. (See Chapter XIV for theory.)

In Germany Messrs. Haas and Dietzius have shown [3] in an excellent paper how the cross-section may be worked out by trial and error. Their paper deals with nonrigids and shows the results of tests on models and of ships in flight. It also deals with shear stresses and deflections, showing that the latter are not large—perhaps 15 per cent of the bending deflections.

These methods were not sufficient for an investigation which the author made of the United States Army Airship *RS*-1, recently built. The complete algebraic theory was therefore worked out (see Chapter XIV), and from this was prepared a diagram (Figure 76) that permits of the solution of any portion, or the complete section, of any flexible cylindrical envelope subjected to gas pressure.

[2] Rendiconti Esperienze e studi dello stab. Costr. Aeron. Vol. III, anno 1914.
[3] Third Annual Report, N. A. C. A., pp. 219-242.

All of these methods presuppose a truly cylindrical form, and take no cognizance of the effect of longitudinal curvature. Also except Haas and Dietzius, the authors omit any reference to the distortion of the section by shearing stresses that must be resisted by the fabric if any part of the bending is carried by the envelope itself; the algebraic complications introduced by considering either of these factors have thus far not been surmounted. In the parallel body, or amidships section, the first does not appear, and the second is probably small for normal conditions of superpressure. But in any event it is advisable to check the shape adopted by testing a water model made to conform to it.

Longitudinal Profile of Italian Airships

The customary equation of the sine curve is not adapted for use in determining a profile.

Assume that the longitudinal profile of the ship is sinusoidal, of quarter wave length, and referred to its chord. (See Figures 48, 49 and 50.)

Let γ = Angle of chord = Nose angle

ϕ = Tail angle

x, y = Coordinates referred to the chord (origin at tail)

u, v = Coordinates of sine wave

Then $v = k \sin u$; $\tan \gamma = \dfrac{2k}{\pi}$; $\sin \gamma = \dfrac{k}{L}$; $\cos \gamma = \dfrac{\pi}{2L}$

$L = \frac{1}{2}\sqrt{\pi^2 + 4k^2}$

Now $x = v \sin \gamma + u \cos \gamma = \dfrac{k^2 \sin u}{L} + \dfrac{\pi u}{2L}$;

$y = v \cos \gamma - u \sin \gamma = \dfrac{k\pi \sin u}{2L} - \dfrac{ku}{L}$

To determine the value of k to produce a ship of elongation ratio, $n = \dfrac{L}{D} = \dfrac{L}{2y_m}$, differentiate and find the maximum value of y.

$$\frac{dy}{du} = \frac{k\pi}{2L} \cos u - \frac{k}{L} = 0; \quad \text{hence } \cos u_m = \frac{2}{\pi}; \; u_m = 0.88;$$

$$\sin u_m = 0.77$$

and $y_m = \frac{k}{3L}; \; x_m = \frac{0.77k^2 + 1.385}{L}$

and $n = \frac{L}{2y_m} = \frac{3L^2}{2k} = \frac{3}{8k}(\pi^2 + 4k^2)$

Solving for k, we have $k = \frac{n}{3} \pm \sqrt{\left(\frac{n}{3}\right)^2 - \left(\frac{\pi}{2}\right)^2}$ (36)

This equation shows that no ship can be built with sinusoidal shape whose theoretical elongation ratio is less than $\frac{3\pi}{2}$, for which value $k = \frac{\pi}{2}$; also that there are two different shapes for each value of n, depending on whether the positive or negative value is used. In the tables and curves that follow, only the positive value has been used. The other gives a shape in which y_m occurs near the half length.

Now $\frac{dv}{du} = k \cos u = $ slope of sine wave

Thus $\tan (\gamma + \phi) = k$

But $\tan \gamma = \frac{2k}{\pi}; \quad$ hence $\tan \phi = \frac{k(\pi - 2)}{2k^2 + \pi}$

From the formulas on page 160.

$$\frac{x}{L} = \frac{1}{L^2}\left(k^2 \sin u + \frac{\pi}{2}u\right)$$ (37)

$$\frac{y}{L} = \frac{k}{L^2}\left(\frac{\pi}{2}\sin u - u\right)$$ (38)

The following table gives values of ratios $\frac{x}{L}$ and $\frac{y}{L}$ for shapes having certain values of n. The shapes are also shown drawn to scale. The actual value of n is usually somewhat smaller than the theoretical due to modification of curves to eliminate the thin tail and to improve the nose form.

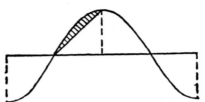

Figure 48.   Sinusoidal Development

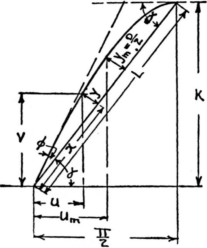

Figure 49.   Curve Showing Profile Factors
(All dimensions are in radian units)

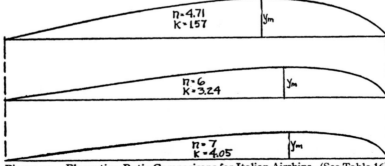

Figure 50.   Elongation Ratio Comparisons for Italian Airships. (See Table 16)

TABLE 16—COORDINATES OF SINUSOIDAL PROFILE

u	$n = \frac{3\pi}{2} = 4.71$ $k = \frac{1}{2}\pi = 1.57$		$n = 6$ $k = 3.24$		$n = 7$ $k = 4.05$	
	$\dfrac{x}{L}$	$\dfrac{y}{L}$	$\dfrac{x}{L}$	$\dfrac{y}{L}$	$\dfrac{x}{L}$	$\dfrac{y}{L}$
0°...................	0.000	0.0000	0.000	0.0000	0.000	0.0000
10°...................	0.142	0.0311	0.162	0.0246	0.165	0.0210
20°...................	0.282	0.0598	0.320	0.0472	0.326	0.0403
30°...................	0.415	0.0831	0.468	0.0656	0.478	0.0560
40°...................	0.539	0.0987	0.605	0.0778	0.616	0.0665
0 88 radian.........	0.667	0.1060	0.730	0.0833	0.743	0.0714
60°...................	0.767	0.0987	0.829	0.0778	0.840	0.0665
70°...................	0.859	0.0812	0.910	0.0640	0.919	0.0546
80°...................	0.939	0.0478	0.968	0.0376	0.973	0.0321
90°...................	1.000	0.0000	1.000	0.0000	1.000	0.0000

Theory of Bending

All airships are statically indeterminate structures, meaning thereby that they cannot be computed by the three static conditions of equilibrium alone, but must be solved by the aid of the theory of deflections, by the Theory of Least Work, or by the making of certain assumptions such as that the "Theory of Plane Bending" applies,[4] although "plane bending" holds only for a circular section.[5]   In nonrigids the indeterminateness is customarily ignored and the envelope designed to carry the full moment without assistance from the truss action of the car suspenders.   In rigids the effect is not large because the cover is weak, compared with the full rigid frame, and gives additional strength.   But in semirigids the situation must be clearly recognized.   The envelope by itself may have sufficient strength and stiffness to resist all moments;   the keel may do so also.   These factors

[4] Third Annual Report, N. A. C. A. (U. S. A., 1917), pp. 211–214 and 218.
[5] Technical Note No. 140, N. A. C. A. (U. S. A.), "General Theory of Stresses in Rigid Airship ZR-1," by W. Watters Pagon.

being nearly equal the nature of the assembly requires that both act jointly.

Rigid keel type.[6] Ordinarily an indeterminate structure is composed of rigid members and has a shape that is indeformable except within the limits of elasticity of its several members. In a semirigid the keel itself complies with this requirement, so far as its internal stresses are concerned. But the envelope receives its form and characteristics both from the nature of the fabric and from the gas pressure. If the pressure is reduced, not only does the longitudinal pressure diminish, possibly below that required to neutralize the compressive bending stresses in the lower elements, but the cross-sectional shape deforms as shown in the theory given later. If the fabrics had *no* shearing stiffness or were cylindrical throughout, the elements of any short length of envelope would rise freely, affecting the joint bending strength only in so far as their own moment of inertia varied thereby. But there *is* shear stiffness in the fabric, hence the resultant effect is that the two elements move apart, differentially, the keel sagging somewhat, or vice versa. The amount of the stresses produced by such effect cannot be accurately computed, although the writer attempted to approximate them in a paper submitted to the Special Committee on Airship *RS-1*, appointed by the National Advisory Committee for Aeronautics. The stresses, however, are of considerable magnitude only if the superpressure becomes small (0.75 in. or 19 mm. of water); and if ample provision is made against drop in pressure, they need not be considered.

Apart from the effect just described, which must be provided for by some positive means (see Blower and Scoops), the keel and envelope must act jointly in bending if certain conditions are met. For instance, it is essential that the envelope be securely lashed to the keel at every point of sus-

[6] Papers by Wm. Hovgaard and W. Watters Pagon to Special Committee on Airship *RS-1*.

pension, in order that there may be perfect transfer of longitudinal shear between fabric and keel; the early Basenach type, for instance, was incapable of such shearing. Again the superpressure must be sufficient always to maintain tension in the lower fabric, because shear cannot be transferred effectively through a flabby sheet.

Assuming these conditions all to have been met, let us consider the joint action in bending. Aerodynamic forces and gas lift act directly on the envelope itself, as does the fabric weight; fuel, ballast, car weights, etc., all act on the keel directly. Because there is equilibrium between lift and load, holding the elements apart, there can be no deflection of either without a corresponding deflection of the other— subject to the condition that the envelope does not change its shape. Again the two elements are constrained by the suspension lashings to move longitudinally as though one beam. Hence the structure is clearly a composite beam composed of two materials, both parts of which have identical deflections. From the theory given in the textbooks for composite beams, and from the references given below for composite bending with articulated keel, if the product, EI, the modulus of elasticity times moment of inertia, in comparable units, be found for envelope and keel, then their respective shares of the bending moments will be inversely proportional to EI for each. Thus if keel and envelope are equally stiff they will share the bending equally. Further, the keel will act in the nature of reinforcing for the fabric, much after the manner in which steel bars act in a reinforced concrete beam. If n be the ratio of E_k to E_f, the respective moduli of elasticity of the keel and fabric materials, then we may consider that the keel acts as would an increased amount of fabric having a cross-sectional area n times as great. From all which discussion there results that the compound girder may be computed as a simple beam, using the moment of inertia of envelope and keel about their common center of gravity and considering the keel to be replaced by fabric having *n* times its area.

This theory Prof. Wm. Hovgaard has shown [7] to be general and it applies to the semirigid so long as the envelope does not alter its shape. Should the shears or breathing produce an alteration, there will be a change in the joint action, which in the present state of knowledge cannot clearly be defined, hence until more experimental results have been published it is the author's belief that the keel should be made strong enough for the entire moments. Tests have shown that the full theoretical effect of the envelope is not realized.

In transverse bending a new set of conditions obtain. It is well known that unsymmetrical structural members undergo a torsional deflection when subjected to pure bending. For moments due to side winds or aerodynamic forces in turning, the ship is unsymmetrical in shape and is moreover reinforced by the keel on one side only, and at the neutral plane. At most the keel would assist only to the extent that it might be required to deflect by the same amount as the envelope. No further action is possible because the keel lies in the neutral plane and cannot reinforce the fabric as described above. But the resistance to bending offered by the keel will introduce torsion into the fabric and it is the author's belief, and that of others, that the bending strength and stiffness of the fabric will offer such resistance that the keel will have opportunity to carry but little, relatively, of the bending. Hence the envelope should have strength and be inflated to such superpressure that it may assume the entire lateral bending moments.

In this connection it is submitted that ships of the Italian "Military" type are at a disadvantage in transverse bend-

[7] *Journal of Mathematics and Physics,* Vol. II, No. 4, December, 1923. "A New Proof of the Theory of Ordinary Bending and Its Extension to Beams of Non-homogeneous Materials," by Prof. Wm. Hovgaard.

ing, because of the re-entrant angles at the top. Such angles, in a flexible fabric, are ill-fitted to carry longitudinal shear due to lateral bending, and longitudinal shear is maximum at the neutral plane, in which the apex of the angle lies.

In ships of the Forlanini type it is undoubtedly true that the additional cover assists in resisting bending. It also appears probable that the longitudinal diaphragms assist in vertical bending and in torsion. These ships should also be better in lateral bending because they have the outer cover and no sharp re-entrant angles.

Articulated keel type. An "articulated keel" has been defined as one composed of lines of columns, each divided into numerous straight members fitted to the shape of the envelope and provided with ball and socket joints, the lines being braced laterally with struts at the joints and with double crossed-wire diagonals. The columns have two functions, (1) to resist the loads from the car suspensions, and (2) to serve as reinforcing for the lower fabric.

In serving to help carry the loads the action is that of resisting the horizontal components of the suspenders, because the lift forces are purely vertical. If the fabric had no shear strength, then clearly each pair of suspenders would have a vertical load at their top equal to the lift of one panel, there being catenary ropes sewed to the fabric to concentrate the lift at the joints. In so far as there is shear stiffness, it is possible to have a lift of greater or less amount. But assuming that each joint has a lift of one panel, and that there are no redundant suspenders, it is then possible to draw an equilibrium polygon and determine the stresses in the suspenders and keel members, making due allowance for the inclination of the cables to the plane—or really the curved surface—of the aggregation in proportion to the secant of the angle of deviation from the vertical. The connections to the cars are disposed in practice so as to obtain convenient points of attachment. In some designs it is sufficiently accurate to assume that all cables meet at a common, but imaginary, point below the car, forming a "bundle" of rays. In other designs some cables are attached nearer midlength of the car, and it will be more accurate to consider the car body as the lower chord of a truss. In either event the stresses are computed as though all cables lay in a vertical plane through the axis of the ship, and the actual stresses found by increasing these stresses in proportion to their inclination to this axial plane, both for suspenders and for keel members. The cross-strut stresses can then be found by considering the equilibrium of each joint.

But if there are redundant members some modification must be made. Any such will alter the stresses only in the adjacent members. A stress of 1 lb., or 100 lbs., may be assumed in the redundant member, and the stresses caused thereby found. If this unit stress now be increased progressively, clearly one or other of the adjacent cables will soon develop a compression greater than its load tension, after which that cable will go out of action and the structure will become determinate. Hence we may either arrange so that the redundant members are set up with a specified initial stress, or we may find the maximum or minimum stresses in all members and provide strength for the greatest stress. It should be noted that if there are more than one redundant member, some cables may receive simultaneous stresses from two such members, and allowance must be made for this condition.

For safety the cables whose direction is nearly vertical, i.e., the ones directly over the car or cars, should be made of strength sufficient to carry more than the computed load, because the envelope and keel combined are not a rigid structure, hence the loads on the fore and aft cables may be reduced quite a little by deflection. Again, "martingales" are frequently provided, being cables carried from the rear end of car to the forward part of keel, and vice versa, whose function is to resist the *horizontal* forces caused by the propeller thrust, by wind resistance on the cars, and by the parallel component of gravity when the ship is pitched up or down. But these lie at a flat angle, so that frequently they may be neglected, when determining stress in the other suspenders.

The second function of the keel members is to reinforce the fabric where the longitudinal tension due to inflation pressure is least, and where negative moments cause diminution of this tension. The principle under which the columns act is similar to that of the reinforced concrete beam. Briefly stated, if the keel is so lashed to the envelope and the inflation, or superpressure, is maintained sufficiently high so that the fabric will not alter its shape materially nor buckle, we may replace the columns by an equivalent width of fabric, n times larger, where $n = \dfrac{E_k}{E_f}$. Note that E_f is based on the modulus of elasticity per unit width of fabric, for stresses in the longitudinal direction (usually the warp), hence n is a reciprocal of a linear dimension. The center of gravity height, h_g, of the unreinforced fabric may easily be obtained from the envelope theory. Then the total moment of inertia is

$$I = I_f + nI_k + Se^2 + nA_k e_1^2 \tag{39}$$

Where I_f = Moment of inertia of fabric arc about its center of gravity

I_k = Moment of inertia of keel about its center of gravity

S = Perimeter of fabric in linear units

A_k = Area of keel

e = Vertical distance from center of gravity of fabric arc to that of fabric and keel combined

e_1 = Vertical distance from center of gravity of keel columns alone to that of fabric and keel combined

From the moment of inertia the section moduli for top fabric and for keel may be found, and dividing into the bending moments, the fabric and keel stresses. Clearly the top fabric stresses may be more or less than for a ship without keel, depending upon the relative section moduli.

Stresses in the cross-struts are caused by the change of direction of the keel members at the joints, because the lines of columns converge fore and aft. These stresses are small. Other stresses are caused by the fact that the envelope meets the keel at an angle, β, to the horizontal, causing a tension in the struts counter-balancing the compression caused by the inclination of the cables to the horizontal. For such lateral bending as is carried by the keel, these struts and their diagonal wires receive stresses as part of a horizontal truss.

Breathing [8]

Changes in the cross-sectional shape of the envelope are aptly described by the caption, "breathing." As the superpressure varies, i.e., the pressure at the lowest element of the largest cross-section, the envelope undergoes distention or contraction vertically and horizontally. Under large superpressure the ratio of top and bottom pressures is nearly unity, whereas for zero superpressure this ratio is infinity. For the first condition the envelope approaches the circular form—either one circular arc or several, depending upon the number of points of suspension; for the latter the curvature at the bottom is zero. It is only for low superpressures, however, that any marked variation occurs; for example during a drop from 2.6 lbs. per sq. ft. (½ in. or 12 mm. of water) to zero, the movement of certain elements may be three to four times as great in a cardiodal

[8] Papers by Wm. Hovgaard and W. Watters Pagon to Special Committee on Design of Airship *RS-1*; also N. A. C. A. Report No. 211 (1925) by L. B. Tuckerman, "Water Model Tests for Semirigid Airships."

$C = .055$ lb./cu. ft. for helium $y = h - h_0$

q	S	T	β	α	y_n	y_g
0	119 2	81 0	35° 15′	231° 05′	72 9	42.1
1 0	115 0	107 25	23° 12′	219° 0′	70 2	39.8
2 6	113 2	154 5	13° 45′	208° 05′	67 9	36.8
5 2	112 56	236 35	6° 0′	201° 04′	66 9	36.0

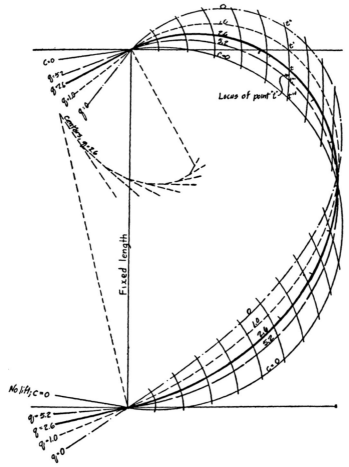

Figure 51.   Cross-Section of Bi-Lobed Envelope for Varying Superpressures

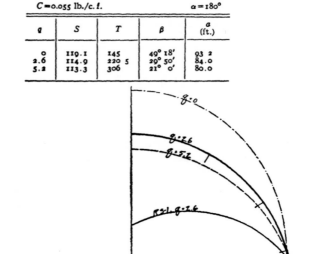

| $C = 0.055$ lb./c. f. | | | | $\alpha = 180°$ |
q	S	T	β	a (ft.)
0	119.1	145	49° 18′	93 2
2.6	114.9	220 5	29° 50′	84.0
5.2	113.3	306	21° 0′	80.0

Figure 52. Cross-Section of Envelope with Bottom Suspension Only for Varying Superpressures

Curve A—multilobed section at 2.6 lbs. superpressure
   "   B—multilobed   "   "   0   "   "
   "   C—bilobed   "   "   2.6 "   "
   "   D—bilobed   "   "   1.0 "   "

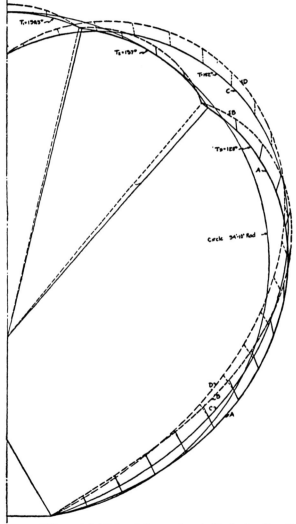

Figure 53.   Effect of Additional Suspenders in Reducing Breathing

design as during a corresponding increase from 2.6 lbs. to 5.2 lbs. (1 in. or 25 mm. of water). See Figures 51, 52 and 53. The effect described occurs in both semirigids and nonrigids but in the latter causes only bending and shear in the envelope.

If the longitudinal profile of the envelope were cylindrical, breathing would not affect the stresses in the ship. But, except for the short parallel body, every section of the ship has different top and bottom pressure heights above the line of zero pressure, and a different ratio of the two. Hence when the superpressure varies, every such section alters its shape in its own peculiar manner. As explained above, the shearing stiffness of the envelope prevents the envelope from assuming all of this deformation, hence part of the vertical change, operating through the keel, produces bending in the keel (also in the envelope, of course). When at a pitch angle there is an exaggerated effect. Again effects similar to breathing are produced by inflation of the ballonet as gas is lost, because the pressure in the ballonet is due to air only and is constant at all heights. Therefore the fabric "flanks" of the ballonet when inflated will have a circular shape, and the whole section must adjust itself to a new composite shape.

This subject is treated more completely in Chapter XV where the author has derived methods of determining these stresses. The results agree closely with results from tests.

Nose Cap

As in nonrigids, it is necessary to provide some form of stiffening for the nose of the envelope to prevent caving in under wind pressure. Two forms have been used; (a) a set of battens similar to that used for nonrigids, and (b) a rigid or semirigid metal cone fastened to the keel structure.

Batten type, nonrigid.[9] The design of a batten type for nonrigids has been well described by Prof. Edw. P. Warner [10]; the following is adapted therefrom, to illustrate the principles. The pressure at the point of nose is the full pitot tube pressure $\frac{\rho V^2}{2} = \frac{9.09 V^2}{3,600}$ for air weighing .07635 lbs. per cu. ft. (at sea level), where V is in M.p.h. and pressure is in lbs. per sq. ft. Since 5.2 lbs. per sq. ft. equals 1 in. of water, a speed of 60 M.p.h. (97 km.p.h.) gives a pressure of 9.09 lbs. or 1.75 in. (44 mm.) of water. An internal pressure of this amount will just prevent caving in at the point of nose for level flight. Allowing as factor of safety a speed variation of 15 M.p.h., (25 km.p.h.) the internal pressure should be in the ratio of the squares of 75 and 60, or 56 per cent greater. If the ship is pitched downward the internal pressure at the nose is lowered .068 for every vertical foot for hydrogen, (0.055 for helium) by which the nose is lowered. The internal pressure may be maintained by means of a blower or by scoops lowered into the slip stream. Since the speed in the slip stream may be considered 30 per cent greater than ship's speed, the pitot pressure in the scoops, neglecting friction in the scoops, is 69 per cent greater. This is sufficient to prevent collapse of the nose point in level flight, especially when it is remembered that the gas lift may increase the internal pressure at the nose above that in the ballonet.

For a pitch angle ϕ, and no air in ballonet, the nose pressure is

$$q + cd \cos \phi - cL \sin \phi \tag{40}$$

When $\tan \phi > \dfrac{d}{L}$ then the nose pressure is less than q. But

---

*In Chapter III, Mr. Blakemore provides tabular data and the sequence of operations for solving a design problem relating to Nose Stiffening. Mr. Pagon discusses this essential feature of pressure airships somewhat more at length. Because of the importance of the subject, both presentations are retained for the information of the reader.—Editor.

[10] Technical Memorandum No. 221, N. A. C. A., August, 1923, "The Effect of Bow Stiffeners in Nonrigid Airships," by Prof. E. P. Warner; a paper prepared for the International Air Congress, London, 1923.

if the ballonet is inflated to height, d', with its top level or without tension, then the pressure is

$$q + c\,(d - d')\cos\phi - cL'\sin\phi \qquad (41)$$

in which case when $\tan\phi > \dfrac{(d - d')}{L}$, the nose pressure is less than scoop pressure. In practice d' will rarely exceed d.

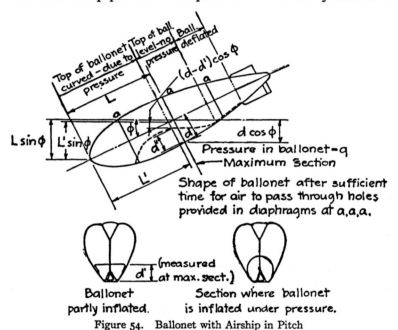

Figure 54. Ballonet with Airship in Pitch

The ballonet has transverse diaphragms, but these are punctured to permit slow passage of air, hence on a long descent, the result is the same as if there were no diaphragms.

For present purposes let us arbitrarily assume with Prof. Warner that for pitch it is necessary to allow 75 per cent of the pitot head, H, for 60 M.p.h. (97 km.p.h.). Then there is required a pressure of $1.56H + 0.75H = 2.31H$, against which the scoops can furnish only $1.69H$. Clearly then some means of stiffening must be employed, even for the point of the nose.

But this is not the whole problem. Tests on ships in flight and on wind tunnel models show that there is a considerable region near the nose, all of which is subjected to inward-acting (positive) external forces, diminishing rearward, followed by a larger region of outward-acting (negative) forces. When flying in pitch or yaw the pressure curve is not symmetrical on all radial planes, but on the windward side the positive forces are greater and extend aft a greater distance than on the leeward side. Hence not only are the internal pressures determined by these greater forces, but the whole nose portion of the ship is subjected to a cantilever bending moment as well.

Now considering axial or level flight, it is clear that at any transverse section through the envelope and keel (Case I) the total axial internal force must exceed by a safe amount the sum of the axial components of the external forces forward of the section, and also (Case II) after allowing for gas and other moments the lower fabric gas tension must safely exceed the fabric compression due to the axial component of the external forces; otherwise (I) the envelope as a whole or (II) the lower portion where the tension is least, will crumple and allow the nose to cave in. Every such section should be considered, back to the region where crumpling cannot occur.

The problem cannot be solved as a general case, because the nose pressures are a function of the longitudinal profile. The article referred to above, however, gives two cases which illustrate the procedure; one that of a ship of the Parseval type, the other that of the U-721, which is said to offer less resistance than any form yet developed. Figure 55 shows three sets of curves: (a) the longitudinal profile of each ship, (b) the external, normal, unit pressures, and (c) the total axial component of external pressures forward of any given section. The latter curves, therefore, give the internal pressure that must be exerted to prevent collapse. Clearly the positive pressure region (axial flight, no pitch) extends back 23 per cent of the maximum diameter for U-721—marked p_0—and 33 per cent for the Parseval—marked p_0'; and clearly these are the maximum limits of the region which can have need of stiffening, under any circumstances. If now we neglect the variation of the internal pressure, due to gas lift (Case II of preceding paragraph), around the

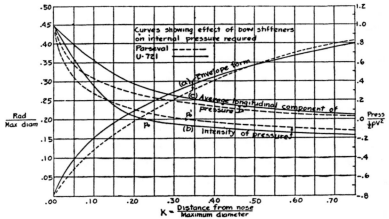

Figure 55. Effect of Bow Stiffening on Internal Pressure Required

periphery of the section, because the diameter of envelope at rear end of battens is not large, then it is only necessary to select a point on the curves (c) where the proper condition is met.

Thus allowing $1.69H$ for superpressure, q as maintained by the air scoops; deducting $0.75H$ to allow arbitrarily for pitch angle; there remains $0.94H$ effective internal pressure, which must be divided by the safety factor of 1.56, leaving $0.60H$. Therefore the battens must extend aft to a point where the axial component of external pressure is reduced to $0.60H$. In U-721 this is found at the section where K is 0.105, i.e., $0.105D$ from the nose; and in the Parseval type where K is 0.045.

Thus the length of battens is determined. There still remains to be considered the strength. The shape of nose is a known curve, hence the distance between battens at every point is easily determined, and thus, the external and internal pressure on the batten (see theory of batten pressures). The sum of the axial components of these must be equal, as determined above (note a qualification of this in the theory), but the components normal to the axis and the moments remain to be found. A diagram showing the data for a specific problem is then prepared from these curves. The loads are computed on the basis of the theory given herein, and are concentrated at short intervals for convenience. Inasmuch as the batten is hinged at the nose it is necessary that the fabric at the rear end act as a circumferential tension band. Undoubtedly such a band must have considerable width and hence does not act at the end of the batten entirely, but for computing bending moments the assumption is safe. An equilibrium polygon is prepared, giving the thrust through the batten, and its eccentricity, from which all moments can be figured. The design of batten is then simple. This completes the design of such a nose cone, if the fabric tension band has sufficient strength. If not, then wires must be sewed to the fabric for the purpose. It should be noted that the foregoing theory does not consider the additional external load due to bulge as proved in the section on theory.

Clearly there is some "breathing" effect in the nose, and clearly the degree of lateral stiffening from the fabric is small, because each portion of the fabric is likely to have lost its restraining effect when most needed, yet some restraint must be assumed in order to make a batten possible.

The foregoing method presupposes an internal pressure of considerable magnitude. But the principal advantage of the semirigid ship is that, for bending, it may have smaller inflation pressure, yet if the superpressure, for instance, be ½ in. (12 mm.) of water, or $\dfrac{2.6}{1.56 \times 9.09} = 0.18H$, the battens must extend a distance $0.33D$ for Parseval and $0.40D$ for U-721 making them perhaps 20 to 30 ft. (6.0 to 9.0 m.) actual length.

Semirigid type. Let us consider therefore the case where the internal pressure is insufficient to equalize the axial component of external pressure, in which event the hinged connection to the keel must supply sufficient horizontal force for equilibrium. Each batten has then a known horizontal force at its forward end. The batten is pivoted here, and is subjected to the pressures computed above. Hence it must have bearing near its free end on fabric that is sufficiently inflated to resist. Such condition can only exist aft of the point of zero net pressure. Because of the hinged end the batten will tend to press in at each point an amount which is proportional to the distance from the hinge, unless it is so limber that it may curve out radially, and at the free end there is certain to be an added restraint because of the "end effect," described in the theory, unless the batten bends sufficiently to lift out here, when the effect will be reversed. The supporting forces then will be a distributed load of variable amount and an end concentration. Thus any length of batten (past the zero pressure point) may be used, but length (also strength) of batten is equated against the degree of depression in the fabric (the amount of support being dependent upon the tension and the depth of depression) greater length giving less depression, but higher bending moment, due to increased lever arm. The theory given herein is sufficient for a solution.

The writer has suggested a modification of this idea,[11] whereby the envelope is fluted between battens so that there is a definite depression into the fabric. When there is no wind pressure the outer cover serves to resist the internal pressure on the battens, and if not strong enough there will be circumferential wires fastened to the battens. Based on a set of assumed loads, which closely approximate those of an actual ship, a complete design has been set forth in Chapter XVI. The computation of all loads and stresses is given, showing how the design is developed.

Rigid or bell type. Recent Italian ships have been provided with a fully rigid nose cone of umbrella-like design, e.g., the *Roma*. Radial cantilever battens are secured to a hub which in turn is connected rigidly to the forward end of the keel. With such design it is unnecessary that there be any internal pressure on the battens if the structure can be made sufficiently strong to carry the wind forces. But for pitch or yaw there are unequal forces on windward and leeward sides, causing a bending moment of the whole cap, and while the keel is properly placed to resist this moment if caused by pitch, it is not so placed for moments in yaw, because the moment and keel are not in the same plane, and therefore torsion in the keel comes in to modify the stresses. The keel is not well fitted for torsion, hence it is the writer's belief that the envelope must resist the moment in yaw, as, in fact, it must all other moments in yaw.

Such a nose cap is made of trussed metal battens, of a length nearly to the point of zero pressure, with circumferential struts and bracing between them. The struts are rigid also, (see theory) so that the effect is to make an indeterminate structure composed of a group of cantilevers set in a dome (which is, however, supported at its top like a bell, instead of its base). The space between battens and en-

---

[11] Papers by Wm. Hovgaard and W. Watters Pagon to Special Committee on Airship RS-1.

velope may be inflated with air from the nose valve at pitot tube pressure, hence the outer cover may have an outward pressure except at point of nose and if the envelope is secured to the battens there may be a net inward load on the inner chords. But if the envelope be not attached to the battens, and if it should have a simple form, without flutes, then neither support nor load can come to the battens. If in the latter case the ship be pitched up at considerable angle, the forward drag of the gas may cause some little support, but it should be noted that for recent Italian designs it has been claimed that the cap is self-supporting without assistance from internal pressure. It should also be noted that when the ship is pitched downward, gas pressure tends to draw the envelope back from the nose, throwing some additional backward pull on the ends of the battens where there is a connection, and in flight much of the friction drag will come to the same point. These loads must be considered. In this rigid type it is also possible to flute the envelope so as to obtain definite support, using the circumferential struts to withhold this pressure when not in flight.

In any event the loads on the batten are computed, and the unbalanced moment in pitch or yaw must be resisted by the connection to the hub at the nose. If consideration is to be taken of the struts, then the load carried by struts and by cantilevers must be arbitrarily decided or it can be actually computed at great length by one of the deflection methods. The hub must be so designed as to carry into the keel all unbalanced moment from the entire cap.

Tube types. Some of the smaller Italian airships have a nose stiffening composed of tubes located along the meridians and parallels of the envelope. The former act as do the battens of other types, but the latter act in accordance with the theory presented in this volume; they offer some resistance to the battens, both transversely and radially. On the parallels in the empennage, similar tubes are used to stiffen the fixed surfaces when the airship is partly inflated.

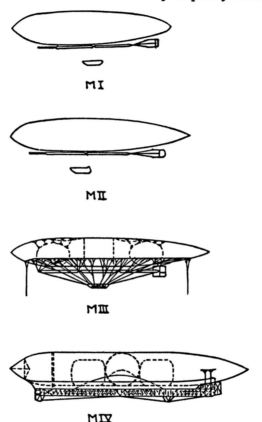

Figure 56.   Basenach Airships, Types *M*-I, *M*-II, *M*-III, and *M*-IV

Figure 56 (the *M*-IV) shows how the Basenach type of nose depends upon a strut terminating in a special diaphragm.

Tail Surfaces

In the Basenach airships, the tail of the envelope was carried to a point, and in some cases it supported two horizontal

fins.   Usually the fins and control surfaces were on the keel.
The Italian Military type ships have the tail cut off abruptly.
In the articulated type there is generally a prismatic, trussed,
lower fin forming an extension of the keel.   This carries the
rudder and the elevators, which in the earlier ships were of
box-kite design.   In the new rigid keel ships the cruciform
empennage has been copied from German rigids.   Four triangular fins lie on horizontal and vertical planes through the
ship's axis; these are braced with external wires and usually
have several circumferential tube struts, shaped to the
envelope, to support them when the ship is not fully inflated.

The Forlanini ships have had a more pointed streamlined
tail.   The earlier ships had a single lower fin forming part of
the keel, and box-kite type control surfaces supported on the
rear of this fin and on the car.   The latest proposed design
has a full rigid empennage with false, streamlined tail.

Blower and Scoops [12]

There are two methods of maintaining the superpressure
in the envelope, by a separate blower, or air scoops.   The
scoop method was the earlier and consists of providing tubes
of fabric projecting from the envelope into the slip stream,
and a nose valve, so as to take in air.   When the ballonet, or
in the Forlanini type the annular space between cover and
envelope, is sufficiently inflated, the scoops serve merely to
maintain a pressure which is equal to the static head due to
the wind velocity in the slip stream, or at the nose.   To
prevent this static head becoming too great for the strength
of the fabric, there is provided a set of air release valves,
(and cover is also made porous in Forlanini ships) which
permits some air to escape, thereby maintaining a safe
pressure.   Until the loss of gas is so great that the ballonet
is completely filled, the upper fabric of the ballonet is subject

[12] See also this title in Part I for blower and air scoop information pertaining to nonrigid airships.

only to the air pressure within and the gas pressure just above it, which must therefore be equal. Thus there is set up a superpressure on the lower boundary of the gas in the envelope. But if the loss of gas is so great that the ballonet is completely filled, its upper surface will bulge upward and fabric tension will act with the gas above, so that the superpressure on the gas will be reduced (see Figure 54). In the Forlanini ships there is one scoop at the point of the nose, where of course the wind pressure on the envelope is maximum. The static pressure here is exerted on the air surrounding the envelope, within the cover, so that the fabric tensions in the several sectors of the fabric are reduced, or in other words these tensions may be computed for the lift of the gas only, without superpressure. An escape valve is provided at the stern.

When the ship is not in flight, or is flying at low speed, the superpressure if produced by scoops is naturally reduced— as the square of the velocity. Later Italian designs have provided a blower in one of the cars, connected to the engine, so that a pressure can always be maintained. The blower is of the centrifugal type, and must have sufficient air capacity for the steepest descent; also it must be able to maintain a static head of sufficient amount even though no air is passing into the ballonet.

The scoops are not different in principle from the ones used in nonrigid ships. The blower offers a disadvantage in adding dead weight to the ship, but it is positive in action at all times, and if scoops are provided in addition there can be little danger of loss of pressure.

To determine the air capacity required of scoops or blower, assume that the ship is flying at velocity, V, in miles per hour, (or V in km.p.h.) and at a downward pitch angle ϕ. Then the rate of descent is $V \sin \phi$, or $88V \sin \phi$ if expressed in feet per minute ($15.67V \sin \phi$ in meters per minute).

At sea level the outside air density increases 0.07635 lbs. per sq. ft. per foot of vertical descent (1.22 kg. per sq. m. per meter) or $6.72V$ sin ϕ lbs. per sq. ft. per minute ($19.11V$ sin ϕ kg. per sq. m. per minute). Hence $\frac{0.39}{V \sin \phi}$ minutes $\left(\frac{.66}{V \sin \phi}\right)$ are required to effect a change of $\frac{1}{2}$ in. of water (12.6 lbs. per sq. ft., or 12 mm.). Change of temperature of the gas and air due to compression will expand it, hence it is on the safe side to neglect temperature change. We may then regard pv, pressure times volume in envelope plus ballonet, as a constant. The average pressure in the envelope is ch_g, which must be converted into absolute pressure. In 1 min. this is increased by $6.72V$ sin ϕ. ($19.11V$ sin ϕ). From this the new volume, and the change of volume, can be found. The blower must have sufficient capacity, at least, to furnish air amounting to this change of volume.

If scoops and blower should both fail, the reduction of volume of gas and air will cause the envelope to rise and at the same time to contract laterally, in other words to breathe, which can be analyzed as discussed in Chapter XV, Breathing.

(Figures 56, 57, 58, 59, 62a, 62b, and 65, are reproduced to the same scale, thereby illustrating the comparative sizes of the airships.)

CHAPTER XIII

DESCRIPTION OF TYPES

French Types

Clement-Bayard. Two French automobile manufacturers, Messrs. Clement and Bayard, built a number of ships which are commonly considered nonrigids. The *CB*-II, however, was provided with a long "girder-car," so that it belongs in the semirigid class, and led to later developments of semirigids in other countries. This ship had a capacity of 247,000 cu. ft. (7,000 cu. m.), a length of 251 ft. (77 m.), a maximum diameter of 43.3 ft. (13 m.), and was provided with two ballonets. The girder-car was suspended by steel cables, secured to crow-foots, and consisted of a latticed girder 167.6 ft. (51 m.) in length, triangular in section except at the car where it was quadrangular. This girder, or keel, carried the fins and rudders, with a biplane elevator amidships. Two 100 h.p. Clement-Bayard motors were used, provided with clutch and inclined shafts to tractor propellers set up on pylons. Either motor could drive both propellers at reduced speed. There was a passenger cabin in the rear of the car.

The *CB*-II was sold to the London *Daily Mail* in October 1910, and made a famous trip to London. The *CB*-V had a shorter girder, with the stabilizers and rudders attached to the envelope.

Lebaudy type. A number of semirigids were built by the Ateliers Lebaudy Fréres, Moisson par La Roche-Guyon,

Seine-et-Oise.[1] The cars were short and were suspended
from a long keel, hung close to the envelope and largely
faired in with fire-proof fabric. At the rear end the keel
was expanded into fixed vertical and horizontal fins, each
with rudder or elevator. There were thin fins attached
to the rear end of the envelope. Airplane fins were fitted
to the keel, forward.

The Lebaudy I was rebuilt as II for the French military
service. *La Patrie* and *La Republique* for the same service,
were wrecked. *La Russie* was sold to Russia. *La Liberté,
Capitaine Marschall* and *Lieut. Selle de Beauchamp* were for
military use. The Lebaudy III, *Morning Post,* built for
British military service, was wrecked. One Austrian ship
was designed along similar lines. Characteristics of three
ships follow:

TABLE 17

		La Liberté	Capitaine Marschall	Selle de Beauchamp
Year....................		1910	1911	1912
Volume.................	(cu. ft.)	170,000	263,000	280,000
	(cu. m.)	4,800	7,500	8,000
Length..................	(ft.)	220	279	292
	(m.)	67	85	89
Diameter................	(ft.)	35 5	42	48
	(m.)	10.8	12.8	14.6
Lift, total...............	(lbs.)	9,000	—	18,000
	(kg.)	4,100	—	8,100
Motors, Panhard..........	(No.—hp)	1–135	2–80	2–80
Maximum Speed..........	(M.p.h.)	31	28	28
	(km.p.h.)	50	45	45
Len./Diameter Ratio......	....	6.2	6.6	6.1

---

[1] Jane, "All the World's Aircraft," 1917.

German Types

Basenach.[2] These ships are named after their designer, Nikolaus Basenach, although they are sometimes called "Gross," after the commander of the Battalion which built them, at Berlin-Reinickendorf, and sometimes referred to as "Gross-Basenach." A small experimental ship was first tried in 1907, modeled largely after the Lebaudy type. From the lessons learned thereby the M-I and M-II were constructed (Figure 56). The essential characteristic was the suspended keel, divided into jointed sections, which supported the car and the tail surfaces. The suspension was by a somewhat complicated system of cables. Two 8-cylinder 75 h.p. engines, built especially by Körtung were used. The elevator was double surfaced and was later moved from the rear keel section to the forward one. Horizontal fins were placed on the rear end of the envelope at axial height. There were two ballonets filled by a "ventilator." A later ship of 5,500 c. m. capacity had the following weights:

	Kg.	Lbs.
Envelope, Ballonets, Fins, etc.	1,741	3,840
Elevators, Rudders, Tanks, etc.	723	1,600
Rigging	284	630
Car, Cooling Water, etc.	1,950	4,300
	4,698	10,370

In order to secure greater speed and lift, M-III was built, in 1909 (Figure 56). It was provided with four 75 h.p. Körtung engines each driving two coupled propellers. The corresponding weights were:

	Kg.	Lbs.
Envelope, Ballonets, Fins, etc.	1,923	4,250
Elevators, Rudders, Tanks, etc.	784	1,730
Rigging	283	630
Car, Cooling Water, etc.	3,605	7,950
	6,595	14,560

[2] Reference. *Motor*, September, October, 1920, "Die Entwicklung der Deutschen M-Luftschiffe," von Hauptmann Koreuber. See also Table of Characteristics, page 230.

In the test flights of January, 1910, the speed developed was 59 km. per hr. (36.7 M.p.h.), which was nearly 11 km. per hr. (6.8 M.p.h.) faster than the then existing Zeppelins.

To increase the useful lift, two cars were decided upon, and the M-IV was built (Figure 56). This contained three ballonets, one at higher pressure than the others, the keel was raised and connected directly to the fabric, serving as a keel corridor and space for control and two machinery rooms, fuel, bombs, ballast, etc. The keel was entirely covered with water-tight fabric so that the ship could alight on the water. Two sheet-steel floats were also provided below the keel, and the ship was actually landed in the water. There were three Maybach 160 h.p. engines, one in the forward machinery room driving two 2-bladed reversible propellers, and two in the rear machinery room, placed oppositely and each driving a 4-bladed propeller. Lorenz propellers were used. Above the envelope at the nose was an observation platform, connected to the keel corridor. In the summer of 1914 the ship was enlarged to 19,500 cu. m. (690,000 cu. ft.), with a useful lift of 7,000 kg. (15,400 lbs.). Provision was made in these ships for towing them from the stern of a warship, and this was actually accomplished.[3] Two ships were projected of similar design but not built, and since the war there has been little activity. The ship was operated at a superpressure of 30 mm. of water (1.18 in. or 6.15 lbs. per sq. ft.), the nose at 80 mm. (3.15 in., 16.4 lbs. per sq. ft.).

Italian Types

Military type. There are a number of types that are usually referred to as the "military" type, such as *P* (piccolo = small), *M* (medio = medium), *A* (alto = high), *V* (veloce = swift), *E* (Esploratore = scout), *SCA* (meaning Stabilimento di Costruzione Aeronautiche), etc. They have all

[3] See cover picture, *Aviation*, February 14, 1921.

been built by the Stabilimento (Aeronautic Constructing Establishment) which is a Section of the Commissariat of Aeronautics, of the Italian Government, for many years under the direction of Col. Ing. (now General) Umberto Nobile: the headquarters of the section are at Rome.

The only types constructed up to 1908 were the *P* and *M*. These early types were provided with an "articulated" keel. Later there was developed the full triangular keel, which in these types is always inverted, apex down, in contradistinction to the Forlanini keel which is erect, apex up. Therefore the keel is necessarily external, forming a large indentation on each side where connected to the envelope, on all ships except the recent *N* type. In this type the keel is nearly tangent to the envelope. In earlier ships like the *P* and *M*, there was no central suspension from the top of the envelope, but in later designs, as the *V*, *Roma*, *N*, etc., there has been a central suspension, which may also be bridled at the top to two catenary bands, causing one or two grooves in the top fabric, extending longitudinally. Other characteristics of a general nature follow:[4]

Profile. The forms used for airship envelopes have all been obtained by modifying the original one which was derived from a sine curve in the manner shown in Figure 48.

The elongation ratio, which can be changed by varying the pitch and amplitude of the sine curve, is thought to be 6, or 8 to 1 for minimum resistance; the former value was employed for the original *P* envelope. The fine tail of this form was found to be objectionable in practice and it has been shortened, making the elongation 5½. Experiments on models indicate an increase in resistance of about 2 per cent due to such shortening. The envelope of the *M* type has been further shortened and has an elongation ratio of 4.7; that of the *A* type, which has been produced from *M* by

---

[4] Abstracted from Aeronautical Research Committee, Reports and Memoranda No. 692, "Notes on French and Italian Aeronautical Practice with Particular Regard to Airships."

the addition of cylindrical body, is 5½. The method of design adopted leads to a bluff head and much truncated tail.

Some of the later designs have been somewhat modified in dimensions because of the necessity of housing them in the existing hangar at Ciampino.

Keel columns. Typical girders (*i.e.*, keel columns), consist of three longitudinal steel tubes spaced at corners of an equilateral triangle. These main tubes are free from holes or other similar sources of weakness and are joined in parallel on the three sides by steel tubing about one quarter the size of the larger (Figure 60). This small tubing is continuous on any one side but zigzags back and forth in a series of triangles. At each corner where it touches one of the main tubes the small tube is split on one side and flattened out against the large tube. It is there firmly tin-soldered, and wired into place. (Figure 47.)

In most of these girders the cross-bracing of any two sides meets at a common point. This differs from Zeppelin practice, and precludes the possibility of setting the bracing itself in symmetrical triangles. Any one leg of the bracing is thus always longer (or shorter) than its adjacent one on the same side. The distance between brace attachments on any one longitudinal tube is about 41 per cent greater than the spacing of the main tubes from each other.

All three main tubes are brought together (sometimes bent, sometimes by elbow fittings) at each end into a single ball and socket joint, which may also have various attachments for connection of other girders, cables, etc. All tubes are well greased inside before attaching the final fittings.

A quality of steel is used which will not be damaged by the soldering, and all tubes are tinned outside. This general type of girder is used in different sizes for various parts of the ship including the fins.

These girders are of much simpler construction than the Zeppelin type; but no information is available as to their relative strengths.

Cars. The cars used in the later types of airship have been constructed of aluminum and steel, having trussed longitudinal girders with curved transverse ribs and sheet metal covering. In earlier types they were constructed either of wood or of a combination of wood and metal, with two-ply diagonal planking of poplar, cedar or mahogany and a layer of proofed fabric between. In later types the control car has been formed as part of the keel, but the engine cars in these types and all cars in the earlier types were hung below with wire or cable suspensions. For a more detailed description refer to a paper by Col. Rodolfo Verduzio.[5]

Scoops. In the earlier types accordion scoops were used,[6] but in the latest type a valve has been provided in or near the nose cap, with fabric trunks through the keel to feed the compartments of the ballonet.

Valves. The theory and practice of the valves used is covered in detail by Col. R. Verduzio.[7] In the latest type ships the manual control of the gas valves has been pneumatic.

Pontoons. Pontoons are provided under the cars, and inflated from a power air pump in the car. Because of operation in high altitudes safety valves have been used to prevent bursting.

Envelope construction.[8] The envelopes are constructed on the gore strip principle, that is with longitudinal strips sewed together on the meridians. At each point of suspension a fabric band passes around the envelope, but frequently

[5] Calcolo della Navicella e degli Organi Accessori nei Dirigibili, by Ing. Rodolfo Verduzio, *Supplemento ai Rendiconti Technici,* 15 Marzo, 1925, Rome.
[6] Aeronautical Research Committee, Reports and Memoranda, No. 692, "Notes on French and Italian Aeronautical Practice with Particular Regard to Airships."
[7] Calcolo della Navicella e degli Organi Accessori nei Dirigibili, by Ing. Rodolfo Verduzio, *Supplemento ai Rendiconti Technici,* 15 Marzo, 1925, Rome.
[8] "Calculation of The Hull and of the Car-Suspension Systems of Airships," by R. Verduzio, Technical Memorandum, No. 285, N. A. C. A., translated from *Rendiconti Technici,* 15 Marzo, 1924, Rome.

after the envelope has stretched considerably these bands have caused a marked corrugated effect.

Controls. In the earlier ships the control surfaces were of the Crocco automatic form. In later types a change was made to cruciform type, with rigid support of the bottom and horizontal fins from the keel. In N-50,000 the top fin will also be supported rigidly. Prior to the N types and the Mr a system of circumferential rings was used, secured to the fabric and supporting the bases of the fins: the outer edges were secured by wire cross-bracing, causing considerable air resistance. In all types the upper fin appears to be fitted after completion [9] if it is thought that turning is so rapid as to set up undue stresses in the ship, and in some ships it is omitted. In the types with cruciform empennage the horizontal fins are placed on the longitudinal axis of the airship, except in the N-7000.

Nose cap. The bow stiffening is extended beyond the point at which the pressure becomes zero. In the early types this consisted of longitudinal tubes ending in a catenary band. For speeds above 75 km.p.h. (47 M.p.h.) rings of tubes were fitted to prevent the stiffeners buckling sideways. Commencing with the A type the nose cap on all ships has consisted of a rigid structure in the form of a dome or bell, having longitudinal and transverse tubes with diagonal bracing wires in each panel. This is secured to the end of the keel.

Range of size. The maximum size to which the military types with flexible keel can be constructed is probably 20,000 cu. m. (710,000 cu. ft.), but there is now being built an N type airship of 50,000 cu. m. (1,760,000 cu. ft.) capacity. In the smaller ships only bottom suspension is used, but in the larger types two or more top suspensions are added in order to reduce the central height and also to reduce fabric tension.

---

[9] Aeronautical Research Committee, Reports and Memoranda, No. 692, "Notes on French and Italian Aeronautical Practice with Particular Regard to Airships."

Wind resistance. The original M type was adopted on the basis of experiments which showed it to have minimum resistance. Tests on a model of the *Roma* with and without the flutes where the top suspenders are made fast showed a difference in resistance of only about 2 per cent. In the earlier types no attempt was made to reduce the resistance of the accessory parts, none of the tubes even being faired which supported the control surfaces. In the latest types, however, every effort has been made to improve this condition, because in type M the envelope caused only about 53 per cent of the total resistance.

Factor of safety. The following factors of safety are used in design:[10]

Part of Ship	Factor
Planes, Maximum Pressure at 85 km/hr. taken at 12 kg./sq.m. (53 M/hr; 2.5 lbs./sq. ft.).	6
Automatic Control Mechanism.	6
Wire Ropes for Plane Controls.	8–10
Fixed Fins, Pressure on Lower Surface assumed at 5 kg./sq. m. (1.0 lbs./ sq. ft.), on upper, 4 kg./sq. m. (0.8 lbs./sq. ft.).	5
Keel Stresses calculated for extreme pitch angle of 17°.	5–6
Car Suspensions.	6–7
Envelope at 25 mm. (1.0 in.) Pressure at Valve with Airship Horizontal. . . .	8–10

Fabric. One striking feature of the envelope is the low diffusion. Ing. Umberto Nobile reported[11] that in the *N*-1 (*Norge*), between September 1, 1923, the date of inflation, and March 1, 1924, the date of its first flight, the loss due to osmosis amounted to 1 g. per cu. m., or a total of 20 cu. m. per day (710 cu. ft.). It has been reported[12] that a Forlanini ship showed a loss of 28 cu. m. per day (1,000 cu. ft.). This low diffusion is undoubtedly due in part to the low superpressure used as compared with nonrigids. The fabric stretches about 2 to 4 per cent transversely, and shortens slightly longitudinally. In the *N*-1 the main cross-section varies from a circle of equal perimeter by about 2

---

[10] Reports and Memoranda 692.
[11] *Rendiconti Technici,* 15 Giugno, 1924, Rome, pp. 4 to 12. This reference gives also a detailed discussion of weights for the *N*-1 and of the fabric construction and stresses.
[12] Reports and Memoranda, 692.

per cent, which thus is about equal to the stretch. In general the envelope fabric is 3-ply. The diaphragms are of Italian silk weighing 60 g. per sq. m. (1.8 oz. per sq. yd.), which when treated with linseed oil to make it semi-gastight has a total weight of 115 g. per sq. m. (3.0 oz. per sq. yd.). For the ballonets silk and sometimes cotton is used.

WEIGHT OF PROOFING COATS PER SQUARE METER FOR VARIOUS FABRICS [13]
(Grams, also ounces avoirdupois per sq. yd.)

		Type O	Type P	Type M	Ballonet
1st Ply	(g./sq. m.)	60	80	85	65
	(oz./sq. yd.)	1.8	2.3	2.5	1.9
Gas Film	(g./sq. m.)	100	160	100	130
	(oz./sq. yd.)	3.0	4.8	3.0	3.9
2nd Ply	(g./sq. m.)	60	80	85	65
	(oz./sq. yd.)	1.8	2.3	2.5	1.9
Gas Film	(g./sq. m.)	50	100	100	....
	(oz./sq. yd.)	1.4	3.0	3.0	....
3rd Ply	(g./sq. m.)	60	80	85	....
	(oz./sq. yd.)	1.8	2.3	2.5	....
Weather Coat	(g./sq. m.)	15	15	15	....
	(oz./sq. yd.)	0.5	0.5	0.5	....

Special Characteristics of Each Type

Type P (Figure 57). Type P was one of the earlier productions, being of small capacity, with bottom suspension only, having an articulated keel and steel tube nose battens. The car was of boat shape, open, with engines on steel tube gantries on both sides, with dual control. Two 75 h.p. Fiat engines were used, with reversible propellers. Gasoline was carried in the car and water ballast beneath the floor. (See Table of Characteristics, page 230). This type is used mostly for instruction of pilots. About 6 built of this type.

[13] Comparison with American fabrics may be made by reference to tables in Part III, volume "Free and Captive Balloons," Ronald Aeronautic Library.

Type PV (Figure 57).   In 1918 a change was made in the *P* type to increase its speed.   The length remained the same, but the cross-section was slightly increased, and with

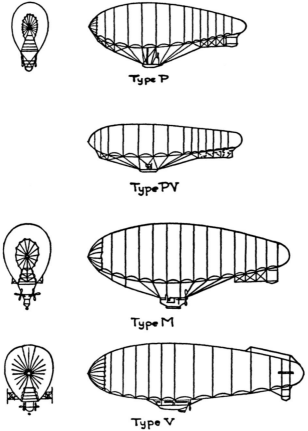

Figure 57.   Italian "Military" Type Airships, *P*, *PV*, *M*, and *V*

it the volume.   The power was increased from 140 to 380 h.p., and the velocity from 65 km. (40 M.) to 90 km.ph. (56 M.p.h.).   Hence the added designation, *V*, "veloce." About 10 built.

Type M (Figure 57). Type M probably gave the best service during the World War of all the military types. It was extensively used for carrying bombs. It is one of the earlier types, of medium capacity, with bottom suspension only, and with an articulated keel. Steel tube nose battens are used, ending in a catenary band as in the P, and for velocities above 75 km.p.h. (47 M.p.h.) tubes are placed on the "parallels" of the nose so as to serve as struts. A single car is used, but these were of different types. For bombing, the Army uses a steel car with two 220-hp. Itala engines; for scouting, the Navy uses two 200-hp. Itala engines and a heavier steel car. A wooden car that is lighter than either, and yet as strong, can also be used for scouting and similar work. The ballonet has a capacity of 45.9 per cent of the volume of the envelope, permitting a rise of 15,000 ft. One ship is said to have made 17,000 ft. with a crew of five men. These ships have carried 1 ton of bombs. They have six envelope compartments, with twelve gas and fourteen air valves. The metal cars can be equipped with 65 mm. guns, and a picture of an unenclosed, tubular steel car with gun mounted is shown in "Il Dirigibili Semirigido Italiano," by Col. G. Arturo Crocco, 1922. Experiments were made also with a 37 mm. gun. Like the P type, the keel changes to a triangular form at the stern and is covered in to serve as a lower fin. To this are fastened the control surfaces. There are no fins or rudders on the envelope. One of these ships was sold to England and became the SR-1. About 22 built in all. One M ship is being fitted (1926) for mooring to a mast.

Type V (Figure 57). Type V was developed about 1916 (see also Table of Characteristics). It had an internal rigid keel, and a bridled top suspension. The car was raised and connected directly to the keel, and a large top fin added. The lower fin was reduced to small size and the rudders and elevators were suspended below the keel. Two ships built.

Type E or DE (Figure 58). The title, "Dirigibili Esplor-atore," or "Scout," indicates the character of the *E* class, which were used for coast patrol. The car was boat shaped,

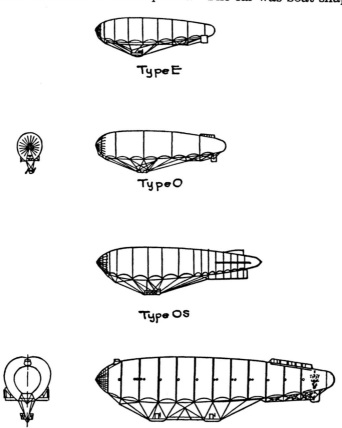

Type E

Type O

Type OS

Type A

Figure 58.   Italian "Military" Type Airships, *E*, *DE*, *O*, *OS*, and *A*

with a single 100-hp. Fiat engine, six cylinders, mounted on a cantilever above and abaft of the car. There were no seating accommodations; the rudder and elevators were similar to the *M* type. There was a single 2-bladed propeller. About eight built of *DE* type.

Types O and OS (Figure 58). The *O* ships are of small size, are provided with articulated keel, a boat type car (see general discussion, page 193), and a steel tube batten type of nose stiffening. There is a large lower fin, and small top fin and horizontal fins secured to the envelope. The rudders and elevators are of the box-kite type supported on the lower fin. Ship *O–1* was sold to the United States Navy for experimental purposes; another to the Argentine Republic. In 1921 one of these ships was fitted with a new type of tail, the now common cruciform type, with steel tubes shaped to the envelope for the purpose of stiffening the horizontal and upper fins. The successful outcome of the tests led to the adoption of this form of tail for all types. Type *OS* had somewhat larger dimensions and capacity, was articulated, had an enclosed wooden car with six passenger seats, two 110-hp. Colombo engines, two 2-bladed wooden propellers of the Crocco variable pitch type, and a tail of cruciform shape with four steel tubes for support. The cost of such a ship is about 800,000 lire ($120,000 at normal exchange). It was provided with eight compartments, and the nose cap consisted of steel tube battens with steel tube struts on the parallels, similar to that of the *Roma*. Ten *O* ships built.

Type A (Figure 58). The name of this type (alto) indicates its purpose. With somewhat greater dimensions than the *M* type it was heavily powered (see Table of Characteristics at end of this chapter). In general it resembled the *M*, but with a short parallel body. There were two cars with two 225 h.p. *SPA* engines, mounted on tubular gantries, with direct drive. The coefficient of utilization was high. The cars had a rigid crawling way between them. Only two ships built.

Type SCA (Figure 59).　Type *SCA* was named from the Stabilimento di Costruzione Aeronautiche.　Two ships of the type were sold to Spain.　There were no ships of

Type SCA

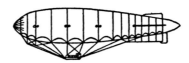

Type PM

Usuelli Type

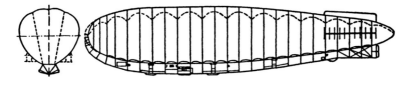

Roma

Figure 59.　Italian "Military" Type Airships, *SCA*, *PM*, Usuelli, and *T*-34 (*Roma*)

semirigid type smaller than these when they were first built, their size being only about 1/23 that of the *Roma*. They were designed for scout ships, also for sport ships. They have articulated keels; nose stiffening of steel tube

battens and one strut; cruciform tail with stiffening tubes.
Fuel consumption 33 lbs. per engine per hr.; cruising speed
37 M.p.h. (60 km.p.h.); range at maximum speed 500 M.
(800 km.); at cruising speed, 800 M. (1,300 km.); service
ceiling 6,000 ft. (1,830 m.); one rudder only.

Type PM (Figure 59). This is a recent type. In keel,
nose and tail it is similar to *SCA* and *OS* types. It is slightly
longer than the *PV* type, has about the same volume, but
a higher useful lift. The power is the same.

Type Usuelli (Figure 59). Named after Sig. Ing.
Celestino Usuelli. A ship of somewhat smaller size than the
P. The fabric was 1-ply, doped. There were two internal
ballonets, a rigid, external, triangular keel, with lifting
planes amidships. Two 100 h.p. Fiat Colombo engines
(see Type *T*). Only two of this type built.

Type T—Roma (Figure 59). The ship *T*-34 was projected by Ing. Usuelli, but the design was actually carried
out by a group of engineers, consisting of Usuelli, Nobile,
Prassone and Crocco. It was built by the Stabilimento,
named the *Roma*, and after completion was sold to the
United States for $475,000 (2,500,000 lira), but the actual
payment at 1920 rate of exchange was $185,000. The
dimensions are given in the Table of Characteristics, showing it to be the largest semirigid prior to Type *N*. This was
the first ship in which was adopted the rigid nose cap, with
full fabric cover, consisting of steel tubes connected to a
hub that formed part of the keel, the tubes being braced
with struts and diagonal wires to form a rigid, cantilever
structure (see Chapter XVI). Only 1 ship of the *T* type
was   built.

The *Roma* was provided with eleven gas and six air
compartments. Control was by one of the early type of
box-kite-like structure, with three horizontal planes and
elevators and eight vertical planes and rudders. On the

envelope there were also one top and two horizontal fins. The envelope was 4-lobed, with three catenaries of 25 ft. (7.6 m.) maximum depth, each having thirteen catenary loops of 10 m. (32 ft. 10 in.) axial length and one each fore and aft of odd length. The center catenary had a steel cable 5 to 8 mm. (0.2 to 0.33 in.) diameter; the side ones 4 to 7 mm. (0.16 to 0.28 in.). These were looped around a nickel steel bull's-eye. At the top of the ballonet the center suspenders were fastened to a double eye, and the lower cable extended down to the lower keel joints. The lower edge of the envelope was provided with 5 m. (16 ft. 5 in.) loops, with bull's-eyes to which the top suspenders also connected and lashed to the keel. Around the envelope there were 8 in. (20 cm.) bands of heavy fabric at each keel joint.

The gas cell fabric was of silk weighing 2.2 oz. per sq. yd. (75 g. per sq. m.), with 3.1 oz. (105 g.) of rubber, making a total of 5.3 oz. (180 g.). Ballonet fabric was of 2 plies of cotton weighing 1.8 oz. each (60 g.), with 3.0 oz. (100 g.) of rubber, making a total weight of 6.6 oz. (225 g.). The envelope varied in weight, but the heaviest section comprised 3 cotton plies at 4.2 oz. each (143 g.), of which one was diagonal, one outside rubber ply at 3.0 oz. (100 g.), and one inside ply at 1.6 oz. (55 g.); and an aluminum coating at 1.1 oz. (37.5 g.); making a total weight of 18.3 oz. (620 g.). The bottom of ballonet, as also the cover for nose cap and keel, was of single ply cotton weighing 4.0 oz. (136 g.). The thread count, warp and fill, was as follows:

	Gas Cell		Ballonet		Envel. (hvy.)		Bott. of Ball.	
Per 1 in. width	132	104	120	112	130	112	73	69
Per 1 cm. width...............	52	41	47	44	51	44	29	27

The keel, Figure 60, was made of tinned steel tubing in 5 m. (16 ft. 5 in.) lengths, straight except at the ends where the tubes were double bent and threaded into the couplings

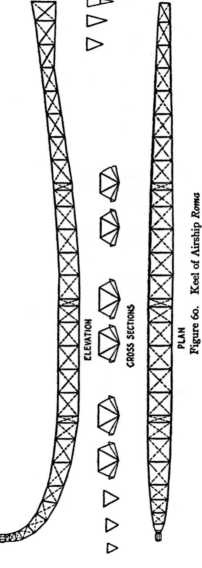

Figure 60. Keel of Airship *Roma*

(Figure 61). Sizes of tubes were as shown in Table 19.

TABLE 19.—SIZE OF KEEL TUBES, AIRSHIP *Roma*

Diameter of Tubes										Thickness			
mm.	in.	mm.	in.	mm.	in.	mm.	in.	mm.	in.	mm.	in.	mm.	in.
8	0.32	10	0.39	12	0.47	15	0.59	18	0.71	0 5	0.02	..	..
18	0.71	20	0.79	25	0.99	30	1.18	..	..	0.8	0.03	..	..
25	0.99	30	1.18	35	1.38	..	..	..	..	1.0	0.04	..	..
35	1.38	45	1.77	..	..	..	..	..	..	1.2	0.05	..	..
35	1.38	45	1.77	..	..	..	..	..	..	1.5	0.06	..	..
45	1.77	..	..	..	..	..	..	..	..	2.0	0.08	2.5	0.10

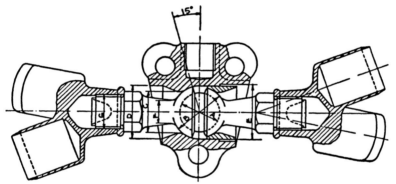

Figure 61. Flexible Keel Connection of *Roma*

Keel Joint	A Ball Diameter	B	C	D	E *	F	G *
I.........	38 1 =1½"	58	38	58	60	30	33
II	38 1 =1½"	53	35	53	55	24	30
III........	30 16=1⅟₄"	42	26	42	44	20	22
IV.........	25 4 =1"	35	26	36	38	16	22

* 16 threads per inch.

Analysis of the tubing showed Carbon .42 to .44; Phosphorous .072; Sulphur .050; Manganese .56. Yield point 104,860 lbs. per sq. in. (7,370 kg. per sq. cm.); ultimate strength 113,400 lbs. per sq. in. (8,000 kg. per sq. cm.).

Elongation in 2 in. (5 cm.) 11 per cent; in 8 in. (20 cm.) 4.75 per cent. Analysis of the wiring used (diameter 0.034 in., 0.83 mm.) showed 71,590 lbs. per sq. in. (5,000 kg. per sq. cm.) and an elongation in 2 in. (5.0 cm.) of 25 per cent. The ball and socket joints were made of nickel steel.

The nose cap was 19 ft. 8 in. in height (6 m.) with a diameter of 45 ft. 9 in. (14 m.). There was a 6 ft. (1.8 m.) aluminum cap on the point. The controls were made with steel tube frame, 65 ft. 5 in. x 16 ft. 5 in. x 8 ft. 10 in. (20 m. x 5 m. x 2.7 m.) and were attached to the keel. The elevators extended across full length, with a width in the central portion of 3 ft. 3 in. (1 m.), and a width outside of the rudders equal to the full depth of the surfaces to serve as balancing surfaces. The 8 rudders were of the same depth by 16 ft. 5 in. (5 m.) in height, but were cut off at an angle so as to permit motion of the elevators. There were wires secured to patches on the envelope which stabilized the upper surface so as to prevent oscillation, and similar wires forward to the keel to prevent horizontal oscillation.

The engines were placed on streamlined outriggers. They were set at angles of 12°, 10° and 0° respectively to the ship's axis, to prevent interference of the slip streams. The width between engines was 3.8 m. (12 ft. 6 in.). Fuel capacity was 2,231 gal. (8,500 litres). With two engines running the radius of operation was 4,500 km. (2,796 M.); with six engines, 2,750 km. (1,709 M.). Engine speed was 1,650 r.p.m. Design speed 80 M.p.h. (130 km.p.h.).

The crew consisted of the Commanding Officer, Chief Pilot, four Pilots (these latter also acting as Supply Officer, Chief Engineer, Radio Officer, and Chief Rigger), four enlisted riggers, six motor mechanics, and two radio operators; a total of eighteen. For flights longer than 12 hrs., an additional Navigating Officer and six motor mechanics increased the number to twenty-five.

There was a 3-ply veneer cat-walk, with tube supports hung on cables, and with a single wire railing. Along this there were three hand blowers. The cabin was of plywood on a tubular frame, with upholstered, wicker porch furniture. Beneath were three pontoons with 4 in. (10 cm.) valves. Control wires 5/16 in. in diameter (8 mm.) passed through the keel over double-sheave guides to drums under the pilot's cabin. The coefficient of utilization of weight was 46.5 per cent, giving 36,000 lbs. (16,300 kg.) useful lift. Fixed weight was 41,280 lbs. (18,700 kg.); crew of 25 totalled 4,000 lbs. (1,810 kg.); water ballast 2,424 lbs. (1,100 kg.); gasoline and oil 17,840 lbs. (8,100 kg.).

The *Roma* was destroyed by fire February 21, 1922, caused by striking high-tension electric wires while out of control. The Board of Officers that investigated the accident was unable to determine the specific reason for the loss of maneuvering control, but the evidence presented to the Board indicated negative internal pressure probably caused by stoppage of an air duct leading from a scoop to ballonet. The *Roma* was flying at too low an altitude to allow discharging ballast in the short time available. Important features for improved design of later airships that were brought out by the investigation include the following: Means for releasing large quantities of ballast quickly by controls direct from the pilot cabin; Fuel tanks to be of the slip type capable of being dropped quickly as emergency ballast; A master switch for stopping all engines from the pilot cabin; The use of helium instead of hydrogen as the inflation gas; That all trial flights be conducted at altitudes sufficient to permit a static control in case rudder controls become inoperative from any cause.

Type N[14] (Figure 62a).   The first ship of the *N* class, the *N-1*, was launched in the Spring of 1924, and in 1926 was bought by Amundsen and used successfully for his Polar

[14] Information from "Technıche di Aeronautica," March 1924, Rome.

flight, making a voyage from Rome to Teller, Alaska. It is
the second of large volume constructed since the war and
includes very notable improvements, which neither com-
plicate the structure nor specialize the construction, constituting an undoubted advance with respect to all previous
airships.

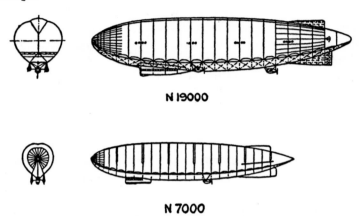

N 19000

N 7000

Figure 62a.   Italian "Military" Type Airships, *N*-19,000 cu. m. and
N-7,000 cu. m.

The characteristics which essentially differentiate this airship from those which preceded it may be summed up thus:

> Adoption of a profile of better penetration.
>
> Stiffening the stern by a cruciform empennage.
>
> Adoption of cars separated from the keel.
>
> Adoption of control car tapered to the rear with good, easy
> visibility for the pilot and in direct communication with
> the metal frame, which is used in this airship as storage
> space for gasoline and water.
>
> Reduction to the minimum of all passive resistances, and
> adoption of a form of good penetration for all the structures
> exposed to the wind.

A system of two internal catenaries collects the lift forces

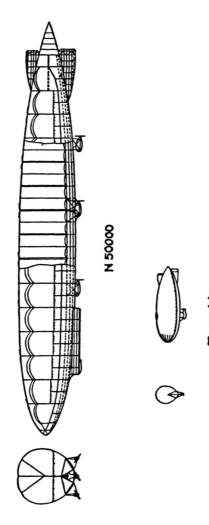

N 50000

Type Mr

Figure 62b.   Italian "Military" Type Airships, N–50,000 cu. m. and Mr

of the part above the keel, carrying them to the apices of the frame.

The keel is of triangular section, apex below, except at the control car where it is trapezoidal. It is built of the same type units as all other ships. The passenger cabin has a capacity of twenty persons, with "cellon" windows, of which some are movable, and has a luxurious private cabin fitted with bed, wardrobe, etc. There is a kitchen and lavatory with hot and cold running water. The width of keel is much greater than in previous ships so that the sides are substantially tangent to the envelope, thus eliminating the grooves which were notable in the *Roma*. In *Aviation*, April 7, 1924, it is stated that the keel is "designed to withstand without danger abnormal stresses such as might develop in case one of the gas compartments should suddenly become deflated."

There are three individual power cars of streamlined form (Figure 63), which marks an important change from the previous practice of placing engines in the control car or on gantries. Each car contains a 260 h.p. Maybach engine with reversing gear, also a space for the mechanics. The engine radiator is placed in the nose, with a shutter. The propellers are of wood, driven by friction clutches. Cars are hung by a simple system of steel cables from two upper keel joints, with martingales fore and aft, and rigid struts horizontally to the lower keel joints (for the two side cars). These cars are entirely enclosed. A walkway runs the length of the keel, connecting to these cars, to the control car, and through a hatchway to the top of the envelope, which is strengthened with wires so as to permit walking on it. The envelope is divided into 10 compartments. The nose is of the rigid type, like the *Roma*. The tail is cruciform like the *SCA* and *OS*, with larger tubes, as are the control surfaces, but the upper rudder was omitted in the

construction.   For inflating the ballonets there are air passages in the keel.   The elevators are balanced, the rudder
unbalanced.

An airship, the *N*-3 is being built for the Japanese
Government, and test flights were made on June 9, 1926.

Type N-2 (Figure 62a).   To replace the *N*-1, or *Norge*,
the Stabilimento in July, 1925, tried out a similar Type *N*

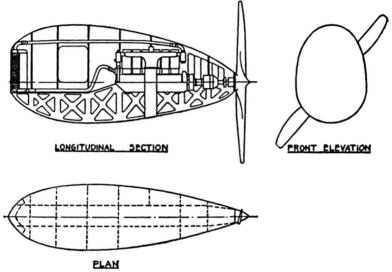

LONGITUDINAL   SECTION

FRONT ELEVATION

PLAN

Figure 63.   Power Car of Italian Type *N* Airships

ship of 7,000 cu. m. capacity.   In this model the aerodynamic form has been improved and there has been inserted
amidships a short length of parallel body; the rear end has
been drawn out into a conical point, and changes made in
the empennage; the nose cap is rigid but has tube extensions
bearing on the envelope; a single, central suspender system
makes the cross-section nearly flat at the top; the cars are
hung on flexible cable suspenders so as to prevent damage
due to striking the ground; the envelope is divided into seven

compartments of about 1,000 cu. m. (35,300 cu. ft.) connected at the bottom; the gas valves are pneumatically controlled, and the air valves are of a new and lighter type. There are two Isotta Fraschini *V*6 engines of 260 h.p. each, 1,650 r.p.m., with direct driven wood propellers.

Type N-50,000 (Figure 62b). There will be launched in 1927 an *N* ship of approximately 50,000 cu. m. (1,765,000 cu. ft.), which will thus be about 1½ times the size of the *Roma*. It is similar to *N*-1 in most respects, but has an entirely different type of keel. This new type (see Figure

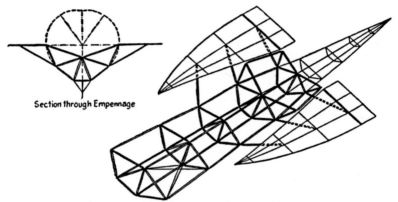

Section through Empennage

Figure 64.   Keel Structure of Airship *N*-50,000

64) is pentagonal in section throughout, except at the empennage where it is heptagonal in order to provide a determinate form of support for the horizontal fins. With this shape there are certain advantages; the horizontal fins are rigidly supported and no tube struts are used, thus the control of the rudders is improved; the keel depth can be increased where bending is large; the lower portion of the envelope cross-section can be made more circular, with less change of shape due to pressure variations; the car suspension systems are improved and the cars can be placed out of line so as to improve propeller efficiency; there is no loss of

gas volume, because there can be gas cells on either side of the keel walkway. The shape of the cars has been improved so as to lower their wind resistance; there are five cars, four with a single 245 h.p., 1,400 r.p.m., engine each, and one rear car with two such engines driving 1 reversible wood propeller; the radiators are made in two movable parts, either of which can be disconnected.

Type Mr (Figure 62). On June 5, 1924, the first ship of the *Mr* type made its maiden flight. It is the smallest semi-rigid ever built, and compares with the smallest Zodiac non-rigid as follows:

	Mr		*Zodiac*	
Capacity	960 cu. m.	33,885 cu. ft.	1,000 cu. m.	35,000 cu. ft.
Useful Lift	450 kg.	990 lbs.	260 kg.	572 lbs.
Coefficient of Util	42.5%	....	26%	....

It is largely an experimental ship. There is an external triangular keel, with only two customary articulated joints, the others being of grooved type. The nose is framed of tube struts and rings like the *OS* and *PM*. There is a cruciform empennage, supported from the keel. The fabric is 2-ply, rubber-covered cotton, with aluminized surface. Two complete and two partial diaphragms divide the envelope into five compartments. Suspension is at the bottom only. It can be operated by one man, if necessary. The static ceiling is said to be 3,300 m. (10,800 ft.).

Forlanini Type Airships

Description (Figure 65). Forlanini airships are named for Sig. Ing. Enrico Forlanini, chief engineer of the Società Leonardo da Vinci, Milan. The first three were not successful, and even the *F*-4 envelope was found to be very porous. The ships, like other Italian types, were primarily designed to carry bombs, and no great attention was paid to speed in the earlier designs. The notable characteristics are the triangular internal keel, the multi-lobed design, the outer cover, the use of the annular space between cover and envelope as a ballonet, and the method of suspension. The keel is entirely within the circular outer cover; it is tri-

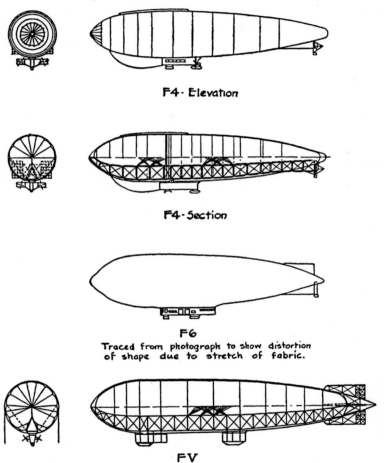

F4· Elevation

F4·Section

F6

Traced from photograph to show distortion
of shape due to stretch of fabric.

FV

Figure 65.   Forlanini Type Airships *F*-4, *F*-6 and *FV*

angular with apex on top, constructed of ball-jointed-steel columns each consisting of three steel tubes triangularly braced with smaller tubes. The suspension consists of diagonal steel cables passing from a keel joint up to the central diaphragm and down again to the keel at the second or third joint beyond; from the diaphragm a number of longitudinal silk diaphragms pass radially out to the envelope, which is held thereby in a multi-lobed or scalloped shape that will lie within the circle of the outer cover. The longitudinal profile of the cover is a surface of revolution formed by a curve which consists of two cubic parabolas whose common axis is normal to the axis of the ship at its maximum diameter.

The manufacturers claim that in impermeability their fabric is superior to that of any other airship; that the envelope is subjected only to the lift of the gas; that the envelope is protected from the sun by the cover; that the gas also is so protected that the rate and amount of change in volume is greatly reduced; that in aerodynamic qualities it has no superior. Chapter XV shows that these ships are subject to breathing stresses only to a slight degree.

Fabric. The Forlanini type of airship [15] is different in fabric practice from the Military type. The Forlanini bag contains no material except silk, which is dyed yellow to protect it from the actinic effect of the sun. The gas bag proper is made from 2 plies of 32 g. (0.9 oz.) silk, with 40 g. (1.17 oz.) of gas film between the plies and 40 g. of gas film on the outside. (See page 195 re Military type). This is afterwards coated on the outside with linseed oil varnish, further to protect it against the weather and reduce the diffusion loss. The diffusion specification is 4 litres per sq. m. per day.

Diaphragms separating the gas bag into gas-tight compartments, are made of 2-ply silk, one straight and one bias, with 50 g. (1.44 oz.) of rubber between the plies and 20 g. (0.59 oz.) of rubber on one side. Two coats of linseed oil varnish, weighing about 15 g. per sq. m. per coat (.45 oz.), are applied to the rubber surface.

---

[15] British Aeronautical Research Committee, Reports and Memoranda, No. 692.

The radial diaphragms for holding the gas bag in the "orange shape" are made from single-ply of 40 g. (1.17 oz.) silk and are all joined together to a supporting band made from 9 plies of 65 g. (1.89 oz.) rubbered silk, every other ply being on the bias.   This band connects the envelope to the rigid keel by means of supporting wires.

The outer cover of the balloon, which also forms the ballonet, is made from 1 ply of 80 g. silk (2.34 oz.).   This silk is run through a bath of linseed oil and dried.   The outer cover is then made up to shape, and reinforced both longitudinally and circumferentially at intervals of 2 ft. (60 cm.) by silk ribbon sewed on the inside; the ribbon running around the balloon is about twice as strong as the ribbon running lengthwise.

The outside of the envelope exposed to weather is painted with a second coat of linseed oil varnish, and finally with a very light coat of aluminum, leaving approximately only 5 g. of aluminum per sq. m.   The last coat of linseed oil and the coat of aluminum are applied to the bag after it is assembled.

Silk thread is used throughout.   In the Forlanini type every possible means of saving weight has been adopted in the gas bag, regardless of expense, and this saving of weight has been carried to a greater extent than by anyone else in the allied countries, for either rigid or semirigid gas bags.

Ballonet.   The ballonet consists of the space between the outer cover and the gas bag, and is continuous from end to end.   When the gas bag is not full the lower compartments are closed by the air pressure in the ballonet, and as the volume of gas continues to diminish other compartments begin to close in.   The ballonet capacity is thus of the same order as the volume of the envelope and the maximum altitude attainable is only limited by the density at which the mass of air displaced is equal to the weight of the ship.   The maximum altitude attainable is said to be about 20.000 ft.

The ship is not designed to be sufficiently strong to carry a full charge of gas at ground level, the large capacity being mainly for the purpose of gaining great heights.

Size. The Forlanini type can be constructed in much larger sizes than the Military type Italian ships with flexible keels.

Keel. The keel in this design is quite rigid and has a triangular form in cross-section (see Figure 65), the individual girders also being triangular. The girders are constructed of steel tubes connected by sockets and braced by wires, the sockets are of 3 per cent nickel steel cut from the solid, and sometimes take as many as six tubes. Such a socket takes a man three days to rough out on a milling machine.

Gas valves. All these valves are placed along the extreme top of the ship, one to each compartment, and are of the inward opening type. The disc opening of each is about 12 in. (30 cm.) in diameter, and a petticoat is fitted at each valve to facilitate removal without loss of gas. The automatic action of these valves is dependent on the Forlanini design of the gas bag. The automatic operating wire is fastened to the bottom of the valve dome and runs straight down to the bottom of the inside envelope branching out to a connection on either side. The valve opens automatically only when the air is all out of the bottom of the balloon and there is a slight pressure besides. Adjustment is made by regulating the length of the internal wire, a sleeve being fitted in the bottom of the inside envelope as a means of access.

A large steel compression spring fitted around the stem of the valve, combined with the gas pressure underneath, serves to force the valve back again after opening. In the stem above the dome is also the pressure cylinder by which the valve can be controlled by the pilot. This pressure cylinder is about 3 in. (7.5 cm.) in diameter, and contains within it a cylindrical accordion container made of fabric, which is an assurance against leakage past the piston. The inside of this space is entirely free, the stem being in reality formed by the outside casing of the cylinder in which is also placed the closing spring above mentioned.

The gasket is of the usual soft rubber cushion type. The controls for the valves are simply a row of small wire levers placed directly under the corresponding manometers for the different gas compartments. The control tubes leading up to the valves are about ¼ in. internal diameter, the wall being only slightly stiffened. For allowing the gas valves to close again, air is released through the same tubes when the control lever is returned to its "closed" position. These control levers are arranged to remain open when pulled down until it is desired to close them again. This was considered to be a fault by one of the pilots who thought that it involved unnecessary risk. In fact, an accident was caused by one of these valves being accidentally opened.

The pressure is derived from a cylindrical tank in the car which is supplied by a small 2-cylinder pump. This tank is about 5 ft. in length by 1 ft. diameter (1.5 m. × 0.3 m.) and carries pressures up to 5 m. of water (7 lbs. per sq. in.).

Air valves. The air valves were simple and light, but no pains were taken to make them air-tight as there is large leakage through the outside envelope. The air valves are entirely automatically operated by the direct air pressure against them. To reduce the air pressure intentionally, the pilot simply shuts off the scoop and blower, and the air escapes by itself, through the fabric.

Blower. The blower is of the axial flow type, driven by connection with one of the main motors; it is used just before starting and after landing.

Fabric stretch. The envelope capacity increases with time due to stretch of the fabric; it was estimated that an increase of 1½ per cent took place in a year.

Power. The power plant on *F*-6 consists of four Isotta Fraschini engines of 180 hp. each, and two similar units on *F*-5. There are only two airscrews, and the engines drive through long shafts and bevel gearings. A short transverse shaft is carried in order that any engine may drive either airscrew. The airscrews are of metal, 4-bladed, reversible, and have ball and socket joints at the base of the blades. The maximum speed was given as 55 M.p.h. for the *F*-6 (88 km.p.h.).

Manometers. The manometers employed are of the concentric U-tube type. Those for gas pressure measure the difference between the gas bag and the ballonet, the connecting tube being flushed out so as to be full of air. On other types of Italian ships the tubes are filled with gas. The pressure in the ballonet is measured relative to that in the car, and for full speed it is maintained at from 25 to 30 mm. of water (1.0 to 1.18 in.). The pressure in the car is also used as a datum in measurement of speed by means of a pitot tube. On the *F*-5, pitot and static tubes were fixed about 3 ft. from the side of the car, and there was said to be no appreciable difference of pressure between the static tube and the interior of the car.

Controls. The upper vertical fin is relatively longer than on the Military type, there being no fixed vertical surface below the envelope. The forward supports for this fin pass through the outer cover, and are attached to a structure resting on the gas bag; the supports from the rear end are fixed to the after end of the keel.

The movable fins are flexible, and practically the whole area is used in controlling the ship. These surfaces are rigid for a short distance near their leading edges, and the control cables are attached near the trailing edge. In operation the surfaces are flexed; these controls are claimed to be 40 per cent more efficient than the ordinary type which is not flexed. They are said to be quite easy to operate though they are unbalanced; this is no doubt largely accounted for by their small dimension along the wind. The load on the planes is assumed to be 25 kg. per sq. m. (5 lbs. per sq. ft.), and they are designed for a factor of safety of two. The planes which were fitted amidships on earlier types (the F-3) to give dynamic lift, have been abandoned on F-5 and F-6.

General. All ships carry a barograph for recording altitude; one record showed a rise of 4,250 ft. in 7½ min.

These ships appear to have given satisfaction during the World War.

There are four 24 in. automatic valves near the forward edge of the rudders, which open automatically at 30 mm.of water, so that the stresses and pressures are kept low. The rudders are of an area of about 70 sq. m. total (755 sq. ft.), and are made of steel wires which are fixed at one end and connected to an oval steel tube at the other, being covered on both sides with varnished silk secured together. Compressed air is used in the fuel system, the gas valves and for inflating the bumper or float bags. The blower is provided with a fabric non-return valve. The keel members are designed of variable thickness, for the actual stresses expected. The floats have a capacity of 70 cu. ft. (2.9 cu. m.) and 105 cu. ft., (3.0 cu. m.) fore and aft, respectively, and are made of rubberized fabric, with release valves to reduce the shock of landing.

Ship F-6 has nearly the same characteristics as F-5, except that there are four engines of about equal capacity. Two propellers are driven by either pair of engines. The cover has a theoretical factor of safety of 8, or ultimate strength for about 240 mm. of water.

In flight it has been observed that the torsional rigidity of the keel is not sufficient to prevent rolling of the control surfaces. The ships are very complicated in construction costing about 1,200,000 lire ($231,000 at normal exchange). Ship F-5 was burned in its hangar.

Type FV (Figure 65). In a circular of October, 1922, the Società Leonardo da Vinci gave the general details of a projected ship to be known as *FV*. Two cars are provided instead of one, each containing two engines driving two independent propellers, with a total horsepower of 1,200. Passengers and baggage are accommodated in the forward cabin as well as the control room. In the rear car, where they will cause the least noise, will be the engines and a cabin for the mechanics. Communication is through the keel, where ballast and fuel will be stored. The tail has been completely revised, having a cruciform empennage similar to that on the rigid airships, consisting of four axial fins each with a rudder or elevator. The top fin and the two side fins are braced to the keel at the forward end by struts similar to keel columns for the first time in the Italian ships. The volume is given as 23,000 cu. m. (813,000 cu. ft.), the length 110 m. (361 ft.), the maximum diameter 21 m. (69 ft.), the velocity 110 km.p.h. (68.3 M.p.h.) maximum. Later information indicates that a ship of 40,000 cu. m. (1,410,000 cu. ft.) is proposed. In this it will be noted that the nose cap remains of the same type, namely a rigid cap which is prolonged by a series of elastic battens. Being part of the cover of the ballonet, the static pressure of the air at the nose valve serves to give an internal pressure which is greater than the external pressure, save at the point of the nose, where they are equal.

Proposed German Type

Parseval. On pages 25–26 of this volume, the author of Part I has abstracted a description of a new type of pressure airship construction that is quite a radical departure

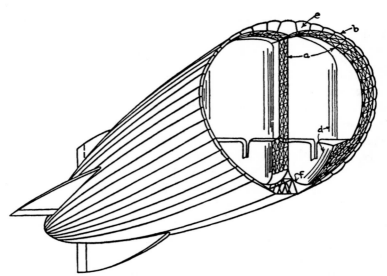

Figure 66.   Parseval Design of Metal Mesh Airship

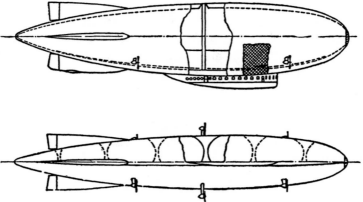

Figure 67.   Parseval Design of Metal Mesh Airship

from principles employed heretofore. Although this new development by the Luftfahrzeug-Gesellschaft of Berlin (Parseval type manufacturers) is called by them a nonrigid type airship, the longitudinal steel mesh partition serves much the same purpose as the keel construction of semirigids, consequently it may be classed as either type and it exemplifies the observation that there is no distinct structural division between nonrigids and semirigids. Figures 66 and 67 illustrate the proposed new type referred to. A complete description by H. Naatz has been translated and published by the National Advisory Committee for Aeronautics.[16]

United States Types

Type RS-1 (Figure 68). There was fabricated at the plant of the Goodyear Tire and Rubber Co., for the United States Army Air Service, the first American built semirigid.

 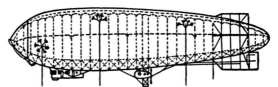

Figure 68. United States Army Airship *RS-1*. (See also Plate XIV)

It was assembled and is stationed at Scott Field, Illinois. The Roma and *O-1* were purchased from Italy by the Army and Navy respectively. The characteristics are given in the table, page 231. The *RS-1* was designed under the direction of the Engineering Division by the Goodyear Tire & Rubber Co.; General Umberto Nobile, of the Stabilimento di Costruzione Aeronautiche, Rome, was consulted. It follows the general features of the Italian "Military" type, although there is no one prototype. The *RS-1* is intended for employment on long range reconnaissance.

The profile was determined by wind tunnel tests, made

[16] N. A. C. A. Technical Memorandum No. 277, "Recent Researches in Airship Construction," Part III, by H. Naatz.

at the Bureau of Standards (Washington) in the light of the experience with previous nonrigids. The cross-section was found by means of a water model, but the theory outlined in this volume was found to check very closely. All cross-sections have been considered similar sections. The keel is designed to carry all bending stresses without assistance from the envelope. The aerodynamic loads were determined by Munk's method. An allowance of 5 per cent in the lift is made for stretch of the fabric. The speed used in computations is 70 M.p.h. (112 km.p.h.) in level flight, and 55 M.p.h. (88.5 km.p.h.) in pitch or yaw. The control surfaces are designed for an average load of 14 lbs. per sq. ft. (68.5 kg. per sq. m.), varying from 18 to 12 lbs. per sq. ft. (88 to 59 kg.). Provision is made for carrying 5,000 lbs. (2,270 kg.) of bombs, and also for a 2,000 lbs. (910 kg.) airplane, together with the mooring stresses produced by a differential speed of the airplane of 10 M.p.h. or less (16 km.p.h.).

The construction of the keel is novel. Instead of the common Italian type of tubular steel columns, there is being used a tapered circular type made of sheets of duralumin, riveted together on the cardinal points, also to nickel-steel ball and socket joints (see Figures 69, 70 and 71). The cross-section of the keel is triangular, with apex erect, making the keel entirely concealed. Steel wires brace the three sides. The envelope is lashed to the lower column joints, which are spaced about 10 ft. (3.05 m.) horizontally. There is a single center suspension, making the envelope bilobed, or cardiodal. Three diaphragms divide the envelope and ballonet, with small holes to permit slow passage of air when the ship is at a pitch angle. The design is made to allow for the use of helium gas having an assumed lift of 55 lbs. per 1,000 cu. ft. (0.88 kg. per cu. m.). The ballonet capacity is 30 per cent of the envelope, giving a computed ceiling of

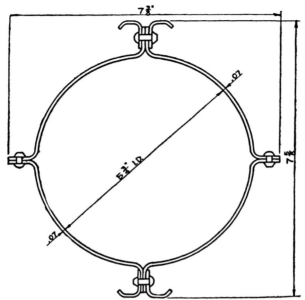

Figure 69.   Cross-Section of Typical Keel Column of *RS*-1 Airship

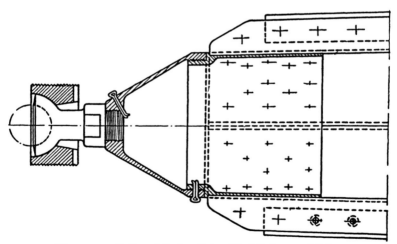

Figure 70.   Ball and Socket Joint, Keel Columns of *RS*-1

12,000 ft. (3,660 m.).　The nose construction is of a novel type (see Chapter XVI), having rigid battens that are pivoted to the hub on the forward end of the keel and yet

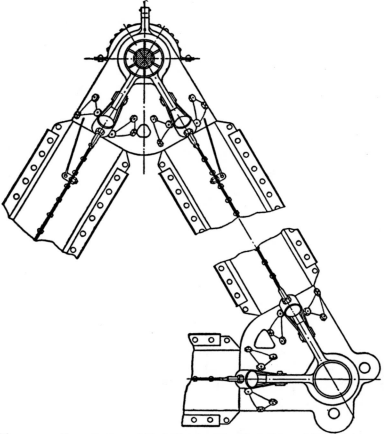

Figure 71.　Cross-Section of Keel Showing Terminal Joint of Keel Columns of *RS-1*

bear near their rear ends on the inflated envelope.　These battens are braced laterally against torsion only.　The tail surfaces are of cruciform type, similar to the latest Italian

(Official Photograph, Air Corps, U. S. Army)

Plate XIV.   United States Army Semirigid Airship *RS-1*

designs, set somewhat forward. Elevators and rudders are balanced with the paddle type arrangement.

There are two power cars and a control car forward (see Plate XIV). The power cars each contain two Liberty engines, throttled to 300 h.p. each, giving a total of 1,200 h. p. The engines are gear connected to 17½ ft. propellers. Maximum computed speed is 70 M.p.h. (112 km.p.h.); cruising speed 56 M.p.h. (90 km.p.h.). Scoops are provided, also a centrifugal blower in a power car. Air and gas valves are of Goodyear automatic type.

The fabric used in the envelope is 3-ply fabric with one diagonal ply and an aluminized surface. Each cotton ply weighs 2.2 oz. per sq. yd. (75 g. per sq.m.), and the rubber films weigh 1.0, 1.6, 3.6 and 0.5 oz., respectively (34, 54, 122 and 17g., respectively), from the outside to the inside. Including 0.7 oz. (24 g.) for the aluminum, the total weight is 14.0 oz. per sq. yd. (475 g. per sq. m.). The ballonet fabric is 2-ply, weighing 7.1 oz. per sq. yd. (240 g. per sq. m.). Each ply weighs 1.4 oz. (47.5 g.) and the gas films weigh 4.3 oz. (146 g.) The cover fabric is single-ply cloth weighing 2.2 oz. (75 g.), with gas films and aluminum weighing 1.6 oz. (54 g.), making a total weight of 3.8 oz. per sq. yd. (130 g. per s. m.). A test sample of the envelope fabric, 5 in. x 1 in., stretched at a speed of 12 in. per min. (12.7 cm. x 2.54 cm., at a speed of 30.5 cm. per min.), shows a stretch of 3½ per cent in the fill and 1 per cent in the warp at a load of 10 lbs. per in. width (178.5 kg. p.m.), with a nearly constant modulus of elasticity of 3,400 and 10,000 lbs. per lin. ft., respectively (5,050 and 17,850 kg. per lin. meter). The fabric has a factor of safety of 8 at design tension. It is laid on circumferentially, instead of in longitudinal gores as in Italian ships. Leakage tests show a diffusion of 15 litres per sq. m. per day. The actual weights are shown by the following summary:

RS–1 Airship Weight Summary

	Sub-Total Pounds	Total Pounds
FIXED WEIGHTS		
1. Hull..		15,629
(a) Envelope, including ballonets, partitions, internal suspension, air lines, gas and air valves, handling and mooring units, keel cover inside and outside, valve control lines, control car fairing and control surface suspension..................................	9,272	
(b) Keel including structure, drag-rope assembly and support assembly, control lines and fittings	5,500	
(c) Nose structure................................	857	
2. Cars..		10,690
(a) Control—including bumper, suspension cables, struts and equipment and instruments................	1,895	
(b) Power cars—2 including 4 Liberty engines, 2 mahogany propellers, transmissions, cooling system, engine accessories, oil reserve tanks, electrical equipment not otherwise noted in this statement......	8,260	
(c) Suspension for power cars........................	535	
3. Fuel system, including tanks, lines, valves and fittings....		821
4. Water ballast system, including emergency and regular ballast bags...		127
5. Control surfaces including control lines to keel..........		1,630
Total Fixed Weight..........................		28,897

WEIGH OFF ON APRIL 19, 1926:
Volume (envelope)............................. 760,000 cu. ft.
Gas Volume................................... 677,442 cu. ft.

Ballonet....................................... 82,558 cu. ft. = 10.85%

Lift = 59. lbs./1,000 under following conditions:
Air Temperature............... 48°F.
Humidity..................... 55
Barometer.................... 30.16″
Purity....................... 89.2₃

Gross Lift = 59 × 677,442 = 40,260
Fixed Weight.............. 28,897

Disposable Weight.......... 11,363

Crew (9)............. 1,800
Fuel................ 6,876
Oil................. 687
Water Ballast........ 2,000

A table of dimensions and strengths of the keel columns follows:

TABLE 20

Nom'l Cap'y lbs.	Diameter		Area		Thickness in.	Ult. Str. lbs.	y in.	Mom. of Inert. in.⁴	I/y	r in.	Theor. Str. lbs.
	End in.	Center in.	End sq. in.	Center sq. in.							
15,000......	2.12	4.38	.64	.92	.05	15,665	2.88	2.52	.88	1.65	16.500
23,000......	3.53	5.5	.81	1.10	.05	24,710	3.44	4.58	1.33	2.04	24,250
30,000......	3.5	5.5	1.03	1.41	.06	29,180	3.56	5.88	1.65	2.04	31.130
45,000......	3.75	5.75	1.63	2.11	.09	46,300	3.38	9.15	2.57	2.08	47.990
60,000......	3.75	5.75	2.27	2.93	.125	67,400	3.62	13.38	3.69	2.13	66,703
80,000......	4.	6.	2.88	3.62	.15	87,150	3.88	18.29	4.72	2.24	84,820

In this table the "theoretical strength" is computed by the formula:

$$P = \left[f + \frac{f^2}{4c\pi^2 E} \left(\frac{L}{v} \right)^2 \right] A$$

TABLE 21. CHARACTERISTICS OF SEMIRIGID AIRSHIPS

Type		BASENACH								ITALIAN MILITARY						
		M-a	M-I	M-II	M-III	M-IV	M-IV	M-IV	M-IV	P	PV	M	M (Enlarged)	M (SR-I) 3 Motors	V-2	E
Year Built		1907	1908	1909	1911	1913	(proj.)	(proj.)	(proj.)	1912	1918	1914	1916	1918	1916	1916
Total Length	(m.)	40.0	65.5	81.5	96.6	98.5	150.0	210.0		62.0	62.0	82.7	82.7	82.7	87.1	48.4
	(ft.)	131.2	214.9	267.4	315.0	323.1	492.1	688.8		203.4	203.4	271.3	271.3	271.3	285.7	158.8
Diameter, Maximum Section	(m.)	8.2	11.1	13.0	14.0	15.3	26.0	36.5		12.6	12.9	16.9	16.9	16.9	20.7	10.1
	(ft.)	26.9	36.4	42.7	45.9	50.2	85.3	119.7		41.3	42.3	55.4	55.4	55.4	67.9	33.1
Elongation Ratio		4.9	5.9	6.3	6.9	6.4				4.9	4.8	4.9	4.9	4.9	4.2	4.8
Theoretical Volume	(cu. m.)									4,750	5,000	12,110	12,110	12,110	15,360	2,510
	(cu. ft.)									167,800	176,500	428,000	428,000	428,000	542,000	88,600
Practical Volume	(cu. m.)	1,800	5,000	7,800	11,000	13,500	25,000	110,000		4,900	5,200	12,500	12,500	12,590	15,700	2,600
	(cu. ft.)	63,500	176,500	275,500	388,000	476,000	883,000	3,883,000		173,000	183,800	441,000	441,000	441,000	554,000	91,900
Total Lift at 1.15 kg.	(kg.)	2,070	5,750	8,680	12,660	15,520	28,750	126,500		5,635	5,980	14,375	14,375	14,375	18,055	2,990
	(lbs.)	4,560	12,680	19,800	27,900	34,200	63,400	279,000		12,410	13,199	31,700	31,700	31,700	39,800	6,600
Dead Weight	(kg.)									3,800	4,000	8,200	7,200	8,500	11,400	1,800
	(lbs.)									8,380	8,820	18,100	15,870	18,760	25,140	3,970
Useful Lift	(kg.)	470	1,360	2,230	2,700	3,200	16,000	90,000		1,835	1,980	6,175	7,175	5,875	6,655	1,190
	(lbs.)	1,030	3,000	4,920	5,950	7,050	35,210	198,000		4,045	4,360	13,610	15,820	12,960	14,680	2,620
Coefficient of Util., ρ		.23	.24	.25	.21	.56	.71			.33	.33	.43	.50	.41	.37	.40
Maximum Power N	(h.p.)	24	150	300	600	480	1,000	2,000		140	380	390	440	640	540	100
Maximum Velocity, V	(kmph.)	32.5	46.0	59.0	61.0	82.5	112.0	128.0		65.0	89.9	70.0	74.0	83.4	78.0	68.0
	(Mph.)	20.0	28.6	36.7	38.0	51.2	69.5	79.4		40.4	55.8	43.4	46.0	51.7	48.5	42.3
$\dfrac{N}{\sqrt[3]{v^{2}}\,V^{3}}$ * (10⁻⁴ Omitted)										1.77	1.74	2.11	2.01	2.05	1.82	1.68

* Giornale del Genio civili, 1921, "L'impiego dei dirigibili nei trasporti di passagieri."

TABLE 21 (Continued)

Type	DE	ITALIAN MILITARY											UNITED STATES	
	DE	O	O (with Rigid Stern)	OS	A	SCA-1	PM	U	T-34 (Roma)	N-1 (Norge)	N-2	N-3	Mr	RS-1
Year Built	......	1918	1921	......	1918	1922	......	1917	1919	1923	1925	(Under Construction)	1924	1925
Total Length (m.)	48.5	54.2	54.2	67.7	98.0	39.5	67.1	55.0	125.0	106.0	82	173.6	32.0	86.0
(ft.)	159.0	177.8	177.8	222.0	321.5	130.0	220.0	180.5	410.1	347.8	269.0	569.5	105.5	282.0
Diameter, Maximum Section (m.)	......	10.8	10.8	13.6	18.5	8.5	13.6	10.6	22.7	19.5	12.8	24.28	7.78	21.3
(ft.)	......	35.4	35.4	44.5	60.7	28.0	44.5	......	74.6	63.9	42.0	79.5	25.5	70.0
Elongation Ratio	......	5.0	5.0	5.0	5.3	4.6	4.9	5.2	5.5	5.4	6.4	7.15	4.1	4.0
Theoretical Volume (cu. m.)	......	3,500	3,500	......	17,500	......	......	......	34,100	......	......	......	......	......
(cu. ft.)	......	123,700	123,700	......	618,000	......	......	......	1,204,000	......	......	......	......	......
Practical Volume (cu. m.)	2,600	3,600	3,600	4,970	18,000	1,500	5,270	4,000	35,100	18,500	7,100	51,000	1,014	21,100
(cu. ft.)	92,000	127,100	127,100	176,000	635,000	53,000	186,000	141,200	1,240,000	654,000	250,000	1,800,000	35,800	745,000
Total Lift at 1.15 kg. (kg.)	2,990	4,140	4,140	5,700	20,700	1,730	......	4,600	40,400	21,275	8,156	58,650	1,166	24,500
(lbs.)	6,600	9,120	9,120	12,560	45,600	3,830	......	10,150	89,000	46,900	17,980	129,200	2,566	54,000
Dead Weight (kg.)	......	2,650	......	......	10,000	1,080	......	3,000	21,400	13,000	4,700	20,000	650	......
(lbs.)	......	5,850	......	......	22,050	2,400	......	6,600	47,200	28,660	10,361	63,933	1,433	......
Useful Lift (kg.)	......	1,490	......	2,500	10,700	650	2,150	1,600	19,000	8,275*	3,456	28,650	516	10,700
(lbs.)	......	3,290	......	5,500	23,600	1,430	4,750	3,500	41,950	18,240*	7,619	63,160	1,133	23,630
Coefficient of Util., ρ	......	.36	......	.44	.51	.38	.53	.35	.47	.39*	.42	.43	.44	.44
Maximum Power, N (h.p.)	......	240	240	480	950	80	380	240	2,100	750	470	1,410	40	1,200
Maximum Velocity, V (kmph.)	64.0	91.0	96.0	85.0	80.0	82.5	94.4	71.7	109.8	113.0	110	110.0	72	112.0
(Mph.)	40.0	56.6	59.7	53.0	49.7	51.0	59.0	44.6	68.3	70.2	68.4	68.4	44.7	70.0
$\dfrac{N}{\sqrt[3]{V^2}}$ (10^{-4} Omitted)	......	1.35	1.15	......	2.70	......	......	2.59	1.45	......	......	......	......	......

* When changed for the polar flight the useful load was increased to 9,525 kg. (21,000 lbs.) and the coefficient of utilisation raised to .45.

TABLE 22—CHARACTERISTICS OF FORLANINI AIRSHIPS

		F-1	F-2	F-3	F-4	F-5	F-6	F-7 Proj
Total Volume	(cu. m.)	3,700	13,000	15,000	15,000	19,000	19,000	30,000
	(cu. ft.)	131,000	460,000	530,000	530,000	672,000	672,000	1,060,000
Length	(m.)	40	72	90	90	90	90	110
	(ft.)	131	236	295	295	295	295	360
Diameter, Mid Height	(m.)	14	18	18	18	20	20	23
	(ft.)	46	59	59	59	65.6	65.6	75.5
Total Volume of Gas	(cu. m.)	3,265	11,800	13,800	13,900	17,800	17,800	28,000
	(cu. ft.)	115,500	417,000	487,000	491,000	629,000	629,000	988,000
Number of Compartments		1	12	12	12	12	12	12
Wt. of Complete Construction (equip, arms, provisions)	(kg.)	2,800	8,400	10,500	9,300	9,700	10,300	15,200
Wt. of Constr. per cu. m. Gas	(lb.)	6,170	18,500	23,100	20,500	21,400	22,700	33,500
	(kg.)	0.857	0.712	0.762	0.668	0.544	0.578	0.544
Wt. of Constr. per cu. ft. Gas	(lbs.)	0.053	0.044	0.048	0.042	0.034	0.036	0.034
Cargo Lift at 4,000 m.	(kg.)	....	....	....	1,400	3,500	2,900	5,500
Cargo Lift at 13,120 ft.	(lbs.)	....	....	....	3,100	7,700	6,400	12,100
Max. ht. [with Dyn. Lift, and Norm. Equip. and Prov. for 300 km. (186 M.)]	(m.)	....	....	3,100	4,500	6,500	6,000	6,500.
	(ft.)	....	....	10,300	14,760	21,300	19,700	21,300
Number of Engines		1	2	4	2	2	4	4
Complete Power Installed	(hp.)	40	170	400	320	480	760	1,400
Max. Effec. Power in Flight	(hp.)	30	160	360	300	300	425	800
Max. Velocity near Earth	(km.p.h.)	50	63	75	73	70	75	80
Max. Velocity near Earth	(M.p.h.)	31	39	47	45	44	47	50
Max. Velocity at 2,000 m.	(km.p.h.)	....	63	74	80	75	81	90
Max. Velocity at 6,560 ft.	(M.p.h.)	....	39	46	50	47	50	56
Max. Velocity at 4,000 m.	(km.p.h.)	....	....	....	78	80	90	97
Max. Velocity at 13,100 ft.	(M.p.h.)	....	....	....	48	50	56	60
Max. Velocity at 5,000 m.	(km.p.h.)	....	....	....	78	79	95	104
Max. Velocity at 16,400 ft.	(M.p.h.)	....	....	....	48	49	59	65
Max. Velocity at 6,000 m.	(km.p.h.)	....	....	....	48	78	100	110
Max. Velocity at 19,700 ft.	(M.p.h.)	....	....	....	....	48	62	68
Cons. of Gasoline and Oil at Cruis. Speed (85%) and for Dist. Indicated	(kg.)	....	....	42	35	45	65	125
	(m.)	....	....	2,500	4,000	4,000	4,000	4,000
	(lbs.)	....	....	93	77	99	144	276
	(ft.)	....	....	8,200	13,100	13,100	13,100	13,100
Ditto, per km. run	(kg.)	0.100	0.355	0.660	0.575	0.665	0.850	1.470
Velocity of Ascent and Descent: 1,000 m.	(min.)	....	....	6.0	5.5	6.0	6.0	6.0
1,000 ft.	(min.)	....	....	1.8	1.7	1.8	1.8	1.8

Above Table (metric units only) taken from "I Dirigibili Tipo F della Società Leonardo da Vinci," Milano, November 1916.

CHAPTER XIV

CROSS-SECTION OF AN AIRSHIP ENVELOPE UNDER GAS PRESSURE

Following is a list of the symbols employed in this chapter.

Symbols

A = Half area of cross-section of bi-lobed ship

A_k = Area of keel columns in cross-section, total

A' = Area of one lobe, for "index curves"

α = Value of Θ at upper limit of fabric arc; also

   = Half angle of fabric bulge between nose battens

b = Positive bulge of fabric between nose battens; also

   = Initial middle ordinate of tube strut

b' = Negative bulge of fabric between nose battens; also

   = Increase in middle ordinate of tube strut, after deflection

β = Value of Θ at lower limit of fabric arc; also

   = Half central angle between nose battens, in vertical plane

c = Lift of gas, per unit of volume

c' = Equivalent lift of gas, after allowing for fabric weight

d = Depth from ship's axis to lowest element of ballonet

d' = Inflated depth of ballonet at maximum cross-section

d_m = Depth of indentation of nose batten at end; also

   = Depth of indentation, in "end effect"

D = Diameter of tube strut; also

   = Diameter of maximum equivalent circular section of envelope

δ = Half angle between nose battens, in normal plane, at any section; also

$= \text{Volumetric efficiency} = \dfrac{v}{\frac{1}{4}LD^2}.$

$\Delta = \sqrt{1 - g^2 \sin^2 \psi} = \cos \epsilon$

$\Delta' = \sqrt{1 - k^2 \sin^2 \epsilon}$

$\Delta_f =$ Deflection of envelope, in breathing

$\Delta_k =$ Deflection of keel, in breathing

$\Delta_{y_0} =$ Vertical movement of any envelope section, in breathing

$\sin \epsilon = g \sin \psi$

$\epsilon =$ Half angle between nose battens, in their plane, at any section

$e =$ Vertical distance from center of gravity of composite ship to center of gravity of fabric alone

$e_1 =$ Vertical distance from center of gravity of composite ship to center of gravity of keel

$E =$ Modulus of elasticity of steel spring, in Crocco's device

$E_k =$ Modulus of elasticity of keel metal

$E_f =$ Modulus of elasticity of envelope fabric

$E =$ "Elliptic integral" of the second kind

$F =$ "Elliptic integral" of the first kind

$f =$ Maximum fiber stress per unit area

$f_k =$ Stress in any keel column, due to breathing

$g^2 = \dfrac{4r_m}{h_m}$, for theory of shape of section

$\gamma =$ Half nose angle of battens, at any section

$H =$ Velocity, or pitot, head $= \frac{1}{2}\rho V^2$

$h =$ Static pressure head of gas; also

$=$ Depth from neutral axis to the outermost element of keel at any section, in breathing theory

$h_m =$ Static pressure head of gas at highest element, $(\Theta = 180°)$

$h_v =$ Static pressure head of gas where $\Theta = 90°$

$h_l =$ Static pressure head of gas at lowest element, $(\Theta = 0°)$

$h_g =$ Static pressure head of gas at center of gravity of any arc of fabric

$h_{cg} =$ Static pressure head of gas at center of gravity of area of gas

$I =$ Total moment of inertia of compound ship; also

$=$ Moment of inertia of spring, in Crocco's device

$I_f =$ Moment of inertia of envelope about its center of gravity

I_k = Moment of inertia of keel about its center of **gravity**

$k = \dfrac{1}{g}$; also

$= \dfrac{b}{\frac{1}{2}L} = \dfrac{-b'}{\frac{1}{2}L}$; also

$=$ The constant multiplier in $v = k \sin u$, for profile of en-velope; also

$=$ Any deflection constant, in breathing theory

$k_1 = \dfrac{b + b'}{\frac{1}{2}l}$

L = Length of ship from nose to maximum section; also

$=$ Length of chord between nose battens, at any section; also

$=$ Length of ship in breathing theory

L' = Length of fabric between nose battens, at any section

l = Length of chord between nose battens, after depression

M = Elongation ratio, $\dfrac{\text{Length}}{\text{Diameter}}$; also

$=$ Bending moment, in breathing theory

$m = \dfrac{I_k}{I_f}$

$n = \dfrac{E_k}{E_f}$

P = End load on tube strut; also

$=$ Indenting load, in "end effect"

p = Internal pressure of gas, per unit area, $= ch$

p_m = Average gas pressure

ϕ = Angle of pitch of ship, to horizontal; also

$=$ Half tail angle of envelope; also

$=$ Slope angle in "end effect"

$\psi = 90° - \frac{1}{2}\Theta$

q = "Superpressure," per unit area

ρ = Density of air; also

$=$ "Coefficient of utilization" of weight

r = Radius of annular element of fabric, undergoing inden-tation; also

$=$ Radius of curvature of fabric, in cross-section

r_m = Radius of curvature of fabric, when $\Theta = 180°$; also

$= $ Radius of outer limits of indentation, in "end effect"
$r_b = $ Radius of contact of P, in "end effect"
$r_0 = $ Initial radius of curvature of tube strut
$r', r'', \ldots r^n = $ Lengths of suspenders in multilobed design
$R = $ Radius of curvature of fabric bulge
$S = $ Perimeter of fabric, in cross-section
$\Theta = $ Angle of tangent to cross-section, measured from horizontal
$t = $ Thickness of fabric; also
$= $ Shearing force in fabric, per unit length; also
$= $ Thickness of metal, in tube struts
$T = $ Fabric tension, per unit width
$u = $ A parameter, in theory of shape of profile; also
$= $ Horizontal coordinate in breathing theory
$V = $ Velocity of axial flight; also
$= $ Lift of unit length of envelope
$v = $ Total volume of ship; also
$= $ Vertical coordinate, in breathing theory
$w = $ Weight of fabric, per unit area
$W = $ Total load on any beam, in breathing theory
$x_c = $ Horizontal distance from center of curvature of topmost element to chord joining ends of arc, S, for "index curves"
$z = $ Distance from nose point to any fabric element

Theory

Let a cross-section of the envelope be as shown in the sketch, with origin at the intersection of zero pressure line and a vertical through the highest element of the envelope. The diagram shown in Figure 72 represents unit gas pressures. Assume fabric to be weightless and without shear. Then fabric tension, T, is constant.

From $\Sigma H = 0$, on vertical section through the origin,

$$\tfrac{1}{2} (ch_m + ch)(h_m - h) - T \cos \Theta - T = 0 \qquad (42)$$

Then
$$h = \pm \sqrt{ h^2_m - \frac{2T(1 + \cos \Theta)}{c} }$$

(Note, only positive sign is required.)   But at any point,

$$T = chr, \text{ where } r = \text{radius of curv.}$$

Hence, $\dfrac{T}{c} = hr = h_m r_m = \frac{1}{4}g^2 h^2{}_m$, if we let $r_m = \frac{1}{4}g^2 h_m$ (43)

Let $\psi = 90° - \frac{1}{2}\Theta$

Then $1 + \cos\Theta = 2\sin^2\psi$, and $\sin\Theta = 2\sin\psi\cos\psi$

and when $\Theta = 180°$, $\psi = 0°$; when $\Theta = 0°$, $\psi = 90°$; and when

$$\Theta = \beta, \psi = 90° - \frac{\beta}{2}$$

Then $h = h_m\sqrt{1 - g^2\sin^2\psi} = h_m\Delta$ (44)

which is an "elliptic function"[2]

$$h_v = h_m\sqrt{1 - \frac{1}{2}g^2}$$ (45)

and $h_l = h_m\sqrt{1 - g^2}$ (46)

And $dh = -\dfrac{\frac{1}{2}g^2 h_m \sin\Theta d\psi}{\Delta}$, since $d\psi = -\frac{1}{2}d\Theta$

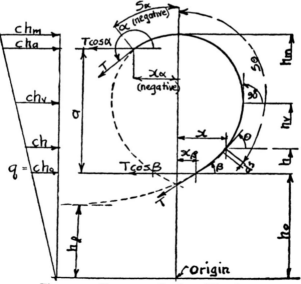

Figure 72.   Transverse Section of Envelope

[2] See Hancock on "Elliptic Integrals" and other authors.

$$ds = \frac{-dh}{\sin \Theta} = + \frac{\frac{1}{2}g^2 h_m d\psi}{\Delta}$$

$$dx = \frac{dh}{\tan \Theta} = + h_m \left[\Delta d\psi - \frac{(1 - \frac{1}{2}g^2)d\psi}{\Delta} \right]$$

Integrating these expressions, and letting

$$F_\pi^\beta = \int_\pi^\beta \frac{d\psi}{\Delta}, E_\pi^\beta = \int_\pi^\beta \Delta d\psi$$

Then $S_\beta = + \frac{1}{2}g^2 h_m F_\beta \ (\psi, g)$ (47)
since $F_\pi^\beta = F_\beta - F_\pi = + F_\beta,$ Note F_π and E_π are
And $x_\beta = + h_m [E_\beta - (1 - \frac{1}{2}g^2)] F_\beta$ zero   (48)
since $E_\pi^\beta = E_\beta - E_\pi = + E_\beta$

Area of lift $= \int_\pi^\beta (h - h_0) dx = \int_\pi^\beta \frac{h dh}{\tan \Theta} - \int_\pi^\beta h_0 dx$

$$= + \frac{T \sin \beta}{c} - h_0 x_\beta \tag{49}$$

Hence, lift $= V = + T \sin \beta - q x_\beta$ (50)
which can also easily be obtained from $\Sigma V = 0$

Also, $V_\alpha^\beta = T (\sin \beta - \sin \alpha) - q (x_\beta - x_\alpha)$

Moment of arc about line, $h = 0$, or the line of zero pressure.

$$\text{Moment} = \int_\pi^\beta h ds = \frac{T (\pi - \beta)}{c} \tag{51}$$

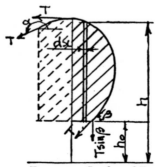

Figure 73.   Transverse Section of Envelope

Therefore, center of gravity height of arc is

$$h_g = \frac{T\,(\pi - \beta)}{cS_\beta} \text{ and } h_g\Big|_\alpha^\beta = \frac{T\,(\alpha - \beta)}{cS_\alpha^\beta} \tag{52}$$

Moments of inertia of arc about line, $h = 0$, and about axis through center of gravity.

$$I_0 = \int_\pi^\beta h^2 ds = \tfrac{1}{2}g^2 h_m{}^3 E_\beta \tag{53}$$

But from equations for S and x,

$$E_\beta = \frac{x_\beta}{h_m} + \frac{2\,(1 - \tfrac{1}{2}g^2)\,S_\beta}{g^2 h_m}$$

Hence,

$$I_0 = \frac{2Tx_\beta}{c} + h^2{}_v S_\beta, \text{ and } I_0\Big|_\alpha^\beta = \frac{2T\,(x_\beta - x_\alpha)}{c} + h^2{}_v S_\alpha^\beta \tag{54}$$

and for arc for which $x_\beta = x_\alpha$, then h_v is the radius of gyration about axis, $h = 0$.

Also,

$$I_g = I_0 - Sh^2{}_g = \frac{2Tx_\beta}{c} + S_\beta(h^2{}_v - h^2{}_g) = \tfrac{1}{2}g^2 h^2{}_m x_\beta$$
$$+ S_\beta\,(h^2{}_v - h^2{}_g) \tag{55}$$

Moment of lift about line, $h = 0$.

$$\text{Moment} = \int_\beta^\pi cxh\,dh = \tfrac{1}{2}cxh^2 - \tfrac{1}{2}c\int_\beta^\pi \frac{h^2 dh}{\tan \theta}$$
$$= \frac{cx_\beta\,(h^2{}_v - 3h^2{}_0)}{6} + \frac{Th_0 \sin \beta}{3} + \frac{TS_\beta}{3} \tag{56}$$

Since the lift, $V = + T \sin \beta - qx$, then the center of gravity of lift is

$$h_{cg} = \frac{cx_\beta\,(h^2{}_v - 3h^2{}_0) + 2Th_0 \sin \beta + 2TS_\beta}{6\,(- qx_\beta + T \sin \beta)} \tag{57}$$

or, if $\quad x_\beta = 0$, then $h_{cg} = \dfrac{h_0 \sin \beta + S_\beta}{3 \sin \beta} \tag{58}$

Also, moment

$$M\Big|_\alpha^\beta = - \frac{c\,(x_\beta - x_\alpha)\,(h^2{}_v - 3h^2{}_0)}{6} +$$
$$\frac{T\,(h_0 \sin \beta - h_a \sin \alpha + S_\alpha^\beta)}{3} \tag{59}$$

These formulas apply when g^2 is less than unity. If it is greater than unity, then Δ is imaginary. Let k be the reciprocal of g. Then clearly k^2 is less than 1 when g^2 is greater than 1.

Let

$$\sin \epsilon = g \sin \psi = g \cos \tfrac{1}{2}\theta;$$

$$\text{then } g \cos \psi = \sqrt{g^2 - \sin^2 \epsilon} = \frac{\Delta'}{k} \tag{60}$$

where $\Delta' = \sqrt{1 - k^2 \sin^2 \epsilon}$. Also $\Delta = \cos \epsilon$, and $d\psi = \dfrac{k \cos \epsilon d\epsilon}{\Delta'}$

Then

$$\Delta d\psi = \Delta' \frac{d\epsilon}{k} + \frac{(k^2 - 1)\, d\epsilon}{k\Delta'}$$

and

$$\frac{d\psi}{\Delta} = k \frac{d\epsilon}{\Delta'}$$

Hence,

$$S_\beta = \tfrac{1}{2} h_m \frac{F_\beta}{k} \tag{61}$$

and

$$x_\beta = \tfrac{1}{2} h_m \frac{(2E_\beta - F_\beta)}{k} \tag{62}$$

The other equations and quantities are independent of g and k, and therefore are the same whether g is greater or less than unity.

Total longitudinal gas pressure:

Let P = Total gas pressure at any section, on the area shown in the figure, which would be half of the total area of cardiodal section.

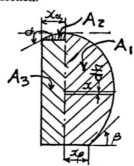

Figure 74. Transverse Section of Envelope

Now,
$$P_\beta^\pi = \int_\beta^\pi chx\,dh$$

But this is the same as the moment of lift about line, $h = 0$

Therefore,
$$P = \frac{c\,(x_\beta - x_\alpha)\,(h^2{}_v - 3h^2{}_0)}{6} + \frac{T\,(h_0 \sin \beta - h_a \sin \alpha + S)}{3} \quad (63)$$

and if
$$x_\alpha = x_\beta,\ P = \frac{T\,(h_0 \sin \beta - h_a \sin \alpha + S)}{3} \quad (64)$$

Moment of gas pressure about line, $h = 0$

Let M_0 = Moment of gas pressure, P about line, $h = 0$

Now,
$$M_0 \text{ for area } A_1 = \int_\beta^\pi chx h\,dh = \frac{ch^3x}{3} - \frac{c}{3}\int_\beta^\pi h^3\,dx$$

$$= \frac{ch^3x}{3} - \frac{T}{3}\int_\beta^\pi h^2 \cos \theta\,d\theta,$$

since
$$\frac{T}{c} = rh = \frac{h\,ds}{d\theta} = \frac{h\,dx}{\cos \theta\,d\theta}$$

$$= -\frac{cx_\beta h^3{}_0}{3} + T\,(h^2{}_0 + h^2{}_v) \sin \beta + \frac{T^2\,(\pi - \beta)}{3c}$$

Also,
$$M_0 \text{ for area } A_2 = \frac{cx_\alpha h^3{}_a}{3} - T\,(h^2{}_a + h^2{}_v) \sin \alpha + \frac{T^2\,(\alpha - \pi)}{3c}$$

and
$$M_0 \text{ for area } A_3 = -cx_\alpha \int_\beta^\alpha h^2\,dh = -\frac{cx_\alpha h^2{}_a}{3} + \frac{cx_\alpha h^3{}_0}{3}$$

Therefore, $M_0 = \dfrac{T}{6}\left[(h^2{}_0 + h^2{}_v) \sin \beta - (h^2{}_a + h^2{}_v) \sin \alpha \right]$

$$+ \frac{T^2\,(\alpha - \beta)}{3c} - \frac{ch^3{}_0\,(x_\beta - x_\alpha)}{3} \quad (65)$$

Gas pressure bending moment:

Let M = Bending moment of gas pressure about center of gravity of envelope for one half total area, i.e., for one side of axis of ship. For an envelope formed of a single curve—on each side of axis—

$$h_g = \frac{T\,(\alpha - \beta)}{cS}, \text{ for envelope only, neglecting keel}$$

But

$$M = M_0 - Ph_g$$

Thus

$$M = \frac{T}{6}\left[(h^2{}_0 + h^2{}_v - 2h_0h_g) \sin \beta - (h^2{}_a + h^2{}_v - 2h_ah_g) \sin \alpha \right]$$

$$-\frac{c}{6}\,(x_\beta - x_\alpha)\,(2h^3{}_0 - 3h^2{}_0h_g + h^2{}_vh_g) \tag{66}$$

When

$$x_\alpha = x_\beta,\ M = \frac{V}{6}\left[(h_v - h_0)^2 + 2h_0\,(h_v - h_g) \right]$$

$$-\frac{T}{6}\,(h_a + h_0 - 2h_g)\,(h_a - h_0)\sin \alpha \tag{67}$$

which is a reduced form not involving small differences.

For the equivalent semicircle, at any value of q, $M = \tfrac{1}{8}c\pi r^4$

Change of Cross-Section Due to Weight of Fabric, and to Shear

Let $w = $ Unit weight of fabric

$t = $ Unit shearing force

Taking summations tangentially and radially, for unit length of ship,

$$(T - T - dT) \cos \tfrac{1}{2}d\Theta + (t + dt - t)ds + wds \sin \Theta = 0$$

or

$$dT = (w \sin \Theta + dt)ds \tag{68}$$

Hence the fabric tension in this case is not constant, but varies with the weight of fabric and with the rate of change of shear per unit of ship's length.

Again, $(T + T + dT)\sin \frac{1}{2}d\Theta - chds - w \cos \Theta ds = 0$

And since $ds = rd\,\Theta$

then $T = r(ch + w \cos \Theta)$ (69)

so that T is dependent not only upon the gas pressure but upon the fabric weight also.

Now if the envelope were circular, $w \cos \Theta$ would vary linearly from bottom to top, changing from positive below

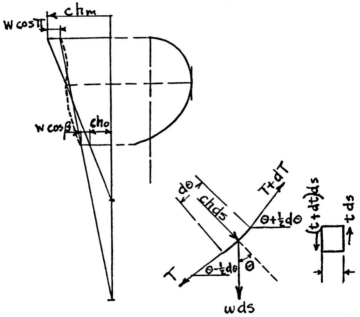

Figure 75. Change of Envelope Shape Due to Weight of Fabric and to Shear

x_v, h_v to negative above. It may be a sufficient approximation to assume it so. From the diagram, however, it is clear that the net pressure can be considered that due to a gas of less lift than c. The equivalent net lift is approximately that of a gas weighing.

$$c' = c - \frac{w\,(1 + \cos\beta)}{h_m - h_0} \tag{70}$$

and $T = rc'h$

If desired, $w \cos \Theta$ can be plotted at actual value when the shape of envelope has been determined for the gas pressure alone, and a straight line drawn through the somewhat irregular points found by plotting it (see dotted line, Figure 75). The slope of this average line is then c', and design is changed correspondingly.

It is much more difficult to make use of the equation

$$dT = (w \sin \Theta + dt)\, ds$$

because all variables are interdependent. If the shape were fixed, and known, and there were no keel, then unit longitudinal shear = shear $\times$ statical moment divided by moment of inertia

or $$t = \frac{\text{shear}\,[T\,(\pi - \Theta) \div c - S_\theta h_g]}{I_g}$$

$$= \frac{\text{shear}\,T\,[\,(\pi - \Theta)\,S_\beta - (\pi - \beta)\,S_\theta]}{c S_\theta I_g} \tag{71}$$

which is only true if the keel does not help in bending, or there is no keel. Since if there is a keel it must assist, then I_g and h_g must be replaced by the corresponding quantities for the combination of envelope and keel. But since t and therefore dt, depend upon center of gravity, shape, etc., it is clear that no simple value can be inserted in the equation for dT, hence the equation can only be used for successive approximations.

Fortunately the effect of fabric weight and shear is small in comparison with the gas pressure. Haas and Dietzius [3] ascribe to shear a maximum effect of the order of 15 per cent, so that usually it can be neglected, or merely approximated.

[3] N. A. C. A. Technical Report No. 16 (1917).

Change of Volume with Pressure

The density of the atmosphere at sea level changes about $3\frac{1}{2}$ per cent for a descent of 1,000 ft. (300 m.), and at an elevation of 6,000 ft. (1,800 m.), about $3\frac{3}{4}$ per cent. Thus a ship having constant volume (i.e., more than 1 in. or 2.5 cm. of water) will undergo a decrease in pressure of 1 in. of water every 75 ft. (1.0 cm. every 9.2 m.). From the index curves it will be found that the semirigid ship shown in Figure 81 will go through the following changes:

Section a: Half perimeter $= S = 106.5$ ft.; $a = 63.5$ ft.
Section b: Half perimeter $= S = $ 92.5 ft.; $a = 56.0$ ft.

the superpressure, h_0, for the latter being 4 ft. greater than for the former.

TABLE 23

Section	S ft.	a ft.	$\dfrac{S}{a}$	q in. water	h_0 ft.	$\dfrac{h_0}{a}$	$\dfrac{\sqrt{A'}}{a}$ from Curves	A' sq. ft.	$\frac{1}{2}a^2\tan\mu$ sq. ft.	A Half Sect. sq. ft.
a	106.5	63.5	1.68	0	0	.0	.640	1,650	180	1,830
				$\frac{1}{4}$	23.6	.37	.653	1,720	180	1,900
				$\frac{1}{2}$	47.2	.75	.665	1,780	180	1,960
				$\frac{3}{4}$	70.8	1.12	.670	1,810	180	1,990
				1	94.4	1.49	.672	1,820	180	2,000
				∞			.672			2,000
b	92.5	56.0	1.65	0	4.0	.07	.635	1,260	140	1,400
				$\frac{1}{4}$	27.6	.49	.650	1,320	140	1,460
				$\frac{1}{2}$	51.2	.92	.657	1,350	140	1,490
				$\frac{3}{4}$	74.8	1.34	.660	1,360	140	1,500
				1	98.4	1.76	.660	1,360	140	1,500
				∞			.6605			1,505

In order approximately to determine changes of volume, the prismoidal formula was applied to the two portions separated by section a as follows (with comparative water model data in parallel):

TABLE 24

Volume Changes, by Computation			Volume Changes, by Water Model		
Superpressure In. of Water	Volume		Superpressure In. of Water	Volume	
	Cu. Ft.	Ratio		Cu. Ft.	Ratio
o	693,000	100.0	o	692,000	100.0
¼	722,000	104.1	¼	725,000	104.8
½	739,000	106.6	½	736,000	106.4
¾	745,000	107.5			
I	746,000	107.6			
∞	748,000	107.8			

From this it is easily seen that, assuming no change in temperature and assuming even that scoops and valves are inoperative, the following changes of altitude are required (in this ship) to produce changes of ¼ in. of water (0.63 cm.):

TABLE 25

Pressure Range		Change of Volume %	Change of Altitude (at Sea Level)	
Inches	Cm.		Feet	Meters
o to ¼	o to 0.63	4.1	1,170	360
¼ to ½	0.63 to 1.27	2.5	720	220
½ to ¾	1.27 to 1.90	0.9	260	80
¾ to I	1.90 to 2.54	0.1	30	10
I to ∞	2.54 to ∞	(Same as constant volume ship)		

It is clear by comparison with the change in pressure for a constant volume ship that the low pressure semirigid is very insensitive to ordinary changes in flying height. In greater and less degree this is true for uni-lobed and for multi-lobed shapes.

Application of Theory in Practice

To apply the foregoing theory and diagram, it is first necessary to know certain fixed design data. First, the lift is fundamental, and when the longitudinal profile of the ship is tentatively adopted, the lift to be developed at every section is known. When the section has been developed it may prove to be necessary to revise the profile, but this has no effect upon the method outlined below. Next the superpressure, q, is a quantity which is fixed upon arbitrarily, depending upon the strength and desired life of the fabric; and c is a characteristic of the gas used, whether hydrogen or helium, and its degree of purity. Finally, if the ship is multi-lobed, or cardiodal, the length of the suspenders must be known or fixed. Having determined these, the mathematical design is based upon a graphic chart.

Figure 76 represents a family of curves, that the author has named "g-curves," which differ from one another only in the value of g. Being based upon tables of Elliptic Integrals, whose characteristic (usually denoted by k instead of g) is expressed not as g but as $\sin^{-1}g$, this is naturally given in whole degrees. Hence the g-curves are denoted by antisine rather than by g. For the value of $\frac{1}{4}g^2$, which is used in finding the lift, a table is given. When $g = 1$, or $\sin^{-1}g = 90°$, it is clear that the elliptic functions become mere trigonometric ones. This curve therefore is a dividing line. From the preceding theory, values greater than unity require the use of modified formulas, hence all formulas are tabulated on the diagram itself. All dimensions and coordinates of the curves are reduced to a scale of tenth parts of h_m by merely dividing the dimensions by h_m; and across the curves is a set of contours showing lengths S, measured from the topmost point. Angles are shown similarly. In order that the curves might not touch each

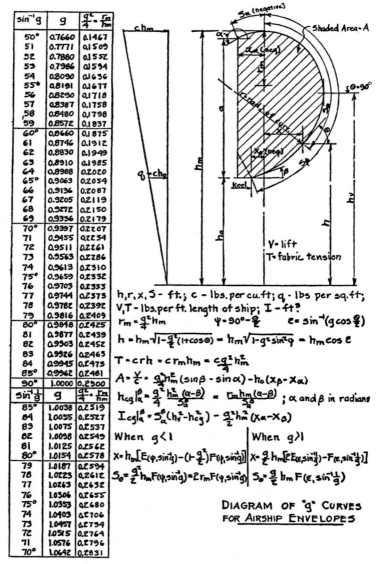

Figure 76b.   "g" Curve Data for Airship Envelope Design

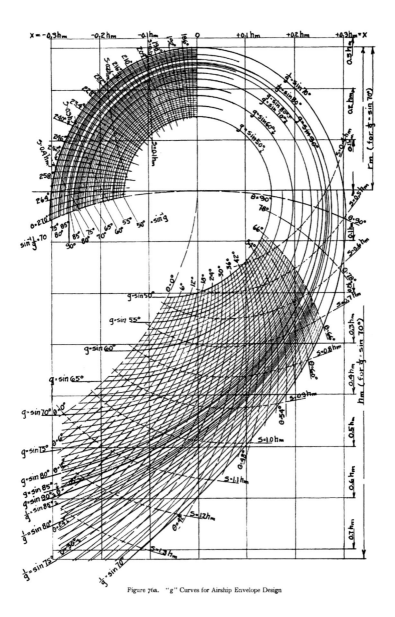

Figure 76a. "g" Curves for Airship Envelope Design

other, they are all plotted to the same center, using the center of curvature of the topmost element in each case. The radius of curvature here is expressed by $\frac{1}{4}g^2$, hence the table just mentioned gives the distance from top to center.

The diagram, Figure 76, has been prepared to show the relationship of g (or k), h_m, S_β and x_β as expressed by these formulas, also the fabric tension, T. Clearly S and x are linear functions of h_m, hence the diagram is based on a scale of tenth parts of h_m. Thus the entire diagram is independent of the pressure heights, which may have any desired values depending upon the conditions of the problem. By using this diagram all elliptic functions are solved, without the use of tables, and in fact without even requiring any knowledge of their theory. If any 2 of the 4 variables are known, the others may quickly be found.

To facilitate changing the value of any function of the g-curves and determining the effect on values of the dependent variables, a modified form of plotting, i.e., a pair of so-called "index curves," is helpful. To meet all conditions that may arise would require more than one such diagram, but for sake of brevity only one pair is given herewith (Figures 77 and 78). It relates to one lobe of a multi-lobed envelope, terminated by a longitudinal section having an angle, μ, to the vertical, and a horizontal distance x_c, from the center of curvature of the topmost element. The area between this plane and the curve is A' (which is of course not the total lift, because of gas within the angle μ). In a bi-lobed ship the tangent of angle μ is the ratio of half keel width to height of center suspender. The length of arc S, determined by the intersections with this plane, will in most cases be constant for any variation likely to be made; pressure heights h_m and h_0 will never vary by equal amounts; in general, x_c is not a constant; and a and μ will be a constant only in a bi-lobed ship, although in a multi-lobed section a may often be assumed constant without serious error.

In order to eliminate the scale factor, curves are drawn for $\frac{x_c}{h_m}$ and $\frac{h_0}{a}$, for convenience, and in the first diagram are plotted on $\frac{1}{4}g^2$ and $\frac{S}{a}$ as coordinate system. If a and μ are determined, as in a bi-lobe, then $\frac{S}{a}$ is a constant for any one section. In the diagram presented here, μ is assumed to be 5°, which is a good average figure.

Now referring to the diagram (Figure 77), let the superpressure (therefore also $\frac{h_0}{a}$) vary, $\frac{S}{a}$ remaining constant. Clearly the intersection point will move across the diagram toward the right, through successive values of $\frac{1}{4}g^2$, from which by reference to the g-curves a clear picture can be obtained of the change of shape.

In order to eliminate the scale effect from the net area, A', the value $\frac{\sqrt{A'}}{a}$ is plotted as ordinate in the next diagram on $\frac{1}{4}g^2$ for abscissa. In this diagram $\frac{x_c}{h_m}$ and $\frac{h_0}{a}$ are plotted giving curves very similar to those in the $\frac{S}{a}$ diagram. The value of A' can readily be found for any point in the $\frac{S}{a}$ diagram (Figure 77). Or if A' is to be varied in a given manner, as when making initial studies of cross-section for a given condition of lift, it is a simple matter to determine the corresponding values of S. This diagram also has superposed on it a few curves of constant $\frac{S}{a}$. Use of these facilitates the determination of change in A' with change in any other variable (e.g., h_0) without having recourse to the diagram on page 251.

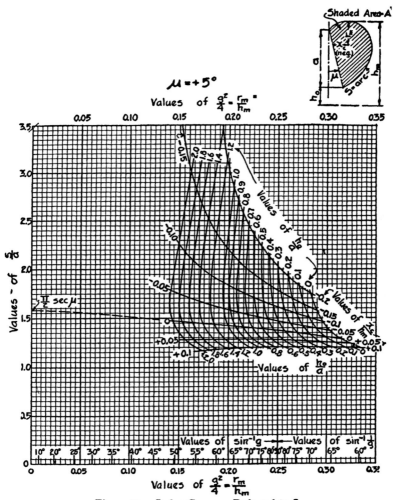

Figure 77.   Index Curves—Referred to S

Index curves such as these are easily drawn because most of the data can be plotted (from data in the g-curves) for any given value of $\frac{S}{a}$, $\frac{\sqrt{A'}}{a}$ or $\frac{1}{4}g^2$, by a single slide rule setting. Once μ is established, the diagram may be applied to any

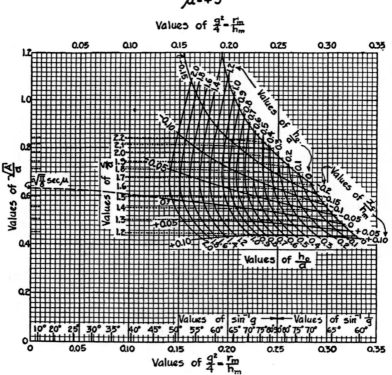

Figure 78. Index Curves—Referred to A'

section of the ship, because customarily the height and width of keel are a constant, or nearly constant, function of the center height of envelope.

(a) *Single, bottom suspension.* $x_\alpha = x_\beta = 0$. (Types P, M, etc.). Height h_m is an unknown quantity as yet, hence assume a reasonable value. Then since $\alpha = 180$ and $x_\beta = 0$, and since $V = \frac{1}{4}c\ g^2\ h^2{}_m \sin \beta$ contains only two unknown quantities, g and β, we assume a value of g, and determine β from the diagram. Using the g-table and a slide rule, see if these values check with V. When a near check is reached, find height $h_m - h_0$ from the diagram, and knowing h_0 find h_m. Using this corrected value continue until the V-equation is satisfied. Then the problem is solved. Also see "index curves," page 250.

(b) *Bi-lobed, or cardiodal design.* $(x_\alpha - x_\beta)$ = half keel width (Types A and $RS-1$). Height of central suspender, a, is known. In this case h_m can be more accurately assumed because it can only be slightly larger than h_α. Hence assume $h_m = 1.05\ (h_0 + a)$, let us say. Then on a piece of tracing cloth, or better a transparent triangle, lay off $\frac{x_\beta}{h_m}$ and $\frac{a}{h_m}$ on two lines at right angles. The ends of these lines then are the points β and α, respectively. Lay this on the diagram and shift until the points lie on the same g-curve. Read the value of $\sin {}^{-1}g$, α and β. From the g-table find $\frac{1}{4}g^2$ and with this and the values for h_m, α and β see what value of V results. Repeat until a near value of V is obtained, then determine accurately the height $h_m - h_\alpha$ and from this determine the accurate value of h_m. Then lay off $\frac{x_\beta}{h_m}$, and $\frac{a}{h_m}$ again to new size, and with these work until a value of V is obtained which meets the specification. Finally recheck h_m, although by now the error will probably be inconsiderable. The length $\frac{S_\beta}{h_m}$ can now be read from the diagram and multiplied by h_m to find the actual length. Also see "index curves," page 250.

The change of shape, due to change of superpressure q, of a section whose dimensions have been found is easily determined. Compute the new value of h_0 from the new value of q, and from this a new approximate value of h_m. Then proceed as follows: Dimensions a, x_β and S_β are the same as before, but $\dfrac{a}{h_m}$, $\dfrac{x_\beta}{h_m}$ and $\dfrac{S_\beta}{h_m}$ are new. Lay off the first two as before and place on the diagram. Bring points α and β on to the same g-curve at distances apart of $\dfrac{S_\beta}{h_m}$ as shown by the contour lines [noting that S is measured right and left from the topmost element of the section (point O, h_m)]. Having found the curve determine $h_m - h_\alpha$ and then check against the assumed value of h_m.

Two diagrams showing the relative shape and size of a section with single bottom suspension and another of the bi-lobed type are shown on Figure 52. These diagrams all show how the shape changes with change of pressure, and the extent of the "breathing action" which is described in Chapter XV.

(c) *Ship partly deflated of gas, with ballonet equally inflated.* Knowing the dimensions of all sections and the amount of gas lost, there can be found by somewhat lengthy but elemental computations approximately how much gas area has been lost from a given section. This area is now made up (more or less, because the total area is somewhat changed also) by the air in the ballonet. But the ballonet is under constant pressure q, and its sides are therefore circular and its top level (except for some sagging of the top due to fabric weight, and except in a ship with a pitch angle, in which case the gas may have less pressure than the ballonet and the ballonet top may thus be curved upward until its tension makes up for the difference of pressure). Hence the lower part of the envelope must be circular for any length that is in contact with the ballonet. If the ballonet is fastened to the sides of the envelope above the keel connection, then the envelope below the seam must be circular, and moreover in this case if the ship is pitched so that the top of ballonet is in tension there will be some drawing in of the sides which must be allowed for in using the diagram. But in any case the method is as described here.

To determine the shape of section, assume h_m as before, and lay off the dimensions $\frac{x_\beta}{h_m}$ and $\frac{a}{h_m}$. Compute $\frac{S_\beta}{h_m}$. Since ballonet pressure is q, the radius of the circular section is $\frac{T}{q}$. Since T is still unknown it is necessary to assume a number of values, and then lay off a series of circular arcs all tangent to each other at a given point, which will be the point $h_0 x_\beta$, and having these on a transparent sheet they may be superposed on the triangle and the diagram so as greatly to simplify the work. Clearly one condition of the shape is that the circular portion must be tangent to the upper portion at the point where the ballonet leaves the envelope, which point must be determined from the required area of the ballonet and an assumed curvature, and later corrected. Slide the triangle and the sheet of circles over the diagram until the terminal points lie on the same g-curve, as before, and at the same time make sure that a circle is tangent to this same g-curve at the top of ballonet or ballonet connection. Having found such a combination find T from the g-table and see if its value is the same as that for the circle chosen. If not try another circle until this condition is met. Then the criterion which must hold is that the total length of envelope between the terminal points must be $\frac{S_\beta}{h_m}$, including the circular portion. Having obtained an approximate solution, check the value of h_m for the g-curve chosen, the curvature of the ballonet, and the assumed height of the ballonet, and make new trials until a solution is reached which meets all the conditions.

(d) *Multi-lobed design* (*Forlanini*) (See Figures 65 and 79) Suspender lengths, r', r'', etc., all known. For this type it will probably be sufficiently accurate to consider that all the short arcs are circular, because each is subjected to an almost constant pressure. Then the g-curves are used for the lower portion. The lengths of suspenders must be known or assumed so that the envelope will clear the outer cover, and

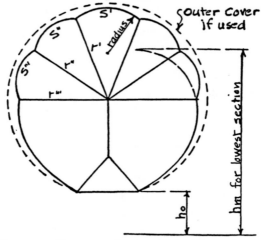

Figure 79.   Transverse Section of Multi-Lobed Design

the lengths of the small arcs must be fixed by general considerations. Then proceed as follows:

1. Assume the radius of the top segment. With the known length of arc S', determine graphically the position of suspender r'. From the scaled average height of arc S' and the known superpressure q, compute pressure and tension $T' = ch'\rho'$, where ρ' is the radius.

2. Assume radius for the second segment, and starting at the end of suspender r' as just determined find T'' in similar manner.

3. By graphical methods determine the components of T' and T'' perpendicular to suspender r'. If these compo-

nents do not balance, try a new radius for S'' until they are equal.

4. In the same manner find the tensions and the positions of the suspenders for all the small arcs up to S_n. The end of the last arc will determine the distances $x_\beta - x_\alpha$ and $h_a - h_0$ for the lowest section.

5. Using the method of paragraph (b) for change of superpressure, where length S is known, find the tension and angle at the top of the lowest section. If the component of this perpendicular to suspender r_n does not balance the similar component of arc S_{n-1}, a new assumption will have to be made for radius of S', and all arcs recomputed as described above until there is equilibrium at the end of r_n. The problem is then solved.

If the shape found as above, based on the assumptions as to lengths of arc and suspenders, does not fit the circular outer cover, it may require still further change. If desired the circular arcs may be discarded and the true shape of arcs determined from Figure 74, but the method is then still more laborious.

If the annular space between envelope and outer cover is used as a ballonet, it should be clearly noted that the superpressure is thereby diminished, and with it all internal pressures.

Figure 53, which shows a design having two suspenders on each side of the vertical axis, was prepared by the method just outlined. This diagram also shows the change of section due to change of superpressure, the altered shape having been determined along the lines described for change of superpressure in paragraph (b). In comparing this with the diagram of paragraph (b), however, it should be noted that the pressure drop is not the same in the two cases, but with less drop in the bi-lobed design there is approximately the same change in height as caused by twice the drop in the multi-lobed.

Theory of Apparatus devised by Col. G. Arturo Crocco, for Deriving the Shape of Cross-Section

The following has been adapted from Colonel Crocco's theory.[4]

Assume a thin, elastic spring, either of full length as shown by dotted lines, or with levers fastened to the ends of

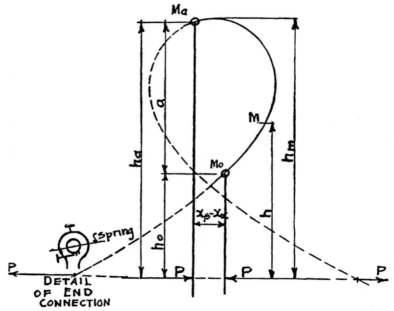

Figure 80.   Flexible Spring Method of Colonel Crocco

the portion shown in solid lines (Figure 80). Let each end of spring, or each lever, have a force, P, applied, the two forces, of course, being concurrent.

$$\text{Let } M = Ph = \text{Moment at any point}$$
$$M_0 = Ph_0 = \text{Moment at } x_\beta h_0$$
$$M_\alpha = Ph_\alpha = \text{Moment at } x_\alpha h_\alpha$$

[4] Rendiconti Esperienze e studi dello Stabilimento Costruzione Aeronautiche. Vol. III anno 1914.

From the theory of straight beams (which is approximately true for thin curved beams)

$$\frac{d^2h}{dx^2} = \frac{M}{EI} = \frac{1}{r}, \text{ or } \frac{1}{r} = \frac{Ph}{EI}$$

Hence, $rh = EI \div P$

But the theory given above shows that in a thin fabric

$$rh = T \div c; \text{ hence } T \div c = EI \div P$$

In a given elastic spring EI is a fixed quantity, dependent only upon the shape and dimensions of the section, and material, hence P may be given a value to comply with the equation. The principle of the apparatus, then, is that by applying a force P at a proper distance below the spring with the levers separated along the perimeter of the spring at a distance S, and normal to their length at a distance $x_\beta - x_\alpha$, it is possible so to curve the spring that its shape will be identical with that of the envelope if subjected to pressures proportional to the heights, h_0, h, etc.

Thus, since $r = \frac{ds}{d\Theta}$, $rh = h\frac{ds}{d\Theta} = \frac{EI}{P}$ = a constant, $(-K)$

Then, $rh = \frac{h\,ds}{d\Theta} = \frac{hdh}{\sin\Theta d\Theta} = \frac{-\,dh^2}{2d\cos\Theta} = -K$

or $h^2 = 2K\cos\Theta + K'$ where K' is a constant of integration

When $h = h_m$, $\Theta = 180°$, and $\cos\Theta = -1$; or $h^2{}_m = -2K + K'$

and

$$h^2{}_m - h^2 = -2K - 2K\cos\Theta, \text{ or } \tfrac{1}{2}(h^2{}_m - h^2) = \frac{EI}{P}(1 + \cos\Theta)$$

and if $\dfrac{T}{c}$ is submitted for $\dfrac{EI}{P}$ there results the same equation as was found on page 236 from equating the horizontal forces on the envelope.   Clearly also, dh, ds and dx have the same relationships as in the theory of the envelope, hence the spring must assume the same shape as the fabric.

The problem then, in the use of this apparatus, is so to

adjust the levers that the heights h are proportional to the pressure heads on the envelope, and that the levers are parallel and at a distance apart equal to the corresponding distance in the envelope. If g is greater than unity, it may be possible to do away with the levers and apply the forces to the free ends of the spring.

Therefore, provide two levers of lengths at least equal to h_0 and h_m, with set screw attachments at their upper end so that their angle to the spring may be adjusted and fixed at any value. Find length $h_0 = \frac{q}{c}$ and $h_a = h_0 + a$. Distance $x_\beta - x_\alpha$ is half the keel width (in a bi-lobed design). Now apply equal forces at distances h_0 and h_a below the spring, maintaining the levers parallel at the given distance apart. At first trial none of these conditions may be met, hence numerous adjustments of the angles must be made by means of the set screws, until there is parallelism with the given distances x, h, etc. When these conditions are met the spring has the desired shape. Then if means are available for measuring the value of P, the value of T can immediately be found from $T = \dfrac{cEI}{P}$, otherwise T must be found by measuring the angles between levers and spring. From these angles T is found by equating all horizontal forces. From the sum of the vertical forces the lift V is found. The length S is measured on the spring, which can be graduated if desired.

Clearly this method depends on trial and error as do all of the others, because it is not possible to solve the equations containing elliptic integrals in any other way. Some persons may prefer one method, some another. All have certain inherent errors which are probably of the same order of magnitude.

CHAPTER XV

STRESSES DUE TO BREATHING

Discussion

The presence of stresses due to breathing has been definitely established.[1] By water model and full size test it has been shown that they are of considerable magnitude when conditions are favorable, and that they are of the order of magnitude proved in the following algebraic analysis. The application of the deflection theory for beams to the curve which represents the movement of the centroids of the envelope sections, and thus to the deflection curve of the keel, has been criticized, but it is an approximation which gives one limit of stress. The other limit is found by assuming the keel to deflect as a parabola. From tests it is found that the actual results lie between the two. Further, it is clear that the differences in deflection between the actual and the theoretical ship lie not in an error of assumption, but upon the resistance to bending offered by the keel itself, which tends to smooth out the deflection curve obtained from the theory, and probably also to certain other factors.

The material that follows is based upon the author's algebraic methods of determining the cross-section of the envelope; in fact these methods were derived in order that the breathing stresses might be studied. The effect of shearing stresses is neglected, however, hence there is proper need for a discussion of them here. The former theory neglects the stretching of the fabric under tension, and its permanent

[1] Papers by Wm. Hovgaard and W. Watters Pagon to Special Committee on Airship' RS-1. Also N. A. C. A. Technical Report No. 211, "Water Model Tests for Semirigid Airships," by Dr. L. B. Tuckerman.

set; and considers that the bag is so fabricated that it has an exact fit with the keel, both when first assembled and after permanent stretch has occurred. It neglects the effect of seams in the bag, which may increase its moment of inertia by as much as 10 per cent. It assumes that the ship is on level keel, although this is seldom the case. For simplicity Figures 51 and 52 treat the keel as a linear beam located under the central axis of the ship, although the methods shown apply with equal ease to a keel of any width. The theory does not discuss the bending of the keel due to the longitudinal shortening (or lengthening) of the bag caused by the lateral enlargement, nor due to longitudinal drag.

This chapter attempts to appraise the bending produced in the keel by the deformations of the bag under variable superpressure. If the fabric were made with no diagonal ply, it could take no shear, hence the aggregation would simulate closely a stiffened suspension bridge. With the diagonal threads provided, however, it is clear that the bag can take some shear (and therefore moment) hence the aggregation becomes indeterminate. The shearing resistance offered has two effects; (1) it tends to hold the bag against deformation as described in Chapter XIV, thereby reducing the forces computed herein, but (2) it forces the keel to deflect by reason of restraining the bag from deflecting freely, and therefore creates a need for this discussion. Without diagonal threads the bag could deform differently at all sections without restraint; with the threads it resists such differential movements, thereby producing bending and shearing stresses. It should be clearly understood that the author assumes that bag and keel have shear deflections proportional to their bending deflections, which is not greatly in error, but it should also be understood that the stresses are computed in the keel as if all the deflection that it takes is a bending deflection. Hence the true stresses will be less than those figured—by the ratio of shearing to total deflection.   In the paper by Haas and Dietzius,[2] on page 246, is a discussion of the relative amount of shear and bending deflection in a nonrigid ship, indicating perhaps 15 per cent as the ratio of shearing deflection to total deflection; on which basis the stresses computed herein would be reduced by 15 per cent. As regards the amount of restraint offered to the pressure deformation of the cross-sections, it is clear that the shear stiffness of the bag is mostly in the nearly vertical side walls. Shear is always higher near the neutral axis, and in this case varies as sin θ ; but in addition the upper and lower portions of the section offer little resistance to the rise and fall of the keel because they are at too flat an angle.   Hence evidently the effect of shear strength in the bag will be to hold the sides more nearly in the unstrained position, giving the loads on the keel an opportunity to draw the keel down; or in other words, the effect of shear in the bag will be to permit a deflection of the keel which is independent of the bending deflection which this chapter aims to discuss.   Because of this shearing deflection, it is fair to conclude that the effect of shear will be more or less neutralized, and the net reduction of the stresses computed later will be perhaps only 15 per cent.   However, see subsequent comments.

The values computed in Chapter XIV are all slightly in error in the length of circumference of the section, but it is known that there is a stretch of the fabric laterally and longitudinally.   The stretch deviates from the normal length in the same way as the errors, hence the computations must closely approximate the actual conditions of the ship when inflated.   Similarly there is an error produced by assuming the keel to have no width, which can be corrected by making x equal to half the width.   The error will tend to reduce the stresses figured herein.

[2] N. A. C. A. Technical Report No. 16 (1918).

In all of the discussions, the author has assumed that the bag and keel will have an exact fit, both initially and after stretching. This assumption is clearly incorrect, but the effect may be either positive or negative depending upon the dimensioning of the fabric. Hence it cannot be considered in any general case, and only by chance will it act to reduce the stresses computed herein. In general, stretch will cause greater length of envelope than that of keel.

When loss of pressure occurs, the bag will tend to elongate at the expense of the lateral dimensions, as discussed by Haas and Dietzius. If the initial fit is exact for $q = 2.6$ then the hogging moment produced in the keel by the loss of pressure will tend to neutralize the stresses computed herein; however, if the fit is not exact but is such as to cause a sagging moment in the keel for $q = 2.6$, then the effect will be nil. Hence this may, by chance, be a qualifying factor.

Seams in the fabric, which may increase the moment of inertia of the bag (alone) by about 10 per cent, tend to make the bag stiffer, and therefore tend to increase the sag of the keel and the stresses produced. However, advantage has not been taken of this fact.

The weight of the fabric is neglected. On the sides it will be of small effect probably, because of the shearing strength of the bag here, but at top and bottom it will tend, if anything, to act with the keel loads. However, since all loads are assumed to be hung on the keel, this may slightly reduce the keel stresses as computed herein.

This discussion deals with the condition of level keel. When the ship is inclined, nose down let us say, the super-pressure near the nose will be diminished (even to zero in places) and the after sections will have increased super-pressures. The effect will be that the forward portion will act as described previously and the aft portion will act oppo-sitely. The result will be to exaggerate the curvature of the keel and increase the stresses. A longitudinal drag is also produced, which will cause some sag of the keel.

The discussion which follows is subject to all of the foregoing variations of condition. Moreover, it is based on an arbitrary design of the keel. Again, it is not claimed that the stresses shown in the tabulation are correct (i.e., exact), because they depend upon the assumption that the keel will bend exactly as shown on the diagram, Figure 81. In fact the keel has considerable stiffness and will tend to bend more in a general curve, somewhat as described later in this chapter. It is nearly impossible to say what this curve will be, because there are so many qualifying factors, and even a water model does not give the shape; but the work will be a minimum, the energy required being that used in compression of the gas during inflation. Some of this energy is given up by the gas on deflation, and absorbed by the structure.

Again for the moment the theory given herein for the division of deflection between bag and keel may be disregarded, and the problem considered purely from a common sense point of view. It is easily possible (even conservative) that a keel may deflect as much as 1 ft. in a length of 300 ft., and it is only in the mathematical computation of the amount and shape of this deflection that there can be any divergence of opinion. Once we concede the 1 ft. deflection it is clear that the minimum possible keel stress comes from the parabolic assumption given on page 261. And clearly from the discussion herein and from actual test the actual stresses will exceed these because the maximum curvature will still be found in the forward part and be greater than the average.

It may not be amiss to point out that this discussion produces a dilemma. Either the bag has sufficient shear strength to resist pressure deformation in part, thereby producing bending in the keel as described, or it has no such shear strength, in which event it cannot assist the keel to carry external bending moments, because moments are produced by shear.

If there is considerable play in the keel joints, the effect is only to cause the keel to deflect more and the bag less, hence the keel stresses will not be materially affected unless there is sufficient play to throw the moment entirely off the keel. But in this event the bag must take the static bending entirely—without any assistance from the keel— which is diametrically opposed to the ordinary basis of design.

Where shear is discussed in this paper it refers to the shear caused by the differential change of cross-section of the bag, which is a second degree force and hence not large. Of course the bag will have static shears, varying through-out its length, but it is a fair assumption that Δy_g will be nearly the same for a section already somewhat changed by shear and for a section of the exact shape produced by internal pressure. Static shears may sometimes force the section into a more circular form, but they may, if acting oppositely, make the section less circular.

When the ship is in flight the air forces tend to constrict the bow and stern sections radially (due to increase of external pressure) and to enlarge the amidships sections radially (due to diminished pressure) thus tending to pro-duce hogging of the keel. At low speeds this is quite small.

Theory

From Chapter XIV it is clear that any given cross-section varies materially in shape as the superpressure q changes. Moreover for a reduction of q the change is quite rapid. Any failure of the air scoops due to disabling of engines may easily cause entire loss of superpressure. Let us therefore consider the effect of such entire loss on the stress conditions.

A longitudinal section of the designed shape is shown on Figure 81. The maximum and one other cross-section are shown also, these being located at the points a and b. The same cross-sections are shown for $q = 0$ (at section a).

The keel is assumed to be fabricated so as to have an exact fit with the envelope for $q = 2.6$, so that there is no internal bending for this condition. If the ship were a cylinder, change of shape would cause no stress. It is not, however. At bow and stern the 2 elements, bag and keel, are reduced to common points, so no change can result here. At all other sections there is a relative change of shape (of envelope) and of relative positions. Both bag and keel are structural members, capable of carrying shear and bending. Assume moment of inertia to be unchanged with variation of q (actually I_0 for envelope changes from 133,000 to 150,000 or about 13 per cent). Then change of height of center of gravity, y_0 for the bag measures the rise (or fall) of each complete cross-section of the bag, or in other words the amount of strain between the two elements, bag and keel.

A compound girder acts after the manner of a reinforced concrete beam.[3] The value of the keel in bending is proportional to its area of section multiplied by the ratio of the relative moduli of elasticity. If the bag distorts with reference to the keel, then the combination will adjust itself by the keel taking (reversed) a part of the bending. For example, suppose that the loss of superpressure causes the bag to deflect as shown in Figure 81. These deflections have been computed in proportion to the square of the ratio of height of section to height of maximum section a, inasmuch as computation of deflection at a and b proved to be

[3] *Journal of Mathematics and Physics,* Vol. II, December, 1923. "A New Proof of the Theory of Ordinary Bending and Its Extension to Beams of Non-Homogeneous Materials," by Prof. Wm. Hovgaard.

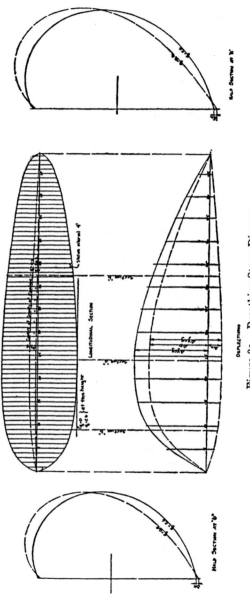

Figure 81. Breathing Stress Diagram

almost exactly as the square of the height. Of course, each section can be computed by the theory of Chapter XIV, but the above method has been followed to reduce the amount of computation required. In Chapter XII it was shown by Figures 51 and 53 that any point t moves over an individual path which differs in direction and amount from all other points. As a result there is produced a differential distortion of the fabric at adjacent cross-sections, which involves the expenditure of energy. The bag in resisting distortion is therefore subjected to bending and shear by being fastened to a rigid (assumed) keel. But the keel is subjected to the same forces (inverted) which because it is not rigid, will cause it to bend in reverse direction with moment and shear equal to those now in the bag.

It is clear therefore that the bag and keel will deflect in opposite directions at each section by amounts approximately proportional to the change of y_θ, the sum of the two deflections being equal to change of y_θ. It is also in accordance with general theory (for beam with constant moment of inertia) that the bag and keel will deflect by the amounts:

$$\Delta_f = \frac{kWL^3}{E_f I_f} \text{ and } \Delta_k = \frac{kWL^3}{E_k I_k} \qquad (72)$$

Therefore,

$$\Delta y_\theta = kWL^3 \left(\frac{1}{E_f I_f} + \frac{1}{E_k I_k} \right) \qquad (73)$$

Therefore,

$$\Delta_f = \Delta y_\theta \frac{E_k I_k}{E_k I_k + E_f I_f} = \Delta y_\theta \frac{nm}{nm + 1} \qquad (74)$$

Where

$$nE_f = E_k \text{ and } mI_f = I_k \qquad (75)$$

and

$$\Delta_k = \Delta y_\theta \frac{E_f I_f}{E_k I_k + E_f I_f} = \Delta y_\theta \frac{1}{nm + 1} \qquad (76)$$

from which the deflection of bag and keel at every section may be determined.

To find the stress produced in the keel by the deflection

Δ_k we know that $\dfrac{d^2v}{du^2} = \dfrac{M}{EI}$ for any elastic curve. But unit stress at each section is $f_k = \dfrac{Mh}{I_k}$, where h is the distance from the neutral axis to the outermost element.

Therefore
$$f_k = \frac{hE_k d^2v}{du^2} \qquad (77)$$

where h and $\dfrac{d^2v}{du^2}$ are in foot units and f_k and E_k are in lbs. per sq. in.

Example. The computation is as follows: Assume $E_f = 2,400$ lbs. per ft. width. $E_k = 9,000,000$. Therefore, $n = 9,000,000 \div 2,400 = 3,750$ ft. per sq. in. Assume the area of the upper keel member as 2.96 sq. in., and lower ones 3.34 sq. in. for two; height of upper above lower, 10.4 ft. Therefore

$$h = \frac{3.34 \times 10.4}{3.34 + 2.96} = 5.5 \text{ ft. for the upper member}$$

and $I_k = 3.34 (10.4 - 5.5)^2 + 2.96 \times 5.5^2 = 170$ sq. in. $\times$ ft.^{2}

From Chapter XIV, $I_f = S (h^2_v - h^2_o)$

Assume this equal to 150,000 ft.^{3} for whole section ($q = 0$)

Therefore $m = 170 \div 150,000 = .00113$ sq. in. per ft.

and $\quad nm = 3,750 \times .00113 = 4.25$ for the maximum section

For the purposes of this computation this ratio, $nm = 4.25$, will be assumed to be constant for all sections, although it will vary actually somewhat from end to end.

Hence
$$\Delta_k = \frac{1}{4.25 + 1} \Delta y_o = 0.19 \Delta y_o \qquad (78)$$

From the curve of Δy_o on Figure 81 it is seen that the minimum radius of curvature occurs between Stations 7 and 24, hence f_k will be maximum in this range. The following tabulation gives the computation of $\dfrac{d^2v}{du^2}$ and f_k.

TABLE 26

Sta.	Δy_g	$\Delta_k =$ $.19\Delta y_g$	dv	d^2v	du	$\dfrac{d^2v}{du^2}$	h	f_k lbs. per sq. in.
7	3.420	.6498						
			.0668		4			
8	3.770	.7164		.0098	4	.00061	4.2	23,000
			.0570		4			
9	4.070	.7734		.0095	4	.00059	4.5	23,000
			.0475		4			
10	4.320	.8209		.0090	4	.00056	4.5	23,000
			.0385		4			
11	4.523	.8594		.0075	4	.00047	5.0	21,000
			.0310		4			
12	4.684	.8904		.0060	4	00038	5 0	17,000
			.0250		4			
13	4.818	.9154		.0047	4	.00029	5 0	13,000
			.0203		4			
14	4.925	.9357		.0037	4	.00023	5.3	11,000
			.0166		4			
15	5.012	.9523		.0030	4	.00019	5.3	9,000
			.0136		4			
16	5.084	.9659		.0026	4	.00016	5 4	7,800
			.0110		4			
17	5.142	.9769		.0022	4	.00014	5.4	6,800
			.0088		4			
18	5.188	.9857		.0019	4	.00012	5.5	6,000
			.0069		4			
19	5.224	.9926		.0016	4	.00010	5.5	5,000
			.0053		4			
20	5.252	.9979		.0014	4	.00009	5.5	4,500
			.0039		4			
21	5.273	1.0018		0012	4	.00008	5.5	4,000
			.0027		4			
22	5.287	1.0045		.0010	4	.00006	5.5	3,000
			.0017		4			
23	5.295	1.0062		.0009	4	.00006	5.5	3,000
			.0008					
24	5.300	1.0070						

This computation is based on the assumption that the elastic curves of the bag and keel will follow the line of centroids of the bag as computed from a consideration of internal pressures acting on the envelope. Actually, however, the elastic curves will not conform to this theoretical curve at all points, but will curve generally from bow to stern, giving a maximum deflection somewhere near the center, and a maximum curvature less than that of the theoretical curve of centroids.

Example. Assuming that the maximum deflection will be the same as before (i.e., 1.0 ft. for the keel), the second approximate computation of maximum stress can be made as follows:

For a beam uniformly loaded,

$$\Delta_{max} = \frac{5}{384} \frac{WL^3}{EI} = \frac{5}{48} \frac{ML^2}{EI}, \quad \text{since } M = \frac{1}{8} WL \tag{79}$$

For a beam with load concentrated at the center,

$$\Delta_{max} = \frac{1}{48} \frac{WL^3}{EI} = \frac{4}{48} \frac{ML^2}{EI}, \quad \text{since } M = \frac{1}{4} WL$$

For the case under consideration the distribution of load causing deflection is in all probability between these two extremes, hence we will adopt the average.

Therefore $$\Delta_{max} = \frac{4.5}{48} \frac{ML^2}{EI} = \frac{.094 \, ML^2}{EI}$$

In these formulas the moment of inertia is assumed to be constant from end to end, but for the airship I varies considerably. If it is assumed that the maximum I is twice the average I of the deflection formula,

Then $$f_k = \frac{Mh}{I_{max}} = \frac{Mh}{2 \, I_{av}} \tag{80}$$

Therefore $$\Delta_{max} = \frac{.094 \times 2 f_k L^2}{h E_k}$$

and $$f_k = \frac{5.3 \, \Delta_{max} h E_k}{L^2} \tag{81}$$

$$= \frac{5.3 \times 1.0 \times 5.5 \times 9,000,000}{280 \times 280}$$

$$f_k = 3,300 \text{ lbs. per sq. in.}$$

In this connection it should be noted that in building design, beams are allowed to deflect $\frac{1}{360}$ part of the span at normal stresses. In this keel 1 ft. is $\frac{1}{300}$ part, or 20 per cent larger. The keel depth is of course less than in such beams, hence the stress is much less than the allowable.

Since the maximum deformation takes place at from $\frac{1}{3}$ to $\frac{1}{2}$ the length of the ship from the bow, the stress would be greater (for a given deflection) than if the deflection occurred at the center. Hence the stress probably lies between these two approximate values of 3,300 and 23,000 lbs. per sq. in., or about 6,000 to 7,000 lbs. per sq. in. maximum.

CHAPTER XVI

NOSE STIFFENING

Pressure on Battens [1]

Internal pressure. Taking components normal to the batten,

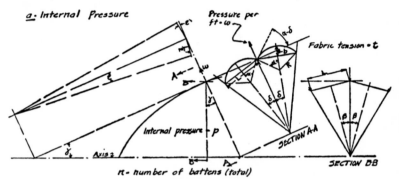

Figure 82. Internal Pressure on Nose Battens

$w = 2t \sin(\alpha - \delta) \cos \epsilon = 2pR (\sin \alpha \cos \delta - \cos \alpha \sin \delta) \cos \epsilon$, since $t = pR$ (neglecting longitudinal curvature)

Now $$R \sin \alpha = \frac{L}{2}, \text{ and } R \cos \alpha = \frac{L}{2} \cot \alpha$$

$$\therefore w = pL (\cos \delta - \cot \alpha \sin \delta) \cos \epsilon$$

Let $$k = \frac{b}{\frac{1}{2}L} = \frac{(1 - \cos \alpha)}{\sin \alpha}$$

Solving for $\sin \alpha$ gives $\sin \alpha = \dfrac{2k}{1 + k^2}$, $\therefore \cot \alpha = \dfrac{1 - k^2}{2k}$

$$\therefore w = pL \left(\cos \delta - \frac{1 - k^2}{2k} \sin \delta\right) \cos \epsilon \quad (82)$$

[1] See this title also in Part I of this volume for data and computations on nose battens for nonrigid airships.

274

Now $\sin \delta = \sin \beta \cos \gamma = \sin \dfrac{\pi}{n} \cos \gamma$, or $\delta = \dfrac{\pi}{n} \cos \gamma$ (approximately; error $\not> 1\%$),

and $\sin \epsilon = \sin \beta \sin \gamma = \sin \dfrac{\pi}{n} \sin \gamma$, or $\epsilon = \dfrac{\pi}{n} \sin \gamma$ (approx.)

For ordinary cases (where β is small) $\cos \epsilon$ may be assumed $= 1$.

When $\gamma = 0$, $\epsilon = 0$, $\delta = \beta$, and $w = pL \left(\cos \dfrac{\pi}{n} - \dfrac{1 - k^2}{2k} \sin \dfrac{\pi}{n} \right)$.

When $\gamma = 90°$, $\delta = 0$, $\epsilon = \beta$, and $w = pL \cos \beta$ regardless of value of k.

Length of arc between battens $= L' = \dfrac{8\,c - C}{3}$ (approx.), where c = chord of half arc and C = chord of whole arc. (Huyghens' approximation)

$$\therefore L' = \dfrac{8\sqrt{\dfrac{L^2}{4} + b^2} - L}{3} = \dfrac{4L\sqrt{1 + k^2} - L}{3}$$

$$= \dfrac{L}{3} \left(4\sqrt{1 + k^2} - 1 \right) \quad (83)$$

For a semicircle $k = 1$ $\therefore L' = \dfrac{L}{3} \left(4\sqrt{2} - 1 \right) = 1.552\,L$

The correct value is $L' = \dfrac{\pi}{2} L = 1.5708\,L$, $\therefore$ error is 1.2 per cent.

When $\alpha = \delta$, $w = 0$, and $k = \dfrac{1 - \cos \delta}{\sin \delta}$.

When $\alpha < \delta$, w is negative.

The maximum value of k occurs when adjacent arcs of fabric are tangent, i.e., when $\alpha = 90° + \delta$, then $k_{max} = \dfrac{1 + \sin \delta}{\cos \delta}$ (84)

This value of k gives $w_{max} = \dfrac{pL}{\cos \delta} \cos \epsilon$

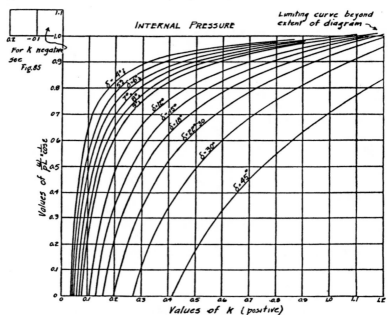

Figure 83.   Nose Stiffening; Internal Pressure Curves

$$\frac{w}{pL \cos \epsilon} = \cos \delta - \frac{1 - k^2}{2k} \sin \delta$$

When $\gamma = 0$; for 24 battens, $\dfrac{\pi}{n} = 7° \ 30' = \delta$

$$\begin{aligned}
22 \quad & \text{``} \quad \frac{\pi}{n} = \ 8° \ 11' = \delta \\
20 \quad & \text{``} \quad \frac{\pi}{n} = \ 9° \ \ 0' = \delta \\
15 \quad & \text{``} \quad \frac{\pi}{n} = 12° \ \ 0' = \delta \\
12 \quad & \text{``} \quad \frac{\pi}{n} = 15° \ \ 0' = \delta \\
10 \quad & \text{``} \quad \frac{\pi}{n} = 18° \ \ 0' = \delta \\
8 \quad & \text{``} \quad \frac{\pi}{n} = 22° \ 30' = \delta \\
6 \quad & \text{``} \quad \frac{\pi}{n} = 30° \ \ 0' = \delta \\
4 \quad & \text{``} \quad \frac{\pi}{n} = 45° \ \ 0' = \delta
\end{aligned}$$

When $\gamma \neq 0$, $\sin \delta = \sin \dfrac{\pi}{n} \cos \gamma$

$$\sin \epsilon = \sin \frac{\pi}{n} \sin \delta$$

External Pressure:

Angles γ, β, etc are as shown in Fig. 82.

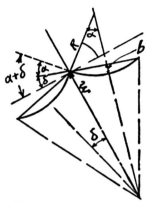

External pressure = p
Figure 84.   External Pressure on Nose Battens

Since bulge is inward, let k be negative, $\therefore$ $k = \dfrac{-b'}{\frac{1}{2}L}$

$$\therefore k = -\frac{(1 - \cos \alpha)}{\sin \alpha}$$

$$\therefore \sin \alpha = \frac{-2k}{1 + k^2}, \text{ and } \cot \alpha = -\frac{1 - k^2}{2k}$$

Now $w = 2t \sin(\alpha + \delta) \cos \epsilon = 2pR (\sin \alpha \cos \delta + \cos \alpha \sin \delta) \cos \epsilon$

$\therefore w = pL (\cos \delta + \cot \alpha \sin \delta) \cos \epsilon$

$$\therefore w = pL \left(\cos \delta - \frac{1 - k^2}{2k} \sin \delta \right) \cos \epsilon \tag{85}$$

This is the same formula as for internal pressure, but k is negative, hence w will be greater than $pL \cos \delta \cos \epsilon$ for all values of k less than 1 and negative.

The minimum value (maximum negative value) of k occurs when $\alpha = 90° - \delta$, then

$$k_{min} = -\frac{(1 - \sin \delta)}{\cos \delta}, \text{ and}$$

$$w_{min} = \frac{pL}{\cos \delta} \cos \epsilon \tag{86}$$

Also $L' = \dfrac{L}{3} (4\sqrt{1 + k^2} - 1)$ as before.

If we assume the battens to be unyielding, and the fabric stretched just taut between them, then if a pressure p be applied to one side, the fabric will stretch, producing a sag b, until the tension t produced elastically by the stretch ΔL is sufficient to balance the pressure.

Then $t = \dfrac{\frac{1}{8}\,pL^2}{b}$ (approx.) $= \frac{1}{4}\,\dfrac{pL}{k}$ since $b = \dfrac{kL}{2}$

Also $t = \dfrac{\Delta L}{L} \times E$ (fabric), and $\dfrac{\Delta L}{L} = \dfrac{L' - L}{L} = \dfrac{4}{3}(\sqrt{1 + k^2} - 1)$

$$\therefore \frac{4}{3}(\sqrt{1 + k^2} - 1)E = \frac{1}{4}\,\frac{pL}{k}$$

$$\therefore \sqrt{1 + k^2} = 1 + \tfrac{3}{16}\,\frac{pL}{Ek}$$

Let $\qquad \tfrac{3}{16}\,\dfrac{pL}{E} = D$, then $1 + k^2 = 1 + \dfrac{2D}{k} + \dfrac{D^2}{k^2}$

$$\therefore k^4 = 2Dk + D^2$$

(Note:—This equation gives the value of k but not its sign; k is always plus for outward bulge and minus for inward bulge.)

Example:

Let $\qquad p = 1.5$ lbs. per sq. ft., $L = 7.6$ ft., $\cos \delta = 0.99$, $\sin \delta = 0.14$
and $\qquad E = 1,500$ lbs./in. $= 18,000$ lbs./ft.

Then $\quad D = \tfrac{3}{16} \times \dfrac{1.5 \times 7.6}{18,000} = .0001175$, and $D^2 = .0000000138$

Since D^2 is small it can be neglected, hence $k^3 = 2D$, (approx.)

$$\therefore k = 0.062$$

Since the pressure is assumed to be external, k must be negative,

$$\therefore w = 1.5 \times 7.6 \left(0.99 + \frac{1 - .062^2}{.124} \times .14\right) = 11.3 \times 2.12$$

$$= 24.0 \text{ lbs./ft.}$$

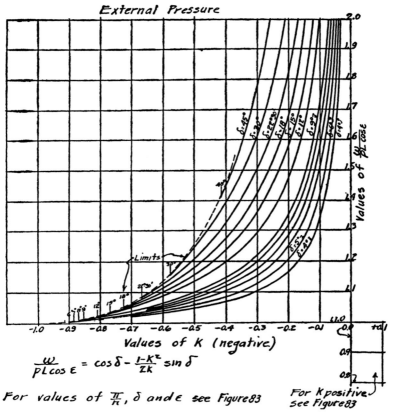

Figure 85.   Nose Stiffening; External Pressure Curves

Design of Nose Battens

Conditions. Fabric designed with flutes in whose depressions the battens rest. (See Figure 87a.)

Relative air speed 70 M.p.h. Impact pressure, $H = \frac{1}{2}pV^2 = 12.48$ lbs./sq. ft.

Pitch to wind 10°

Ballonet pressure 1 in. water = 5.2 lbs./sq. ft.

Inclination 15° down

Top batten figured

TABLE 27. EXTERNAL PRESSURES

Sta.	$\dfrac{p}{H}$	Rad. (Vert.) ft.	L ft.	$\dfrac{pL}{H}$	γ	$\cos \gamma$	δ	b' ft.	k	$\dfrac{w}{pL}$	$\dfrac{w}{H}$	Width of Panel ft.	Panel Load ÷ H	Arm Abt. Nose ft.	Mom. Abt. Nose	Σ Moms. Abt. Nose
0	0.98	0	...	...	...	...	...	...	...	...	...	...	...	...	...	...
1	0.883	3.95	1.13	1.00	56°	0.56	4° 35'	0.11	− 0.2	1.19	1.19	4.37	5.20	4.7	24.4	24.4
2	0.80	7.25	2.07	1.64	53	0.602	5°	0.21	− 0.2	1.21	1.98	4.02	7.97	8 7	69.6	94
3	0.712	10.4	2.97	2.12	49	0.656	5° 20'	0.30	− 0.2	1.23	2.61	3.97	10.37	12.6	131	225
4	0.617	13.25	3.78	2.33	44	0.719	5° 50'	0.38	− 0.2	1.25	2.91	4.0	11.65	16.5	192	417
5	0.518	16.0	4.56	2.36	40	0.766	6° 15'	0.46	− 0.2	1.26	2.97	4.0	11.90	20.3	242	659
6	0.415	18.5	5.28	2.19	36	0.809	6° 35'	0.53	− 0.2	1.27	2.78	3.97	11.05	24.0	265	924
7	0.306	20.7	5.90	1.81	33	0.839	6° 50'	0.59	− 0.2	1.28	2.32	4.0	9.28	27.4	254	1178
8	0.20	22.9	6.53	1.31	30	0.866	7° 05'	0.65	− 0.2	1.29	1.69	4.0	6.76	31.1	211	1389
9	0.095	24.8	7.08	0.67	27	0.891	7° 20'	0.71	− 0.2	1.30	0.87	4.0	3.48	34.6	120	1509
10	− 0.015	...	...	...	...	...	...	...	...	...	...	...	...	...	...	...
11			...	...	...	...	...	...	...	...	...	...	...	...	...	...

TABLE 28. INTERNAL PRESSURES

Sta.	Rad. (Vert.) ft.	Rad. ×.055	Press. p lbs./sq. ft.	$\frac{p}{H}$	L ft.	$\frac{pL}{H}$	γ	cos γ	δ	b ft.	k	$\frac{w}{pL}$	$\frac{w}{H}$	Width Panel ft.	Panel Load ÷ H	Arm Abt. Nose ft.	Mom. Abt. Nose	Σ Moms. Abt. Nose
0	...	...	...	...	...	...	...	...	...	...	...	...	...	...	...	...	...	...
1	...	...	...	...	...	...	...	...	...	...	...	...	...	...	...	...	...	...
2	5.7	0.31	3.51	0.281	1.63	0.46	53°	0.602	5°	0.20	0.25	0.83	0.38	4.0	1.52	8.7	13.5	13.5
3	9.0	0.50	3.70	0.297	2.57	0.76	49	0.656	5° 20'	0.32	0.25	0.82	0.625	4.0	2.50	12.6	31.5	45
4	12.1	0.66	3.86	0.310	3.45	1.07	44	0.719	5° 50'	0.43	0.25	0.80	0.85	4.0	3.40	16.5	56	101
5	14.9	0.82	4.02	0.323	4.25	1.37	40	0.766	6° 15'	0.53	0.25	0.79	1.08	4.0	4.32	20.3	88	189
6	17.4	0.95	4.15	0.333	4.97	1.65	36	0.809	6° 35'	0.62	0.25	0.78	1.29	3.9	5.04	24.0	121	310
7	19.6	1.07	4.27	0.342	5.60	1.91	33	0.839	6° 50'	0.70	0.25	0.77	1.47	3.9	5.74	27.4	157	467
8	21.9	1.20	4.40	0.353	6.25	2.21	30	0.866	7° 05'	0.75	0.24	0.75	1.67	4.0	6.68	31.1	208	675
9	23.8	1.31	4.51	0.362	6.80	2.46	27	0.891	7° 20'	0.75	0.22	0.71	1.75	4.0	7.00	34.6	242	917
10	25.5	1.40	4.60	0.369	7.27	2.68	23	0.920	7° 30'	0.75	0.20	0.68	1.82	4.0	7.28	37.4	272	1189
11	26.7	1.47	4.67	0.375	7.60	2.85	19	0.945	7° 45'	0.75	0.20	0.67	1.91	4.1	7.83	40.7	319	1509

22 battens total $-\dfrac{\pi}{n} = 8°11'$

$\delta = \dfrac{\pi}{n} \cos \gamma$; $\cos \epsilon$ is neglected

Negative pressures are neglected.

End effect not considered in this computation.

Internal pressure at nose = 5.2 lbs./sq. ft. − 140 sin 15° × .055
= 3.2 lbs./sq. ft.

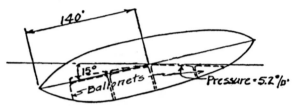

Figure 86.   Nose Batten Design Diagram

TABLE 29. NET LOADS

Sta.	Ext. Load ÷ H	Int. Load ÷ H	Net Ext. Load ÷ H	Net Ext. Load lbs.
1	5.20	0	5.20	64.9
2	7.97	1.52	6.45	80.5
3	10.37	2.50	7.87	98.0
4	11.65	3.40	8.25	102.8
5	11.90	4.32	7.58	94.5
6	11.05	5.04	6.01	75.0
7	9.28	5.74	3.54	44.2
8	6.76	6.68	+ 0.08	+ 10.0
9	3.48	7.00	− 3.52	− 43.9
10	0	7.28	− 7.28	− 91.0
11	0	7.83	− 7.83	− 97.6

Envelope Constructed without Flutes

The foregoing theory presupposes that the envelope is constructed with longitudinal flutes, with each batten bearing in the depression between two flutes. The formulas apply equally if this is not the case, but the envelope is merely a smooth surface and without any depression until

external pressures on the nose force indentation.   In the
latter case the height of bulge *b* is not known as in the
previous case where it is fixed by specification, but the construction is such that when the battens bear lightly on the
envelope the outer cover is just taut.   Therefore in this

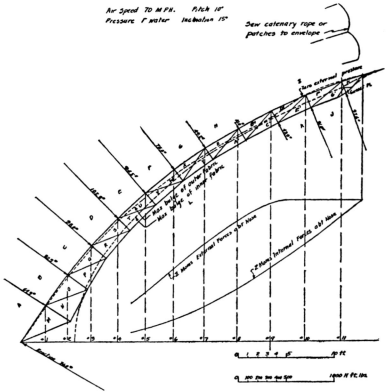

Figure 87a.   Design of Nose Battens

latter case it is necessary to start with an assumed depression
at the free end of the batten, solving as will be shown for *k*,
and then for the external and internal loads.

Envelope depression (Figures 87 and 88).   Assume that
in a cross-section normal to the ship's axis the envelope is

circular, with radius r. If the envelope is not circular, then treat each width adjacent to any batten under consideration as being part of a circular section. Assume also that the section of the bulge on a plane normal to its central element is also circular, although it will lie between a circle and an ellipse, respectively, after and before bulging. Referring to

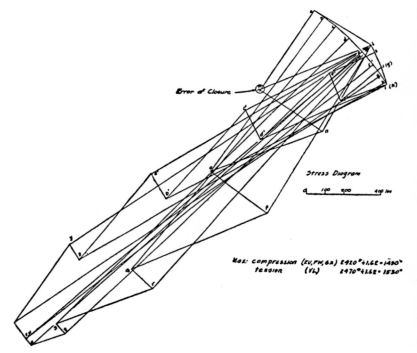

Figure 87b. Design of Nose Battens

previous diagrams, the length of a normal strip of fabric between battens is $L' = 2r_0 \sec \gamma . \delta$ and approximately $L' = L$, the chord length (with an error of the order of $\frac{1}{3}$ per cent). As the battens indent the envelope by a distance d (normally) they converge until the chord distance between them is l, where $l : L :: (r_0 \sec \gamma - d) : r_0 \sec \gamma$.

Hence, $l = L \left(\dfrac{1 - d \cos \gamma}{r} \right)$ (See Figures 87 and 88.)   (87)

From the foregoing, $L' = \dfrac{l}{3} (4\sqrt{1 + k^2} - 1)$

Hence, $k = \sqrt{\left(\dfrac{3L + l}{4l} \right)^2 - 1}$ (88)

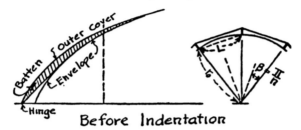

Before Indentation

After Indentation

Figure 88.   Indentation Effects of Nose Battens

From the value of k, determined by this formula from an assumed value of d, may be found through the use of the

k-curves the value of $\dfrac{w}{pl \cos \epsilon}$, and since p and l are now known, the value of w is found. This solution depends upon the assumption that there is no stretch in the fabric, but it is on the safe side, and the error is not great.

Outer cover. As the battens depress into the envelope the outer cover slackens and bulges inward under external pressures. The value of k for the cover is determined in the same manner as that just described for the envelope, noting that $\dfrac{w}{pl \cos \epsilon}$ will always be greater than unity. The fabric is naturally stretched taut under zero pressure (otherwise the case is substantially the first case above) hence its length is of necessity equal to the chord length, L.

It should be noted that the theory is based upon the indenting of battens into the envelope being *normal* to the envelope at all points, each individual short (but finite) axial length of envelope being considered a cone. In the ship the batten will most probably be hinged at a point somewhat forward of the nose of the envelope in order to allow space for the metal hub of the nose cap, hence the indentation will not be strictly normal. However the error introduced thereby is the versed sine of the angle of difference between the cone and a line from the hinge to the element under consideration, which is of necessity a small quantity. If desired, correction can be made for this angle.

Design Procedure for Envelope without Flutes

1. Assume a length of batten. As an initial assumption let it extend to the point of zero external pressure. Lay off the proposed shape of batten, with assumed thicknesses at each short length, so that the curves of envelope and cover are fixed.

2. Assume a maximum depth of indentation, d_m, at the free end of the batten, and from Figure 91 determine the end

load P. Compute the indentation for other points proportionally to the distances, z_1, z_2, etc., from the hinge.

3. Compute external and internal loads on each length thus:

$$L = \frac{2r_0\pi}{n}$$

$$l = L\left(1 - \frac{d\cos\gamma}{r_0}\right) \tag{89}$$

$$k = \sqrt{\left(\frac{3L+l}{4l}\right)^2 - 1} \tag{90}$$

With this value of k the forces can be computed as outlined.

4. Compute moments of external and internal loads about the nose hinge. If the moments do not balance, make a new assumption for d_m and recompute.

5. When the final assumed value of d_m gives loads, including end effect, which balance about the nose hinge, the bending moments and sections of the batten may be found.

Should the length of batten assumed as a trial value give excessive indentation into the envelope, or if the maximum allowable indentation gives insufficient support, a longer batten must be used, and the computations made over.

If the depth of batten be shallow in any part, the outer cover and the envelope may come into contact over a considerable area, and it may be necessary to modify the formulas. In the contact area the external and internal forces will neutralize each other, as if on a single fabric.

The method outlined considers the batten to be rigid. If bending moments cause deflection as a cantilever, the end indentation will be diminished. Allowance must be made for this.

In some of the Italian ships the nose cap is reinforced with thin steel tubes (of a diameter of ⅝ in. and a thickness of No. 10 to No. 20 gauge), lying on the "meridians" and "parallels" of the envelope. Such a cap is substantially a dome, because the circumferential tubes develop ring stresses which support the batten tubes and reduce their deflection. On the short lengths between battens (the maximum spacing is in the neighborhood of 7 ft.) the curvature is so slight that two such tubes acting at each panel point may materially support the batten.

In the airship *Norge* (Italian *N-1*), a full rigid cap similar to that of the *Roma* has been used.

Strength of Tube Struts

The strength of tube struts located on parallels of the envelope and intended to brace circumferentially the nose battens or the control surfaces of the empennage, may be computed as outlined in the following paragraphs.

Tubes assumed to be free ended.   Clearly the circular tube, if between nose battens, may be assumed, with small

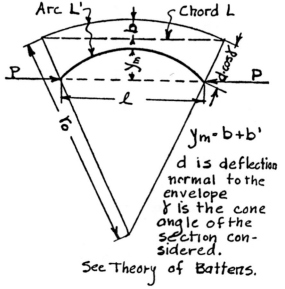

Figure 89.   Strength of Tube Struts

error, to be a parabolic curve. But moments in a beam uniformly loaded are parabolic, and the deflection of such a beam is

$$b' = \frac{5}{384} \times \frac{wl^4}{EI}$$

hence tube deflection will be approximately the same.

Since $M_c = \frac{1}{8}wl^2$

$$b' = \frac{5}{48} \times \frac{M_c l^2}{EI}$$

Also $M_c = \frac{2fI}{D}$, where f = allowable unit stress and D = diameter of tube

$$\therefore b' = \frac{5}{24} \times \frac{fl^2}{ED} = \frac{5}{24} \times \frac{fL^2}{ED} \tag{91}$$

approx. since $l = L$ very nearly

Now $M_c = Py_m = P(b + b')$

$$\therefore P = \frac{M_c}{b+b'} = \frac{2fI}{D(b+b')} = \frac{48fI}{D\left(24b + \dfrac{5fl^2}{ED}\right)} \tag{92}$$

If $b = 0$, $P = \dfrac{9.6EI}{l^2}$ $\left(\text{Euler's formula is } P = \dfrac{\pi^2 EI}{l^2} = \dfrac{9.85EI}{l^2}\right)$

a close check.

For a tube whose metal thickness = t

$$I = \frac{\pi}{8} tD^3$$

$$\therefore P = \frac{\pi ftD^2}{4(b+b')} = \frac{6\pi ftD^2}{24b + \dfrac{5fl^2}{ED}} \tag{93}$$

If f = 32,000 lbs./sq. ft.; $D = \frac{5}{8}$ in., $t = \frac{1}{16}$ in., $b = 2.92$ in., $L = 84$ in., E = 30,000,000 lbs./sq. in.

$$b' = \frac{5 \times 32,000 \times 84^2}{24 \times 30,000,000 \times \frac{5}{8}} = 2.51 \text{ in.}$$

and $\qquad P = \dfrac{\pi \times 32{,}000 \times \frac{1}{16} \times (\frac{5}{8})^2}{4 \times (2.92 + 2.51)} = 113$ lbs. at elastic limit
of tube metal

Now $\qquad L' = \dfrac{L}{3}(4\sqrt{1 + k^2} - 1)$, where $k = \dfrac{b}{\frac{1}{2}L}$

$\qquad\qquad L' = \dfrac{l}{3}(4\sqrt{1 + k_1^2} - 1)$, where $k_1 = \dfrac{b + b'}{\frac{1}{2}l} = \dfrac{y_m}{\frac{1}{2}l}$

and $\qquad l = L\left(1 - \dfrac{d \cdot \cos \gamma}{r_o}\right)$, or $d = \dfrac{r_0}{\cos \gamma}\left(1 - \dfrac{l}{L}\right)$

$\qquad \therefore k_1 = \sqrt{\left(\dfrac{3L' + l}{4l}\right)^2 - 1}$

$\qquad \therefore y_m = \frac{1}{2}lk_1 = \frac{1}{8}\sqrt{(3L' + l)^2 - 16l^2}$ $\qquad$ (94)

If d is known, this equation can be solved for y_m, from which b', M_c, P and f can be found.

If y_m is known,

$$l = L'\left(0.2 + \sqrt{0.64 - 4.27\left(\dfrac{y_m}{L'}\right)^2}\right) = L'\left[1 - \dfrac{8}{3}\left(\dfrac{y_m}{L'}\right)^2 \right.$$
$$\left. - \dfrac{40}{9}\left(\dfrac{y_m}{L'}\right)^4 - \cdots\right]$$

and $\qquad L' = \dfrac{L}{3}(4\sqrt{1 + k^2} - 1)$

$\qquad\qquad d = \dfrac{r_0}{\cos \gamma}\left(1 - \dfrac{l}{L}\right)$

In the preceding example, if

$\qquad\qquad \dfrac{r_o}{\cos \gamma} = 25$ ft. $= 300$ in.

then $\qquad y_m = 2.92 + 2.51 = 5.43$ in.

$\qquad k = \dfrac{2.92}{42} = .07 \;\; \therefore L' = \dfrac{84}{3}(4\sqrt{1 + .07^2} - 1) = 84.5$ in.

$\qquad \dfrac{y_m}{L'} = \dfrac{5.43}{84.5} = .0644 \;\; \therefore l = 84.5\left(1 - \dfrac{8}{3} \times .0644^2\right) = 83.57$ in

$\qquad d = 300\left(1 - \dfrac{83.57}{84}\right) = 1.54$ in.

Hence, deflection d normal to envelope may only be 1.54 in. when the elastic limit of tube is reached. If tubes are straight between battens, then d is only 0.97 in. when elastic limit is reached.

For tubes bracing the fixed surfaces of the empennage, the curvature cannot so nearly be assumed parabolic because of their greater length. The method of computing, however, is similar.

In the nose cap if tubes are cut between battens so that one tube may slide within the other, they offer no resistance to deflection and have no stress therefrom, but they effectively prevent torsion of the nose battens.

If tubes are assumed fixed at their ends the formulas must be modified accordingly and deflections will be less.

Indentation Pressure, or "End Effect"

At the free end of a nose batten there will be a semicircular indentation into the fabric called herein "end effect," which terminates the groove formed by indentation of the batten. In a very flexible batten this effect may disappear because of the concave curvature near the free end. In some of the later Italian types definite provision is made, in the form of flexible cantilever ends, to provide for such effect. The curvature may even be such that the batten will lift entirely free of the normal surface of the envelope, and being secured thereto will draw up the fabric or the crow's foot into a half cone; but if the end is at or aft of the point of zero aerodynamic pressure there can be no element of gas pressure as outlined in the following theory, and the resistance is only the product of fabric tension on a semicircle, or in a crow's foot, and the sine of the angle between the cone elements and the respective tangents to the fabric. This negative case, therefore, needs no further discussion.

The amount of depression for a given end load P cannot be determined accurately because it is dependent upon the dimensions of the batten—which may be increased by stiffness of its chafing pad, and upon the respective gas pressure, longitudinal and circumferential fabric tensions, and the local curvatures of the envelope. Though a complete solution is not possible, an approximation will serve to indicate the magnitude of the end load on the batten.

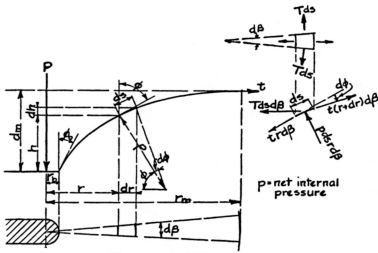

Figure 90.   End Effect Diagram

The longitudinal fabric tension t is determined by the gas pressure and gas bending moment and by the secant of the nose angle at any point being considered. The circumferential tension T has been found by the method of Chapter XIV. When the airship is nosed down, T will exceed t by approximately 20 per cent, on the average; but nevertheless we will assume both tensions equal to T. Assume also that for the depth of depression involved there is no change of either. Neglect the elastic stretch of the fabric, also the initial local curvatures of the envelope.

Consider a semicircular area $\frac{1}{2}\pi r^2_m$ of a size sufficient to support the end load P at net gas pressure p, having clearly in mind that if r_m exceeds half the spacing of the batten ends there will be lateral interference of adjacent battens and a corresponding concentration of support on the center of the arc. Such a condition is more difficult to analyze, even approximately. Consider the batten end to be semicircular and of radius r_b, and, if the chafing pad has bending stiffness, let its equivalent radius be r_b. In either event if r_b is small the depression will be deep and steep sided, so that the fabric may rupture; moreover, for such a case the assumption that fabric tension is unchanged may be seriously in error.

In Figure 90 $ds \approx \rho d\phi$, $dh = \cos \phi ds = \rho \cos \phi d\phi$
$$dr = \sin \phi ds$$

Since Σ (tangential components) = 0

$$[trd\beta - t\,(r + dr)\,d\beta]\cos \tfrac{1}{2}d\phi + 2Tds \sin \tfrac{1}{2}d\,\beta \sin \phi = 0$$

or $$tdr = Tdr$$

Thus $t = T$ = a constant, since both are assumed to be

unchanged.   (95)

Since Σ (normal components) = 0

$$pds\,(r + \tfrac{1}{2}dr)\,d\beta - (2tr + tdr)\sin \tfrac{1}{2}d\phi d\beta + 2Tds \sin \tfrac{1}{2}d\,\beta \cos \phi = 0$$

$$prds - Trd\phi + Tds \cos \phi = 0, \text{ since } t = T. \quad \text{But } ds = \rho d\phi$$

Thus $$pr + T \cos \phi = \frac{rT}{\rho}, \text{ or } \rho = \frac{rT}{pr + T \cos \phi}$$ (96)

Then, $$dh = \rho \cos \phi d\phi = \frac{rT \cos \phi d\phi}{pr + T \cos \phi}$$

Since Σ (vertical components) = 0

$$P = \pi r T \cos \phi + \tfrac{1}{2}\pi r^2 p = \tfrac{1}{2}\pi r^2_m p$$

or $$\frac{pr}{T} = -\cos \phi + \sqrt{\frac{2Pp}{\pi T^2} + \cos^2\phi}$$

Then
$$\frac{pdh}{T} = \frac{-\cos^2\phi\,d\phi}{\sqrt{\dfrac{2Pp}{\pi T^2} + \cos^2\phi}} + \cos\phi\,d\phi$$

Let
$$\kappa^2 = \frac{1}{\left(1 + \dfrac{2Pp}{\pi T^2}\right)}$$

then
$$\sqrt{\frac{2Pp}{\pi T^2} + \cos^2\phi} = \frac{1}{\kappa}\sqrt{1 - \kappa^2\sin^2\phi}$$

and $\dfrac{p}{T}\displaystyle\int dh = -\kappa\int\frac{\cos^2\phi\,d\phi}{\sqrt{1 - \kappa^2\sin^2\phi}} + \int\cos\phi\,d\phi$, between upper

limits of $(0, \phi_0)$ and lower limits of $(d_m, 90°)$

Thus, $\dfrac{p}{T}d_m = -\dfrac{1}{\kappa}\left[E(\kappa, \phi) - (1 - \kappa^2)F(\kappa, \phi)\right]_{\phi_0}^{90°} + 1 - \sin\phi_0$

or $\quad d_m = \dfrac{T}{p}\left[1 - \dfrac{1}{\kappa}\left\{E(\kappa, \phi) - (1 - \kappa^2)F(\kappa, \phi)\right\} - \sin\phi_0\right]$ (97)

where E and F are elliptic integrals having an upper limit of $90°$
and a lower limit of ϕ_0,

where $\kappa = \dfrac{1}{\sqrt{1 + \dfrac{2Pp}{\pi T^2}}} = \dfrac{1}{\sqrt{1 + \dfrac{p^2r^2_m}{T^2}}} =$

$$\frac{1}{\sqrt{1 + \dfrac{pr_b}{T}\left(2\cos\phi_0 + \dfrac{pr_b}{T}\right)}}$$ (98)

where $\dfrac{P}{r_bT} = \pi\cos\phi_0 + \dfrac{1}{2}\dfrac{\pi pr_b}{T} = \dfrac{1}{2}\dfrac{\pi pr^2_m}{r_bT}$ (99)

and $\cos\phi_0 = \dfrac{P}{\pi r_bT} - \dfrac{1}{2}\dfrac{pr_b}{T}$ (100)

It is clear that in this form the equations are dimension-
less and can be plotted as shown in Figure 91. This figure
is plotted on $\dfrac{P}{r_bT}$ for abscissa, and $\dfrac{pd_m}{T}$ for ordinate, with

curves for the reciprocals of $\dfrac{pr_b}{T}$ and for values of ϕ_0. By interpolation it can be used for any case within its range. The depression d_m must of course be that used in the design of the batten, as described on page 284; p, T and r_b are known quantities; hence P can readily be determined. It is clear from the figure that for all values of $\dfrac{T}{pr_b}$ d_m increases with P, and from equation (100) that cos ϕ_0 increases with

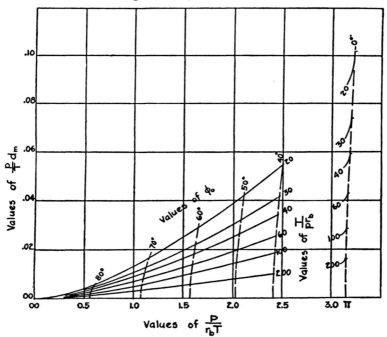

Figure 91. Relation Between Indentation and End Load on Battens

P to a maximum at $\phi_0 = 0$, when $\dfrac{P}{r_b T} = \pi\left(1 + \frac{1}{2}\dfrac{r_b p}{T}\right) = \pi$, approximately, and the fabric is closed around the end of the batten like a cylindrical tube, as would be expected. It should be remembered, however, that for so extreme a case the omitted factor, i.e., the elastic stretch of the fabric, would probably have a large effect, the fabric tensions would probably be different from T, and there might be actual rupture of the fabric; hence the theory should not be carried to this limit.

Example.

Let $d_m = 4$ in. $= 10.2$ cm.

$T = 156$ lbs./ft. $= 232$ kg./m.

$p = 1$ in. water $= 522$ lbs./sq. ft. $= 25.4$ kg./sq.m.

$r_b = 0.3$ ft. $= 9.14$ cm.

Then
$$\frac{T}{pr_b} = \frac{156}{5.2 \times 0.3} = \frac{232}{25.4 \times 0.091} = 100$$

and
$$\frac{pd_m}{T} = \frac{5.2 \times 0.333}{156} = \frac{25.4 \times 0.102}{232} = 0.0112$$

From the figure, $\dfrac{P}{r_b T} = 1.70$

Hence, $P = 1.7 \times 0.3 \times 156 = 80$ lbs.

$\qquad\quad = 1.7 \times 0.091 \times 232 = 36$ kg.

From this example, whose assumed dimensions would fit an airship of the size of the *RS*-1, it is clear that there will be an end load of considerable magnitude if the end depression should amount to 4 in. after allowance is made for the concave curvature of the end of the batten.

APPENDIX I

LOAD FACTORS

The following load factors, for the loading conditions noted, prevail in nonrigid airship design for determining the maximum stresses which are not to exceed the ultimate stresses allowed for the materials specified:

1. *Envelope.* Factor of 4, under full static lift and internal pressure specified. The ultimate strength of fabric shall be that determined by testing in a machine of the inclination balance type, with the pulling clamp operating at a speed of 12 in. per min., the material having been conditioned in an atmosphere of 65 per cent relative humidity at 70° F. for at least 3 hrs.

2. *Nose stiffening.* Factor of 3, dynamic loads calculated from pressure distribution curve for zero degree inclination and 15 m.p.h. in excess of the maximum designed speed of the airship.

3. *Control surfaces.* Factor of 4, under condition of 1½ lbs. per sq. ft. for the movable surfaces and 2½ lbs. per sq. ft. for the fixed surfaces. For air speeds in excess of 55 m.p.h. the load factor should be increased to 5.

4. *Rudder and elevator control mechanism and leads.* Factor of 4 under loading conditions noted under Control Surfaces.

5. *Car suspension.* Factor of 5, car fully loaded.

6. *Car structure.* Factor of 5, full static load.

7. *Fin suspension.* Factor of 5, under unit loading conditions noted under Control Surfaces.

8. *Engine outrigger.* Factor of 4, full static load, combined with 8 for torque at maximum r.p.m. and 4 for thrust

at the rated engine horsepower, propeller efficiency taken at 100 per cent. Where 2 engines are mounted outboard in parallel, each outrigger should be considered loaded as above with the other zero loaded, then both should be considered loaded simultaneously.

9. *Landing gear.* Factor of 4, car fully loaded. Where pontoons are used, the maximum fabric tension shall be calculated on the basis of this load factor with a vertical landing velocity of 8 f.p.s., and considering the stretch of the fabric under load The maximum fabric tension should not exceed $\frac{1}{4}$ of the machine strength as obtained at a speed of jaw separation of 12 in. per min.

APPENDIX II

FABRIC YARDAGES AND WEIGHTS

The following table (30) sets forth cloth and fabric yardages of various nonrigid airship envelopes, which will be of use to the manufacturer in determining the quantities of material required for any ship between the volumes 43,000 and 200,000 cu. ft. There are also noted the weight allowances for seams in the envelope and seams and attachment shoes in the ballonet which the designer needs to consider in a preliminary performance calculation.

From this table the following general rules are formulated:

1. Weight of envelope including seam lap, tape, sewing and cement:

$$W_E = (1 + F_E) \, S_E \frac{G f_g + A f_a}{16}.$$

where W_E = Total weight of envelope

              F_E = Ratio of seam wt. to envelope wt. = .185

              S_E = Surface area of envelope in sq. yds.

              G = Ratio of gas-tight surface to S_E

              A = Ratio of air-tight surface to S_E

              f_g = Gas-tight fabric wt. oz. per sq. yd.

              f_a = Air-tight fabric wt. oz. per sq. yd.

2. Weight of ballonet diaphragm including seam lap, tape, sewing, attachment shoe and cement:

$$W_B = (1 + F_B) \, S_B \frac{f_B}{16}$$

where W_B = Total weight of ballonet

              F_B = Ratio of seam and shoe weight to envelope wt.

                   = .25

              S_B = Surface area of ballonet in sq. yds.

              f_B = Ballonet fabric wt. oz. per sq. yd.

3. Cloth and fabric yardages:

$$R = 1.15\,S$$
$$C = 1.33\,NR$$

where S = Surface area

              R = Rubberized fabric yardage

              C = Raw cloth yardage

NOTE: The above is somewhat in excess of present practice by the Goodyear Tire & Rubber Company; this company gives the following factors:

C = 1.04 $N.R.$ for straight-ply rubberized fabric

    = 1.20 $R.$ for single-ply bias rubberized fabric

    = 2.24 $R.$ for 2-ply straight and bias rubberized fabric

    = 3.28 $R.$ for 3-ply, 2 straight and 1 bias rubberized fabric

and therefore may not include waste allowance as in the above general formulas

TABLE 30—FABRIC YARDAGES AND WEIGHTS FOR NONRIGID AIRSHIPS

		Navy B	Navy C	Navy D	Navy F	Army OB-1	Army MA	Navy J-1	Army TA	Army TC	Army TE-1
Volume	(cu. ft.)	84,000	172,000	180,000	95,000	43,000	180,000	173,000	130,000	200,000	80,000
Length	(ft.)	162	192	198	163	94	169	170½	162	200	136
Diameter	(ft. in.)	32–6	41–9	41–9	33–5	31–0	48–3	45–0	39–5	44–6	34–0
Envelope:											
Surface	(sq. yd.)	1,421	2,217	2,304	1,508	777	2,132	2,100	1,783	2,421	1,277
Fabric	(sq. yd.)	1,640	2,650	2,760	1,745	895	2,460	2,425	2,040	2,770	1,460
Raw Cloth	(sq. yd.)	6,300	10,150	10,600	6,700	2,360	9,450	9,300	7,500	11,250	5,840
Grade and Weight	(oz./sq. yd.)	BB–2.5	BB–2.5	BB–2.5	BB–2.5	BB–2.5	AA–2.0	AA–2.0	AA–2.0	AA–2.0	AA–2.0
Plies—No.		3	3	3	3	2	3	3	3	3	3
(a) Fabric Wt, Gas-Tight		15.0	15.5	15.5	15.0	10.7	13.9	13.9	14.1	14.1	14.1
(a) Fabric Wt, Air-Tight		12.8	13.3	13.3	12.8	9.1	11.9	11.9	12.0	12.0	12.0
Total Finished Wt.[3]	(lbs.)	1,520	2,420	2,500	1,650	587			1,705	2,450	1,200
% Allowance for seams		18.5	18.5	18.0	16.0	17.5			12.5	18.5	18.5
Ballonet:											(1)
Surface	(sq. yd.)	387	745	745	320	148	540	540	300 + 250	356 + 313	345
Fabric	(sq. yd.)	435	860	860	370	170	610	610	630	765	400
Raw Cloth	(sq. yd.)	1,150	2,370	2,370	975	450	1,610	1,610	1,625	2,000	1,040
Grade and Wt.	(oz./sq. yd.)	AA–2.0	AA–2.0	AA–2.0	AA–2.0	AA–2.0	AA–2.0	AA–2.0	AA–2.0	AA–2.0	AA–2.0
Plies No.		2	2	2	2	2	2	2	2	2	2
Fabric Wt.	(oz./sq. yd.)	9.0	9.0	9.0	9.0	8.9	9.1	9.1	8.9	8.9	8.9
Total finished Wt.[3]	(lbs.)	275	450	470	338	105			380	460	240
% Allowance for Seams		26.5				27			24	23.5	25

NOTE (1) Ballonet single with partition. (2) Fabric weight's ounces per sq. yd. maximum. (3) Weight of paraffine not included.

APPENDIX III

CORDAGE SERVING SCHEDULE

Serving, Seizing, and Whipping Ropes and Elastic Cord with Waxed Linen Cord

Diameter of Rope or Cord	Straight Ends and Eyes	Splices and Seizing
Under 1/8 in.	3	3
1/8 and 3/16 in.	6	6
1/4 and 5/16 in.	6	9
3/8 and 7/16 in.	9	12
1/2 and 5/8 in.	12	18
3/4 and 1 in.	18	27

Requirements for Linen Waxed Cord

Ply Cord	Yards per lb.	Tensile Strength lbs.
3	1,870	15
6	930	32
9	620	50
12	465	60
18	310	90
27	210	120

INDEX

THE MAMMOTH DIRIGIBLE:
DOES IT OFFER NEW ADVANTAGES
IN TRANSPORTATION?

An Afterword by Adam Starchild

It would seem strange in our era of advanced technology that transportation of goods around the nation and the world is relatively inefficient and beset with problems. Tractor and trailer combinations are traffic-clogging, relatively slow at any speed limit, in proportion to the amount of payload that they carry, and thus, from the economic viewpoint, somewhat inefficient. Transport ships carry larger loads, but are obviously restricted to areas served by waterways. Trains seem to combine some of the better features of other surface carriers, but seem constantly plagued with a shortage of cars, and are, moreover, restricted to areas where rails and services have been installed. Carrier aircraft, while effectively solving the problem of speed, use enormous amounts of fuel at a time when the need to conserve fuel is pressing. Moreover, goods transported by conventional aircraft almost always have to be transferred to another mode of transportation before they can arrive at their destination.

There is a mode of transportation in the offing, however, that if allowed to be developed, should solve the problems of speed (it is significantly faster than a tractor and trailer combination); capacity (it could easily be designed to carry a high-density load equivalent to the capacity of several freight cars); economy (its fuel consumption is negligible as compared to that of conventional aircraft); and flexibility (it could allow cargo to be loaded and unloaded in undeveloped areas that are served by nothing more than the equivalent of a pack-trail or logging road). What we are talking about, of course, is the dirigible, or airship.

The use of dirigibles to transport enormous cargo loads or large numbers of passengers is not new, nor a concept just off the drawing board, still in need of extensive field testing. As long as seven decades ago, largely through the technology developed by the German, Count von Zeppelin, airships began coming into their own. However, these early airships were ill-fated, from both the viewpoint of military and commercial use, since they acquired an undeservedly poor reputation in safety. Nevertheless, from about 1919 until 1937, when the 804 foot, 6.7 million cubic foot dirigible, the Hindenburg, was destroyed by fire at the New Jersey landing field, dirigibles amassed an impressive number of successful flights, carrying both passengers and cargo. One airship, the Los Angeles, made about 250 flights, including flights to Puerto Rico and Panama, as well as several transcontinental flights, before being decommissioned in 1932.

It is the contention of airship supporters that since, in this era, conventional aircraft had not been fully developed to carry as many passengers as airships, that a safety comparison between airships and conventional aircraft was invalid. Nonetheless, after the Hindenburg disaster, in which 36 of the 92 passengers and crew were killed, the production of commercial airships was virtually discontinued. In recent years, therefore, about the only airships that most Americans have seen have been the small advertising "blimps" (the distinction between a blimp and a dirigible is that a dirigible is of rigid construction, while the blimp is non-rigid).

Since the days of the Hindenburg, vast technological improvements have been made in the materials that can be used for airship construction. The U. S. has developed high-strength, corrosion-resistant alloys for hull structures. For the outer covering, we have tough, durable nylon fabrics. For the gas cell linings, we have impermeable synthetic films. The problem of the highly flammable hydrogen as the buoyancy gas has been overcome through the use of helium gas.

An inherent advantage of the airship over conventional aircraft is that through the use of a buoyant aerostatic lift (conventional aircraft uses a powered aerodynamic lift), the fuel cost of getting and keeping the airship aloft is nothing. Therefore, once aloft, the energy requirements to propel the buoyant airship is dramatically less than for conventional aircraft. In fact, the first mechanically-driven airship (circa 1852) was a 143-foot craft that was propelled at a speed of about 6 miles per hour by a 3-horsepower steam engine.

The advantages of fuel conservation are somewhat offset by the lower operating speed of the airship, which attains an efficient cruising speed between 50 and 120 miles per hour. In theory, higher speeds are obtainable through design, but fuel consumption increases disproportionately as speed is increased over the optimum range. However, considering the fact that dirigibles can be designed to carry a payload of as much as 500 tons, a speed of 100 miles per hour is in viable proportion to the payload.

Since an airship can rise or descend vertically, no runway space is needed for takeoffs and landings. Once airborne, whether taking off or landing, it needs a clear approach; but on the ground all that is needed is level terrain — such as any ordinary field would provide — about twice the length of the craft, to permit movement around a mooring mast.

Many of the calculations on the efficiency, range and fuel consumption of airships have been based on the presumed use of conventional power plants, such as gas turbines or steam engines. But when the possibility of nuclear-powered craft is considered, an even better picture emerges. With a virtually unlimited range of the airship, as compared with a range of about 10,000 miles for conventional aircraft; the elimination of the need for water recovery to compensate for fuel consumption; and extremely large payloads, the airship could become the cargo work horse of the world. In one preliminary design of a 12.5 million cubic foot airship, it was estimated that the weight of an atomic power plant, including the reactor, turbines and shielding, would be about 120,000 pounds, which is a nominal percentage of the gross lift. By comparison, a conventionally powered airship of the same size would have to carry that amount of weight in fuel alone.

The buoyancy of the lighter-than-air airship significantly decreases the danger of an atomic disaster in the case of an accident, since the large space inside the hull acts as a cushion for the reactor. In the case of a mid-air collision, or a ground crash, the reactor is cushioned by springs which would prevent the rupturing that would result in a radiation hazard. Using reactor designs that already exist, a nuclear-powered airship could circle the earth repeatedly without refueling.

Just how large is large, when speaking of airships? Experts are saying that 50 to 100 million cubic feet, and lengths of up to 1,200 or 1,500 feet would be the requirements for a commercially feasible airship. Given their enormous payload capacity, and the range and flexibility of the nuclear-powered craft, their potential as cargo carriers becomes obvious. They could carry bulky loads, of the kind that conventional carriers find economically unfeasible, at the rate of 100 mph, over any kind of terrain, over ice fields, over large expanses of water and into continental interiors, as well as into regions that are undeveloped for surface vehicles. Through the use of winches for loading and unloading, crews of men and equipment would be lowered into logging operations, where logging is done in environmentally fragile areas. Logs could be "yarded" out without resorting to the construction and use of erosion-causing logging roads. Areas could be worked that might be accessible only at extremely high cost — or inaccessible because of present environmental regulations.

Since smaller power plants are required for airship propulsion than for that of power-lifted craft, pollution and noise are considerably decreased. Moreover, because of the larger capacity and buoyancy of the airship, certain kinds of pollution and noise reduction equipment could become an integral part of the craft.

Another advantage of the airship is that, with vibration greatly decreased, it would find a use as a flying laboratory. Other suggested uses for the spacious, quiet craft are the transporting of sightseers, tourists, geologists, surveyors, oceanographers, biologists, rescue crews, archaeologists and medical personnel — and the list could go on. The airship, with its huge size and vibration-free flight, would provide spacious quarters for large crews and their equipment. Facilities almost as luxurious as those provided on luxury liners can be provided for travelers and sightseers. Authorities call the dirigible the most stable and vibration-free airborne device that can be built with our present technology.

Apart from the unusual and exotic uses, the airship would certainly find a use in the transportation of perishable foods. This creates the potential for opening up new markets for fresh fruits and vegetables in such countries as Western

Europe and Japan, where these items cannot be grown on the year-round basis, as in Mexico, Florida, Arizona, Texas and Southern California. Japan is already becoming an important market for American-grown produce. Thus far, foreign markets have been difficult to develop, since the transportation of perishables — especially strawberries and lettuce — for long distances has been problematic. The supporters of airships point out that these perishable items could be transported from a U. S. point of distribution to the market place without the need for transferring shipments.

Given all the advantages of airships over power-lifted craft, then what is slowing their development? There is still the question of safety in the minds of some people, since most remember the dirigible accidents of a few decades, but few people are aware of the relatively good safety record they compiled. It is noteworthy, for example, that the German-founded Zeppelin line carried 40,000 passengers, flying about 25,000 hours in 4,000 flights, without losing a passenger until the Hindenburg accident.

Today, however, with our more accurate knowledge of and ability to predict weather, and the new materials and fuels that have been developed through modern technology, there is no reason to believe that airship disasters will exceed those of conventional aircraft. In fact, most persons who are knowledgeable about flight believe that the airship is the safer of the two modes.

But this is not to say that a large-scale use of airships would not present its problems. The most obvious of these problems is the size of a hangar required to construct an airship. Another problem is the space and facilities needed for ground-handling the airship. Suggested methods for solving the former problem are the use of abandoned shipyards or outdoor facilities.

Several ideas have evolved to solve the problem of ground storage and handling. The foremost problem of storage is the amount of space required to handle just a few of the mammoth airships. Although paved areas and runways are not needed, more land area would be necessary to handle a few airships than would be needed for several airports. While this might be considered a major drawback, one might also consider the savings that could be realized in not having to hard-surface large runway and parking areas.

Wind also presents a problem for the moored airship, and the craft must be free to swing with the wind. Among the ideas brought forth to solve this problem is the use of hangars that float or are mounted on turntables, that would enable the craft to always face into the wind. However, the construction of turntables of sufficient size would be expensive. Another idea is to keep an airship continuously aloft after it has been built, using winches to raise and lower cargo in modules.

In still another suggested method, when the airship lands, it is connected by lines to mobile equipment (U. S. Navy blimp operations used this method in the 1950s and 1960s, and it was also used in the 1930s). A modification of the Navy equipment could be used on rigid airships of up to three million cubic feet, but experts believe that the only way to handle craft in the fifteen-million cubic foot size is by letting it hover.

Still another problem that arises in the loading and unloading of goods is that as goods are unloaded from a hovering craft, ballast must be taken on; and when goods are loaded, ballast must be released, thus decreasing the ability of airships to service undeveloped areas.

Of the two models of airships now under study, one is an all-cargo craft, and the other a passenger-cargo craft with

a capacity of 400 passengers. Because of the large displacement of the new designs, as compared with earlier airships, accommodations can be increased accordingly, making the airship a virtual "flying luxury liner." This could eventually make a dramatic change in
the concept of air travel.

The future of airships looks bright, with most of the technical problems already solved. The problems of getting them into production would seem to center around public relations, and the economics of producing them. Assuming that regulatory bodies will be convinced of their air-worthiness and safety, the final problem would seem to be to attract investment groups with the combined vision and financial clout to launch a new and exciting era in air transportation.

Adam Starchild is an international business consultant and author of over 25 books. He is a life member of the World Future Society and The Lighter-Than-Air Society. His personal website is at http://www.adamstarchild.com